Ion Implantation
and Beam Processing

Ion Implantation and Beam Processing

Edited by

J. S. Williams
Royal Melbourne Institute of Technology
Melbourne, Australia

J. M. Poate
Bell Laboratories
Murray Hill, New Jersey, USA

 1984

ACADEMIC PRESS
A Subsidiary of Harcourt Brace Jovanovich, Publishers

Sydney   New York   London
San Diego   San Francisco   São Paulo   Tokyo   Toronto

ACADEMIC PRESS AUSTRALIA
Centrecourt, 25–27 Paul Street North
North Ryde, N.S.W. 2113

United States Edition published by
ACADEMIC PRESS INC.
111 Fifth Avenue
New York, New York 10003

United Kingdom Edition published by
ACADEMIC PRESS, INC. (LONDON) LTD.
24/28 Oval Road, London NW1 7DX

Copyright © 1984 by
ACADEMIC PRESS AUSTRALIA

Printed in Australia

National Library of Australia Cataloguing-in-Publication Data

---

Ion implantation and beam processing.

Includes bibliographies and index.
ISBN 0 12 756980 4.

1. Semiconductor doping. 2. Ion implantation.
3. Semiconductors. 4. Electron beams. I. Williams,
J. S. (James Stanislaus). II. Poate, J. M.
(John Milo).

621.3815'2

Library of Congress Catalog Card Number: 83-71159

CONTENTS

7 Ion Beam and Laser Mixing: Fundamentals and Applications
B. R. Appleton

8 High-Dose Implantation
D. G. Beanland

9 Trends of Ion Implantation in Silicon Technology
H. S. Rupprecht and A. E. Michel

10 Implantation in GaAs Technology
F. H. Eisen

CONTRIBUTORS

Numbers in parentheses indicate the pages on which the authors' contributions begin.

H. H. Andersen (127), Physical Laboratory II, H. C. Ørsted Institute, Universitets Parken 5, DK 2100 Copenhagen, Denmark

B. R. Appleton (189), Solid State Division, Oak Ridge National Laboratory, Oak Ridge, Tennessee 37830, USA

J. E. E. Baglin (357), IBM Research Centre, Yorktown Heights, New York 10598, USA

D. G. Beanland (261), Faculty of Engineering, Royal Melbourne Institute of Technology, Melbourne, Victoria 3000, Australia

W. L. Brown (99), Bell Laboratories, Murray Hill, New Jersey 07974, USA

L. A. Christel (59), Stanford Electronics Laboratories, Stanford University, California 94305, USA

J. A. Davies (81), Atomic Energy of Canada Ltd Research Company, Chalk River Nuclear Laboratories, Chalk River, Ontario KOJ IJO, Canada

F. H. Eisen (327), Rockwell International Science Centre, Thousand Oaks, California 91360, USA

J. F. Gibbons (59), Stanford Electronics Laboratories, Stanford University, California 94305, USA

H. B. Harrison (357), Microelectronics Technology Centre, Royal Melbourne Institute of Technology, Melbourne, Victoria 3000, Australia

A. E. Michel (311), IBM Research Centre, Yorktown Heights, New York 10598, USA

J. M. Poate (1, 13), Bell Laboratories, Murray Hill, New Jersey 07974, USA

H. S. Rupprecht (311), IBM Research Centre, Yorktown Heights, New York 10598, USA

J. L. Tandon (357), 15251E Don Julian Road, P.O. Box 1212, The City of Industry, California 91749, USA

J. S. Williams (1, 13, 357), Microelectronics Technology Centre, Royal Melbourne Institute of Technology, Melbourne, Victoria 3000, Australia

PREFACE

This book grew out of a specialist international workshop held at Phillip Island, Australia, in 1981. The main purpose of the workshop was to address the scientific and technological advances in the fields of ion implantation and beam processing.

Ion implantation has evolved over the past decade as a mature science and an essential part of semiconductor device technology. More recently, a somewhat analogous technology, that of ultra-rapid heating, using a laser or other pulsed energy sources, has emerged for the processing of surfaces of semiconductors. The convergence of ion implantation and rapid thermal processing is leading to important developments in semiconductor materials science.

Each chapter of the book presents a critical review of these recent developments by experts in the fields of ion implantation and beam processing. The authors concentrate mainly on semiconductors, and materials and processes of relevance to semiconductor technology. Important advances in the understanding of the basic science of ion bombardment and rapid thermal processing of solids are outlined. This new understanding, coupled with the emergence of non-conventional methods of materials processing, is leading to important technological advances of considerable importance in the semiconductor industry. Selected examples of practical applications of these new processing methods are also given. We believe that the issues addressed here are some of the most exciting in present-day materials science and technology.

This book would not have been possible without the support of David Beanland (RMIT) and Walter Brown (Bell Laboratories) in making available funds and facilities for holding the initial workshop and facilitating the editing of manuscripts. We thank Bill Rodney (NSF Washington) and the Australian Department of Science and Technology (Canberra) for indirect financial assistance for the initial meeting of contributors. Finally, we thank Ken Short, Andrew Pogany, Faye Adams, Kevin Rossiter and Lim Neoh of RMIT for their assistance with proof reading, and Wendy McKechnie for compiling the index.

CHAPTER 1

Introduction to Implantation and Beam Processing

J. S. WILLIAMS

Royal Melbourne Institute of Technology
Melbourne, Australia

J. M. POATE

Bell Laboratories
Murray Hill, New Jersey, USA

I. BEAMS AND MATERIALS

The structure and properties of solids can be affected by radiation. There is considerable current interest in the modification of surface layers using ion, electron and laser beams. Surfaces play a vital role in many technologies, varying from the most sophisticated, such as integrated circuit fabrication, to large-scale surface coatings. The most successful and widespread surface modification technique in semiconductor technology is ion implantation. Most integrated circuits are now fabricated using this process. Electrical dopants are introduced directly into a semiconductor surface layer by bombarding it with energetic ions. Ion implantation allows excellent control over

1

ION IMPLANTATION
AND BEAM PROCESSING
ISBN 0 12 756980 4

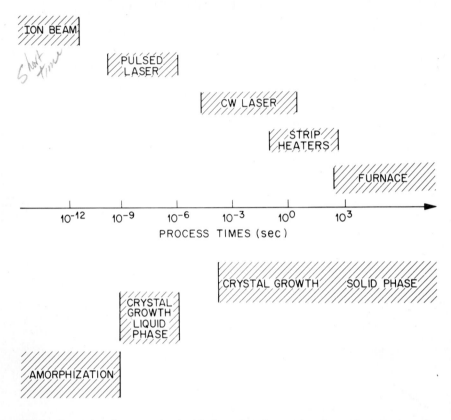

Fig. 1. Processing times associated with the various beam-processing or bulk-heating techniques. Strip heaters refer to the various rapid bulk-heating techniques. The lower part of the figure shows the range of solidification processes in semiconductors.

the number and distribution of atoms that can be injected, and it is undoubtedly this feature that has made the process an indispensable part of semiconductor technology.

This book deals not only with recent developments in ion implantation, but also with other, related beam processing techniques using laser and electron beams. During the past five years there has been a convergence of ideas and interests regarding these disparate techniques. Fig. 1 shows schematically the various process times. The process time can be defined as the time during which either the atoms of the solid are in motion or the solid is significantly above ambient temperatures as a result of the radiation. Energetic ions with ranges of 100 atomic layers will come to rest in $\sim 10^{-13}$ sec, but the excited region created by the incident ions can persist for times of the order of

10^{-11} sec. Pulsed lasers, however, can be used to heat and melt surface layers in the time range 10^{-9} to 10^{-6} sec. Continuous wave lasers can be scanned over the surface layer to give processing times in the range 10^{-5} to 10 sec. Longer processing times can be achieved using rapid bulk heating or conventional furnaces. These various beam processing and heating techniques offer a remarkable range of processing times to the experimentalist.

II. AMORPHIZATION AND CRYSTALLIZATION

The lower half of Fig. 1 illustrates the important amorphization and crystallization regimes in semiconductors which are accessible to the various beam-processing techniques. Irradiation of semiconductors with both energetic ions and pulsed laser beams can result in a crystalline-to-amorphous transition for process times less than about 10^{-9} sec, despite the fact that the energy deposition processes are very different under ion and laser irradiation conditions. Processing with pulsed lasers over a longer time scale (10^{-9} to 10^{-6} sec) can result in local surface melting and rapid resolidification of the crystalline phase.

The series of cross-section electron micrographs in Fig. 2 provides an excellent illustration of amorphization and liquid-phase-crystallization processes in Si. Fig. 2a shows an amorphous surface layer and a deeper band of isolated defects produced by implantation with As^+ ions. Subsequent irradiation with a 30-nsec ruby laser produces the following effects. Figs. 2b and 2c illustrate that, following laser irradiation at low energy densities, an amorphous-to-polycrystalline transition occurs in the outer regions of the amorphous layer. This can be attributed to localized near-surface melting, in which the melt front did not extend into the underlying crystal. Figs. 2d and 2e show an amorphous-to-single crystal transition in which the melt has just penetrated into the underlying crystal during the laser irradiation and then resolidified from the bulk seed crystal towards the surface. Irradiation at a higher energy density (Fig. 2f), which induces melting beyond the region of isolated defects, produces extended-defect-free single crystal via liquid phase epitaxial growth. The entire melting and recrystallization process occurs in a time of less than 100 nsec. Details of such rapid amorphization and crystallization processes are described in detail in Chapter 2.

Heating by continuous wave (cw) lasers, by rapid bulk heating and by conventional furnace processes, for times greater than about 10^{-5} sec, can produce an amorphous-to-crystalline transition via crystal growth within the solid phase. These various amorphization-crystallization regimes have important fundamental and technological consequences for beam processing of semiconductors. In Chapter 2, Poate and Williams give an overview of

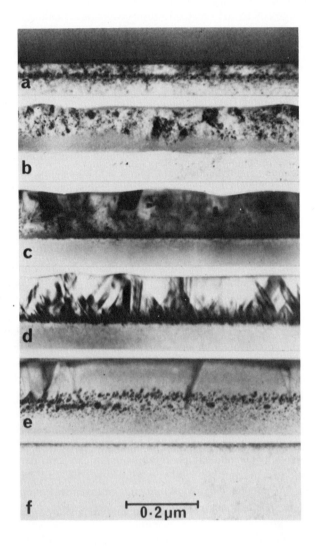

Fig. 2. Transmission electron microscope (TEM) cross-sectional images of an ion-implanted (150 keV As$^+$, 4 × 10^{15} cm^{-2}) amorphous layer on (100) Si. The first image (a) shows the as-implanted layer and the following images (b–f) show deeper melt depths using a pulsed ruby laser (30 nsec); (b) 0.2 J cm^{-2}; (c) 0.35 J cm^{-2}; (d) 0.85 J cm^{-2}; (e) 1.0 J cm^{-2}; and (f) 1.2 J cm^{-2}. From A. G. Cullis (1982). *In* "Laser Annealing of Semiconductors" (J. M. Poate and J. W. Mayer, eds.), Academic Press, New York.

the damage and amorphization processes in semiconductors which are induced by ion implantation, and they review the use of solid-phase and liquid-phase annealing methods to subsequently remove this damage. Indeed, for electronic-device applications, it is vital to follow the implantation process with an annealing step in order to reconstitute the crystal lattice and incorporate the implanted dopant atoms into electrically active lattice sites.

Beam processing over the time spans illustrated in Fig. 1 offers unique possibilities for studying fundamental aspects of crystal growth from both liquid-phase and solid-phase processes. As discussed in Chapter 2, the ability of implantation to produce "clean" amorphous layers has led to recrystallization studies using a range of both beam-processing techniques and more conventional annealing techniques. These have provided new insights into the mechanisms of crystal growth and have allowed fundamental thermodynamic parameters to be measured directly. In particular, non-equilibrium conditions of crystal growth can result in the production of metastable solid solutions.

III. FUNDAMENTAL PROCESSES

Much of this book is concerned with the ion implantation process and, in particular, with those aspects, both fundamental and technological, which constitute current research and development. However, it is important to review briefly the fundamental ion implantation processes so that the topics of both current research interest (Chapters 2 to 8) and current applications (Chapters 5, 8 to 11) may be given a proper perspective.

The four basic processes which directly result from ion bombardment are illustrated schematically in Figs. 3 and 4. As depicted by the ion trajectory in Fig. 3, a single ion of keV energies undergoes a series of energy-loss collisions with both target atoms (nuclear collisions) and electrons (electronic collisions), finally coming to rest some hundreds of atom layers below the surface. When many mono-energetic ions are implanted, the statistical nature of nuclear and electronic energy-loss collisions ensures that not all ions come to rest at precisely the same depth. The ultimate ion-depth distribution follows an approximate Gaussian form, where the peak corresponds to the most probable (projected) ion range. As the dose of incident ions increases, the concentration of implanted atoms increases, thus modifying the near-surface composition of the target. Since the incorporation of a foreign species into a solid by ion implantation is not constrained by equilibrium considerations, non-conventional near-surface alloys can be formed (as discussed in Chapter 2).

The theoretical basis for describing the electronic and nuclear energy-loss

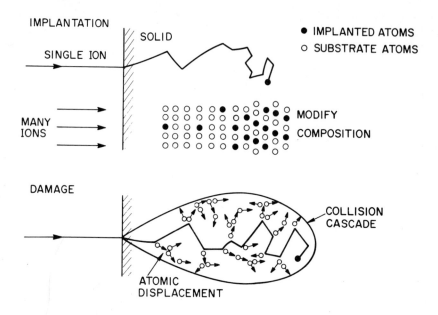

Fig. 3.   Schematic of the implantation and damage processes using energetic ion beams.

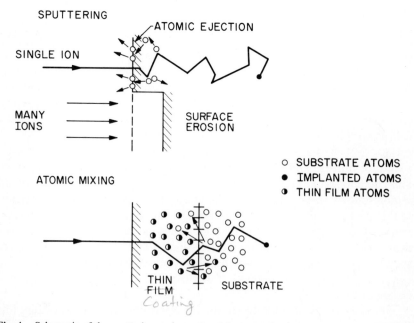

Fig. 4.   Schematic of the sputtering and atomic mixing processes using energetic ion beams.

processes is well established and can be employed to predict accurately the range distributions for energetic ions in solids. In Chapter 3, Gibbons and Christel discuss more recent applications of Boltzmann transport theory to the evaluation of range distributions in multi-layer targets, a situation often encountered during implantation-doping of integrated circuits.

Fig. 3 also illustrates radiation damage, whereby lattice atoms are displaced from their regular sites. A single heavy ion can lead to the displacement of many hundreds of lattice atoms within a volume surrounding the ion trajectory. Although simple models based solely on collisional processes can be used to calculate the expected number and distribution of displaced atoms, the structural damage resulting from ion bombardment is usually determined by several more complex processes. These receive particular attention in Chapters 2 to 8. For example, in Chapter 4, Davies treats 'spike' or high-energy deposition effects within collision cascades. These processes result in the production of completely amorphous zones about ion tracks in semiconductors, the total disordered volume containing many more displaced atoms than would be calculated from "collisional" models. Gibbons and Christel discuss alternate methods of modeling damage and amorphization in Chapter 3. In Chapter 5, Brown describes a process in which electronic energy loss can create considerable radiation damage in insulators, even though the energy transfer during such collisions is too small to displace target atoms directly. Furthermore, defects which are produced by ion irradiation may not be stable at the temperature of implantation, resulting in a "resistance" to irradiation damage. Such annealing processes are particularly important in ion-bombarded metals, but are also clearly observed in semiconductors (as discussed by Poate and Williams in Chapter 2 and Beanland in Chapter 8). For example, the cross-section electron micrograph shown in Fig. 2a illustrates an amorphous surface layer with a deeper band of discrete defects. This structure arises from annealing processes and defect agglomeration which has taken place during the implantation.

Fig. 4 schematically illustrates sputtering, a process in which target atoms are ejected from the surface during ion irradiation. Typically, each incident ion can sputter one or more target atoms. As shown, prolonged irradiation can lead to appreciable surface erosion and ultimately to removal of already implanted atoms. This latter effect, as discussed by Andersen in Chapter 6 and Beanland in Chapter 8, provides an effective limit to the concentration of implanted species which can be attained by ion implantation. Sputtering can often be described adequately by collisional processes (as discussed by Andersen, Chapter 6), but other processes, involving energy spikes (Davies, Chapter 4), electronic effects (Brown, Chapter 5) and complicated diffusional effects (Andersen, Chapter 6), can lead to enhanced sputtering, severe non-linearities and pronounced preferential sputtering of certain elemental constituents of compounds.

The final implantation process depicted in Fig. 4 is atomic mixing. The figure illustrates that ion-beam-induced intermixing can take place across the boundaries of layers of different composition. The mixing process may involve simple collisional mixing or more complicated beam-induced diffusional processes (as discussed in detail by Appleton in Chapter 7). Solid state reactions between appropriate layered components (e.g., metals on silicon to form silicides), metastable phases and novel alloys can be produced by ion beam mixing at temperatures below which these processes occur thermally. Appleton also reviews recent studies of laser mixing of films and discusses the ion beam mixing and laser mixing observations in terms of the different process times and mixing mechanisms.

IV. SEMICONDUCTOR TECHNOLOGY AND APPLICATIONS

Implantation is clearly a well established part of Si technology. However, as detailed by Rupprecht and Michel in Chapter 9, the implementation of VLSI technology is intimately related to developments in implantation. Even greater spatial control is required for shallow contacts. Moreover, high-current implantation machines are required to maintain the high throughput of large-area wafers. The special problems introduced by target heating during implantation at high beam currents, and ways of overcoming them, are discussed by Beanland in Chapter 8.

Although, at present, Si is the most important semiconductor, GaAs is assuming an increasingly important role in specialized high-speed and microwave devices. As Eisen outlines in Chapter 10, integrated circuits are now being fabricated in GaAs. This technology is beautifully illustrated by the optical and scanning electron micrographs in Figs. 5 and 6 of a GaAs integrated circuit fabricated using ion implantation. The micrographs show an 8-bit × 8-bit GaAs multiplier (Fig. 5) and an enlargement of a portion of this GaAs IC (Fig. 6). They were fabricated at Rockwell International using the two-implant process illustrated in Fig. 7c of Chapter 10. The multiplier, which has latched inputs and outputs, contains 1008 logic gates and is the largest GaAs IC fabricated to date. A multiply time, as short as 5.2 ns has been measured, corresponding to an average propagation delay per gate of 150 ps. The typical power dissipation is 1 mW/gate. The enlarged view (Fig. 6) shows FETs, active loads and diodes; the gate length is 1 μm. The white lines are the second layer metallization. The first layers of metallization and ohmic contacts are under a nitride layer and have a different appearance in the scanning electron micrograph. All GaAs integrated circuits are, at present, made by ion implantation, for the physical reasons

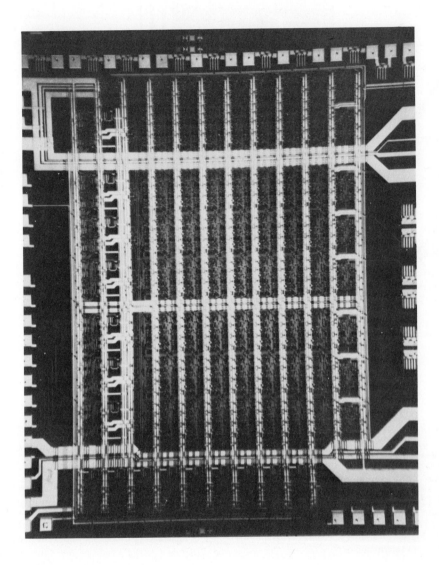

Fig. 5. Optical micrograph of an 8-bit × 8-bit GaAs multiplier. The overall chip size is 2.25 × 2.75 mm². Courtesy of F. H. Eisen, Rockwell International.

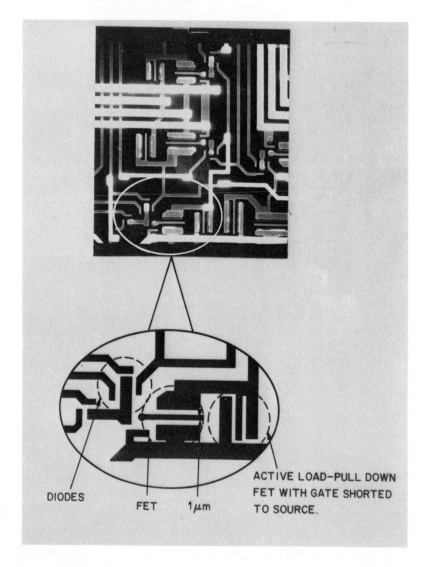

Fig. 6.   Scanning electron micrograph of a section of the GaAs IC in Fig. 5. Courtesy of Rockwell International.

outlined by Eisen in Chapter 10. Compared with Si as a material, GaAs presents many obstacles to planar processing: it is not as thermally stable and its basic metallurgy is more complex. At present, implantation offers the only viable method of localized doping. This is an exciting development in implantation technology.

Once the doped regions have been formed in a semiconductor, contacts and interconnections have to be made to the outside world. At present, contacts are formed by the simple furnace heating of deposited metal films on the bare semiconductor (as described by Baglin *et al.* in Chapter 11). The beam-processing technologies offer alternative methods of contacting. Silicides and contacts to GaAs can be formed by laser heating or ion beam mixing (as described in Chapters 7 and 11).

What role will the pulsed and scanned lasers play in semiconductor processing technology? It is clear that the pulsed sources are opening up new directions in materials science. However, the scanned sources have received more technological attention because, for example, they offer the possibility of crystal growth of deposited Si on amorphous substrates. Localized molten puddles in the Si can be swept across the substrate to give large-area crystallites. Whatever the technological future of laser annealing, there is no doubt that this work has stimulated much interest in basic annealing techniques and processes. For example, the initial observations that amorphous layers could be recrystallized in the solid phase by cw laser heating led to the current widespread interest in rapid bulk heating using more conventional heat sources.

Beam processing is an exciting and continually evolving field. It has produced new developments in materials science and technology. This interplay is well illustrated by Brown in Chapter 5, where the interaction of energetic ion beams with frozen gases of astrophysical interest is shown to have given insights into ion beam lithography using polymeric resists.

ACKNOWLEDGEMENTS

We are indebted to Tony Cullis and Fred Eisen for supplying Figures 2, 5 and 6.

CHAPTER **2**

Amorphization and Crystallization
of Semiconductors

J. M. POATE

Bell Laboratories
Murray Hill, New Jersey, USA

J. S. WILLIAMS

Royal Melbourne Institute of Technology
Melbourne, Australia

13

ION IMPLANTATION
AND BEAM PROCESSING
ISBN   0 12 756980 4

I. INTRODUCTION

The evolution of ion implantation as a successful technology has largely been determined by the ability to anneal implantation damage and produce the requisite electrical activity of the dopants. Research into the annealing process has led to several interesting developments in crystal growth and materials science. We review some of these developments in this chapter. At low implantation doses the semiconductor lattice can maintain its basic integrity, containing only isolated regions of disorder. At higher doses the disordered regions overlap to produce continuous amorphous layers. These amorphous layers produced by implantation have proved very useful for studying Si solid-phase crystallization processes because of their purity and the cleanness of the interface between the crystal and amorphous layer. Indeed, the first complete measurements of solid-phase crystallization kinetics in Si came from the early Caltech studies (Csepregi *et al.*, 1975, 1977) of the furnace annealing of implanted amorphous layers. Moreover, dopants or impurities can be deliberately introduced into the amorphous layer so that their incorporation in the lattice at the crystallizing interface may be studied as a function of temperature, time and orientation. Super-saturated solid solutions have been formed in this way.

The earlier studies on the removal of implantation damage quite naturally concentrated on the use of conventional furnaces. Within the past five years, however, a new field using laser or electron beams to heat surface layers has developed. The most exciting scientific developments have centred around the fact that amorphous and crystalline surface layers can be melted and solidified in remarkably short times. Thus, a new area of liquid-phase crystal growth has emerged.

The convergence of these various techniques and studies has produced new information on the thermodynamic properties of Si. The heat of crystallization of amorphous Si has been measured using implantation and calorimetric techniques. For the first time, amorphous Si has been formed from the melt by ultra-fast laser melting and solidification.

II. IMPLANTATION DAMAGE AND AMORPHIZATION

A. The Production of Amorphous Layers

When an energetic ion penetrates a solid target, sufficient kinetic energy may be imparted to lattice atoms during nuclear collisions to cause atomic displacements. This situation was schematically illustrated in Fig. 3 of Chapter 1, where it was shown that the recoiling lattice atom (secondary projectile)

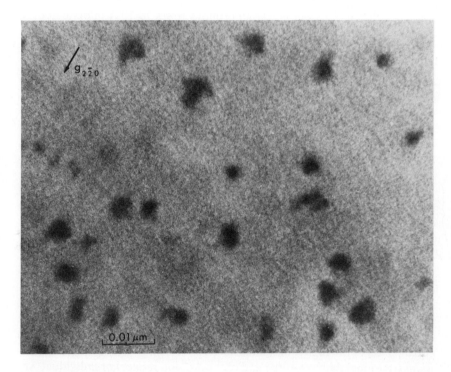

Fig. 1.   Bright-field electron micrographs of amorphous regions in Si produced by bombarding to doses of 3×10^{11} cm^{-2} with 10 keV Bi ions. From Howe and Rainville (1981).

may itself possess sufficient kinetic energy to displace many other lattice atoms. As a result, a cascade of displaced atoms may originate from a single (primary) collision between the implanted ion and a lattice atom. During its path, the implanted ion may initiate many such displacement cascades within a volume surrounding the ion track. In semiconductors, such violent displacement processes cause the accumulation of radiation damage within the lattice. For example, we have already seen (see Fig. 2 of Chapter 1) that bombardment of silicon with As$^+$ ions to a dose of 4×10^{15} cm^{-2} can produce an amorphous surface layer. In this section, we examine typical damage produced in semiconductors by individual heavy and light ions under various implantation conditions. In particular, we illustrate how amorphous damaged layers are built up during bombardment.

A typical example of heavy ion bombardment is illustrated in Fig. 1. The high-resolution transmission electron micrograph (TEM) shows the local lattice damage arising from single 10 keV Bi$^+$ ions implanted into silicon (Howe and Rainville, 1981). Completely amorphous zones 50-70 Å in diameter are observed to surround each ion track, indicating direct-impact amorphization by individual Bi$^+$ ions in a time scale of $< 10^{-11}$ sec. Significantly, each Bi$^+$ ion has directly amorphized a volume containing several thousand silicon atoms. This is a very efficient damaging event, which cannot be modeled using simple collision theory, as we discuss later. In contrast to the observations in Fig. 1, bombardment of silicon with light ions such as B$^+$ does not result in large amorphous zones about individual ion tracks (Chadderton and Eisen, 1971; Baranova et al., 1975; Howe et al., 1980). Indeed, light ion bombardment produces isolated damage clusters which contain few displaced atoms and are separated by several atom spacings along the ion track. Thus, there is a clear distinction between damage produced by individual light and heavy ions in silicon. For light ions, isolated defect clusters are created in essentially crystalline silicon, whereas for heavy ions, distinct amorphous zones are directly produced by individual ion impact (Mazey et al., 1968; Howe and Rainville, 1981).

The evolution of a continuous amorphous layer from the overlap and accumulation of damage formed by individual ions is illustrated by the Rutherford backscattering and channeling spectra in Fig. 2. In this example, damage produced by 1.7 MeV Ar$^+$ ions in silicon is shown to build up from an initial damage distribution which peaks at a depth of ~ 1.3 μm. This depth corresponds to the region of maximum nuclear energy loss and hence maximum collisional damage at the end of the Ar$^+$ ion range. For individual Ar$^+$ ions, such end-of-range damage probably consists mainly of amorphous zones. Closer to the surface, where nuclear collisions are few, the damage would be predominantly that of isolated clusters, somewhat similar to light ion damage. As shown in Fig. 2, both types of damage build up with dose to ultimately give a 1.5 μm thick buried amorphous layer, almost continuous to the surface at a dose of 2×10^{14} cm^{-2}.

A simple qualitative picture can be used to describe amorphization by heavy and light ion bombardment. Typical low-energy, heavy ion damage (as in Fig. 1) builds up with ion dose, via an increase in the density of amorphous zones, until zone overlap eventually leads to the formation of a continuous amorphous layer. From the zone dimensions for the 10 keV Bi$^+$ implants of Fig. 1, the minimum dose required to form a continuous amorphous layer would be $\sim 5 \times 10^{12}$ cm^{-2}. This number is close to those observed experimentally, which are typically $\geq 10^{13}$ cm^{-2} (see Corbett et al., 1981). For light ions, where amorphous layers are produced by the accumulation and overlap of regions of discrete defects, amorphous threshold doses are much higher than for heavy ions (typically $> 10^{15}$ ions cm^{-2}) and the amorphization process is considerably more complex (Thompson, 1981; Corbett et al., 1981).

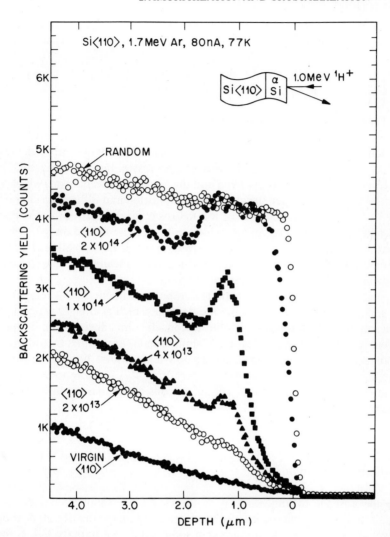

Fig. 2. Channeling spectra of damage accumulation in Si at liquid nitrogen temperature following bombardment with 1.7 MeV Ar$^+$ ions. From Donovan (1982).

Our simple picture for damage build-up and amorphization in semiconductors, although intuitively appealing, belies the complexity of the damaging process. For example, we have not yet considered the thermal stability of bombardment-induced damage. The fact that annealing can take place during bombardment severely complicates an assessment of the nature and degree of damage arising from ion bombardment. Factors influencing the damaging and annealing processes are outlined in the next section.

B. Factors Influencing Damage and Amorphization

At temperatures above absolute zero, the observed damage will be the result of competing disordering and annealing processes. In semiconductors, precise details of the defects involved and the annealing mechanisms which give rise to the final disorder structure are complicated and difficult to characterize. A comprehensive review of the field was given recently by Corbett *et al.* (1981). However, the factors which influence the final damage structure have been reasonably well characterized, and it is now possible to provide a somewhat global picture of ion damaging and annealing processes and how they are influenced by implant conditions.

In semiconductors, it is fortunate that bombardments at low temperature (e.g. 40K) essentially "freeze in" the damage which is directly generated by ion impact. It is therefore possible to consider the effects of the damaging process without the complication of simultaneous annealing. In addition, by comparing the damage produced by low-temperature bombardment with the damage produced at higher temperatures, it is possible to establish the influence of annealing. In this section, we consider the damaging and annealing processes separately.

1. Energy Deposition

In the absence of annealing, it is interesting to examine whether simple collisional theory can be employed to predict damage distributions and the level of ion damage. As discussed in some detail in Chapters 3, 4, 6 and 7, linear cascade theory (Sigmund, 1969; Winterbon *et al.*, 1970) can be employed to generate the expected spatial distribution of displaced atoms from a knowledge of the energy deposited into nuclear collision processes. Such distributions can also be obtained from Monte Carlo methods (Wilson *et al.*, 1977). All treatments give good qualitative agreement with measured ion-damage distributions when realistic interaction potentials are employed (see Chapters 4 and 7). However, linear cascade theory does not account for the level of disorder which is observed (mainly from heavy ion damage) nor for the observed ion mass, dose and energy dependencies of damage in semiconductors (Thompson, 1981). For example, based on simple collisional arguments of Kinchin and Pease (1955), the number of displaced atoms per incident ion, N_d, is given by (Sigmund, 1969)

$$N_d = 0.42 \, \nu(E)/E_d \qquad (1)$$

where $\nu(E)$ is the nuclear component of the ion energy loss which contributes to atomic displacements, and E_d is the mean displacement energy for lattice atoms (~ 13 eV for silicon). For 10 keV Bi^+ ions implanted into silicon at 40K (see Fig. 1), eq. (1) predicts ~ 300 displaced atoms per Bi^+ ion, whereas both TEM (Howe and Rainville, 1981) and ion channeling measurements (Walker and Thompson, 1978) indicate in excess of 6000 (displaced) atoms produced by the Bi^+ collision cascade. How does this discrepancy arise?

The inability of linear cascade theory to accurately predict damage levels for low temperature implantation into semiconductors has been attributed to the effects of energy spikes. (These processes are discussed in some detail by Davies in Chapter 4.) Basically, when the nuclear energy loss per atomic plane is high ($\sim$ several eV), it is possible to conceive of a volume surrounding the ion track as either (a) a thermal spike, in which the average energy supplied to lattice atoms substantially exceeds the heat of melting, or (b) a displacement spike, in which an almost continuous network of displaced atoms is created. Thermal spikes could give rise to excess damage by a process in which the local "hot spot" surrounding the ion track extends out considerably beyond the original collision cascade dimensions. This super-heated region may ultimately quench into an amorphous state in times of the order of 10^{-11} sec to give considerably more damage than expected from collision theory. (Details of thermal spikes and their consequences for damage, sputtering and mixing processes are discussed by Davies, Andersen and Appleton in Chapters 4, 6 and 7, respectively.) Alternatively, displacement spikes could give rise to excess damage by spontaneous collapse to an amorphous state, when the defect (or displacement) density attains a critical level (of the order of 10% of the total atom density for semiconductors). This somewhat *ad hoc* critical-defect-density argument for amorphization was first suggested by Swanson *et al.* (1971) in order to describe ion damage in germanium, and it has recently been employed by Christel *et al.* (1981) to account for the measured thicknesses of amorphous layers and amorphizing doses for low-temperature bombardment of silicon with both light and heavy ions. (Details of such calculations and comparison with experimental results are given by Gibbons and Christel in Chapter 3.)

As discussed by Thompson (1981), the level of isolated damage produced by single light ions (at 40K, for example), is adequately described by linear cascade theory. In fact, for light ions, the initial damage increases almost

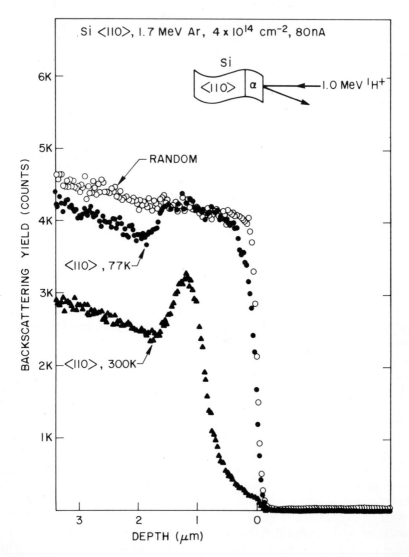

Fig. 3.   Channeling spectra of dependence of damage in Si on substrate temperature after bombardment with 1.7 MeV Ar⁺ ions. From Donovan (1982).

linearly with dose, as expected. However, the relationship is distinctly super-linear for higher doses, where many individual cascades overlap. This region may be indicative either of defect interactions within overlapping cascades or of some sort of lattice collapse into an amorphous state at a critical defect density. On the other hand, the build-up of heavy ion damage follows a linear dependence on ion dose, consistent with the simple accumulation of spike-generated amorphous zones.

2. Annealing Effects

Clearly, dynamic annealing during ion bombardment will reduce the degree of damage and possibly alter the nature of the observed damage structure by the formation of defect complexes. The reduction in disorder level is illustrated in Fig. 3 (Donovan, 1982), where the Rutherford backscattering and channeling spectra compare damage produced at 77K with that resulting from the bombardment of silicon with 1.7 MeV Ar$^+$ ions of a similar dose and dose rate at room temperature. The shape of the distribution of damage at room temperature is interesting. It is clear that dynamic annealing is more "efficient" in both the near-surface and deeper regions of the damage profile. This indicates that the regions containing isolated defects are more likely to anneal during bombardment than those regions near the end of the Ar$^+$ range where amorphous zones are produced. This behavior is typical of the differences in temperature dependence observed for low-energy light and heavy ions. For example, for boron implantation into Si (Eisen, 1970; North and Gibson, 1971; Dennis and Hale, 1978; Corbett et al., 1981), considerable dynamic annealing occurs at room temperature, and the formation of amorphous layers is suppressed (for infinite dose) as the target temperature is increased above about 370K. However, for heavy ions, significant annealing of room-temperature implantation damage in silicon is only observed at the edge of the damage distribution, where cascades are dilute. For heavy ions such as Bi$^+$, temperatures in excess of about 570K are necessary to suppress the formation of amorphous layers completely. An example of end-of-range annealing during heavy ion implantation is shown in Fig. 2 of Chapter 1, where the crystalline defect layer beyond the amorphous-crystalline boundary can be attributed to agglomeration of bombardment-induced defects. (Further examples are given by Beanland in Chapter 8.)

Because of the complexity of the dynamic annealing processes, which can involve interactions between a multitude of discrete defects (Corbett et al., 1981), models to explain the observed dependence of observed damage on target temperature, ion mass, dose, and dose rate have tended to be phenomenological in nature. One model is that of Morehead and Crowder (1970), which interprets the target temperature dependence in terms of annealing via vacancy migration at the periphery of direct impact-induced amorphous zones. Details of this model, and variations of it to account for annealing during light ion bombardment, are given by Gibbons and Christel in Chapter 3, and Beanland in Chapter 8.

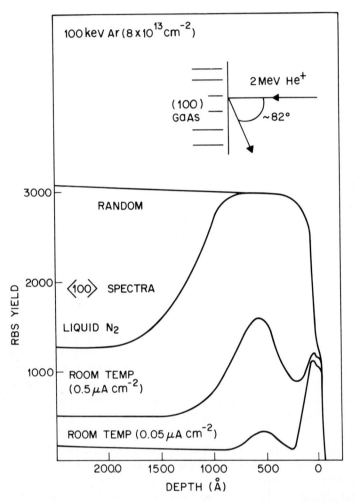

Fig. 4. Channeling spectra of dose rate dependence of damage in GaAs. From Williams (1982b).

It is important to distinguish between the two types of annealing that can take place during implantation; namely, (a) dynamic annealing of damage produced by single ions, and (b) thermal or bulk annealing of damaged layers due to a rise in target temperature during implantation. Studies of dose rate serve to illustrate the differences between the two cases. The Rutherford backscattering and channeling spectra (Fig. 4) illustrate the effects of dose rate in ion-implanted GaAs. In this example, the higher dose rate for Ar^+ implants at room temperature gives rise to *more damage* for the same implanted dose. No dose-rate effect is evident for liquid N_2 implantations, where all bombardment-induced damage is "frozen in" (Williams *et al.*, 1980a). Similar increases in damage have been observed by Moore *et al.* (1975) and Ahmed *et al.* (1980), and this effect is believed to arise from different annealing rates at room temperature for single ion disorder and overlapped damage structures. At higher dose rates, cascades can overlap before the single cascade damage has completely annealed. Similar dose-rate effects have also been observed for light ion bombardment of Si (Eisen, 1970). These observations, where damage increases with dose rate, are indicative of type (a) annealing. As discussed in detail by Beanland (Chapter 8), type (b) (bulk) annealing of damaged layers can result from very high dose and dose-rate implantation conditions which produce a bulk temperature rise during the implantation. In such cases, an increase in dose rate (beam current) can produce *a reduction* in measured damage because of the higher target temperatures attained. This latter (bulk heating) effect can have several consequences for the generation of interesting disorder structures (see Chapter 8). In particular, amorphous layers generated during the initial stages of implantation may regrow as the target temperature rises (even by only a few hundred degrees). Different amorphous thicknesses and types of damage can therefore result for substrates implanted under identical conditions.

To conclude this section, it is interesting to summarize and compare the efficiency of the dynamic annealing of implantation-induced defects for the three semiconductors Si, Ge and GaAs. This summary is given in Table 1 in terms of the approximate target temperature below which the crystalline-to-amorphous transition can be produced by light ions (row 1) and heavy

TABLE I

Approximate target temperatures for which semiconductor crystalline/amorphous phase transitions can occur

	Si	Ge	GaAs
Crystalline-to-amorphous transition during light ion bombardment (e.g. B^+)	$\leq 100°C$	Room temperature and below, depending on dose rate.	Only *significantly* below room temperature, dose-rate dependent.
Crystalline-to-amorphous transition during heavy ion bombardment (e.g. Bi^+)	$<300°C$	$\leq 200°C$	$\leq 100°C$
Amorphous-to-crystalline transition temperature (layers) during furnace annealing	500–600°C	350–400°C	200–250°C

ions (row 2). Clearly, GaAs exhibits the most efficient beam annealing of irradiation defects, whereas damage is most stable in silicon. This behaviour is compared with the typical post-bombardment temperatures at which solid-phase recrystallization of amorphous layers is observed for each substrate (row 3). A typical example of dynamic annealing is given by Nakata and Kajiyama (1982), who observed the recrystallization of amorphous layers 650 Å thick on (100) Si at 300° C by bombardment with a 2.5 MeV heavy ion beam. This behavior arises from dynamic annealing of cascades that overlap the interface, thus giving rise to epitaxial growth.

C. Structural Considerations

As indicated in the previous section, the exact nature and concentration of isolated defects and defect complexes which result from ion bombardment of semiconductors are difficult to characterize. The myriad of possibilities which can exist are reviewed by Corbett et al. (1981). Suffice it to say, that the isolated defects which arise from light ion damage are most difficult to remove by subsequent thermal annealing processes. Elevated temperature and high dose-rate implants can also give rise to discrete crystalline defects, and these are often in the form of extended defects (loops) and clusters. (These structures are discussed in Chapter 8.) They are much more difficult to remove by a subsequent annealing process, compared with the removal of continuous amorphous layers. Unless considerable care is taken to ensure adequate heat sinking, together with implants carried out at low temperatures, amorphizing implants will invariably have a region at the boundary of the amorphous and crystalline layers which contains "annealed" defect complexes (see Fig. 2, Chapter 1). This non-amorphous deep damage is also most difficult to remove completely by subsequent furnace annealing.

Amorphous layers which are generated by ion implantation can possess rather interesting properties not easily obtained with amorphous silicon produced via the more conventional vapor deposition process. For example, by bombarding a crystalline target with pure Si$^+$ ions, it is possible to obtain amorphous layers which are as pure as the substrate and which have an interface with the underlying crystal that is free from contamination. Except under the most careful ultra-high vacuum-deposition conditions, it is not possible to approach such a level of cleanliness. Amorphous layers produced by ion implantation therefore constitute an excellent medium for studying epitaxial growth processes under impurity-free conditions. Details of such measurements have been reviewed by Lau et al. (1981); more recent measurements are given in the following sections of this chapter where both solid-phase and liquid-phase crystallization regimes are described.

Besides impurity differences, possibly more important structural differences between implanted and deposited amorphous silicon layers have been identified. These have been reviewed previously by Poate and Bean (1982). In particular, clean deposited silicon films exhibit different solid-phase recrystallization kinetics (lower activation energies) compared with measurements on implanted layers. It has been suggested that this effect is attributable to the porous, less dense structure of deposited amorphous films compared with those prepared by ion implantation of bulk crystalline targets (Bean and Poate, 1980).

The detailed structure of ion-implanted amorphous silicon has not been examined in detail, but early stress/strain measurements of amorphous layers on bulk substrates established that the amorphous phase produced by ion implantation was about 6% less dense than the crystalline phase (Whan and Arnold, 1970; EerNisse, 1973). Furthermore, EPR and other similar techniques used to probe local atomic arrangements (see Corbett et al., 1981) give information similar to that obtained from amorphous silicon prepared by more conventional processes. Finally, TEM investigations (Mazey et al., 1968; Chadderton and Eisen, 1971; Howe and Rainville, 1981) provide strong evidence of local structure similar to that for deposited amorphous silicon. However, despite these reports, some evidence exists to suggest that there may be differences in the local structures of amorphous layers prepared under different implantation conditions. For example, Thompson et al. (1980), Howe et al. (1980) and Beanland and Williams (1978) report different annealing kinetics for amorphous layers and zones produced by atomic and molecular implants. Recently Narayan and Holland (1982) have observed that the maximum concentration of dopants incorporated in Si during the epitaxial recrystallization of amorphized layers depends upon the implantation parameters. This behaviour has been interpreted in terms of different degrees of amorphicity produced by different implantation conditions. However, such structural differences need further investigation: it would be interesting, for example, to measure accurate activation energies for recrystallization of layers amorphized by light ions (overlap of isolated defects) and heavy ions (direct impact amorphization) as a means of determining possible structural differences.

Finally, possible stoichiometry variations which could arise from ion bombardment of compounds are worth mentioning. For example, in GaAs, displacement damage and spike processes within the collision cascades will undoubtedly produce local departures from stoichiometry. Based solely upon collisional arguments and the use of Boltzmann transport methods,

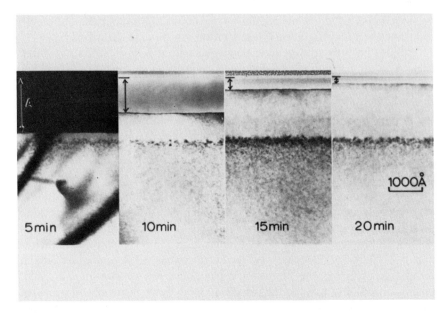

Fig. 5. Transmission electron microscope cross-sectional micrograph for 200 keV Sb$^+$ (6.0 × 10^{15} cm^{-2}) implants in Si annealed at 525°C. From Fletcher *et al.* (1981a).

Gibbons and Christel (Chapter 3) have established that, in GaAs, following amorphization with heavy ions, local regions close to the surface will be rich in As, whereas deeper regions may be significantly rich in Ga. This local non-stoichiometry effect may play an important role in determining the poor-quality epitaxial growth which has been observed for ion-amorphized compound semiconductors, as described in the following section and in Chapter 3.

III. SOLID-PHASE CRYSTALLIZATION

In Table I, we indicated that amorphous layers in semiconductors can be recrystallized in the solid phase by simple heating. Silicon, germanium and gallium arsenide have well-defined temperatures at which crystallization is observed to take place, and these are determined by the activation energy for recrystallization and the growth kinetics. For ion-implanted layers, the recrystallization process usually proceeds epitaxially on the underlying crystalline substrate. This epitaxial growth process is clearly illustrated by the series of cross-section TEM micrographs in Fig. 5. Annealing for various times at 525°C results in regrowth of the amorphous layer produced by the implantation of 200 keV Sb^+ at 4.4 × 10^{15} cm^{-2} into (100) silicon. The epitaxial regrowth rates are about 1.5 Å min^{-1} for these annealing conditions. Note that the dark band of defects at ∿ 1600 Å below the surface corresponds to incompletely annealed end-of-range damage resulting from beam heating. /

Solid-phase epitaxial growth (SPEG) of amorphous semiconductors is conventionally carried out in a furnace at temperatures equal to, or in excess of, those listed in Table I (row 3) for the various substrates (Mayer *et al.*, 1968; Csepregi *et al.*, 1975; Mazey *et al.*, 1968). Alternatively, solid-phase recrystallization can be induced in a much shorter time at higher temperatures by using scanning continuous wave (cw) laser and electron beams (Gat and Gibbons, 1978; Williams *et al.*, 1978; Regolini *et al.*, 1979; McMahon and Ahmed, 1979) or by employing strip heaters, high intensity arc lamps, solar energy or incoherent light sources (Fan *et al.*, 1981; Gat, 1981; Lau *et al.*, 1979; Fulks *et al.*, 1981; Harrison *et al.*, 1982). The laser and e-beam irradiations can locally raise the surface temperature to >900°C for times of the order of milliseconds, whereas the latter heating methods essentially provide heating of the entire wafer to appropriate elevated temperatures for times in the range 1 to 100 seconds. Although solid-phase annealing can be induced over wide time and temperature ranges using the various transient annealing methods, the basic crystallization phenomena are essentially similar. In this section, we concentrate specifically on the crystallization behavior in silicon and GaAs, which has been achieved by furnace annealing.

A. Crystallization of Silicon

Pioneering work at Caltech established that the growth kinetics of impurity-free amorphous layers produced by Si^+ ion implanted into (100) silicon are particularly simple (Csepregi *et al.*, 1975). During regrowth, the planar amorphous-crystalline interface moves towards the surface with a uniform velocity and a well-defined activation energy of between 2.35 and 2.85 eV (Csepregi *et al.*, 1975; Lietoila *et al.*, 1982). In such cases, the regrown epitaxial layer is relatively defect-free (Lau *et al.*, 1981), similar to the regrown layer shown in Fig. 5. When substrates other than (100) are employed and implant species other than Si^+ are used to produce amorphous silicon, the regrowth kinetics and the nature of the regrown layers are often considerably more complex. Indeed, the epitaxial regrowth process depends upon several parameters, such as substrate orientation, and the type and concentration of implanted species (Fig. 6). Considering the (100) regrowth rate data in the middle to upper portion of Fig. 6, low concentrations of implanted arsenic and indium impurities (<2.5 × 10^{20} cm^{-3}) are shown to enhance the

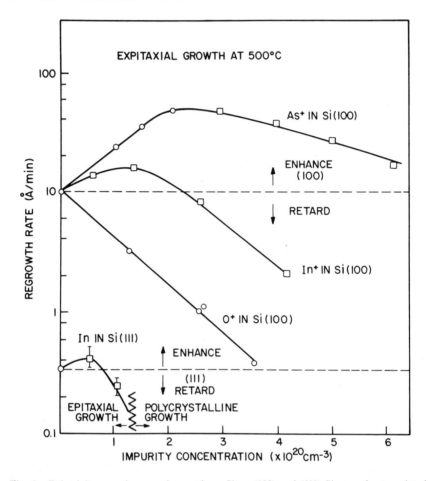

Fig. 6. Epitaxial regrowth rates of amorphous Si on (100) and (111) Si at, and extrapolated to, 500°C as a function of impurity concentration. The circles are data from Csepregi *et al.* (1977) and Kennedy *et al.* (1977), and the squares are data from Williams and Elliman (1980, 1981, 1982).

regrowth, compared with the impurity-free rate of 10 Å min⁻¹ at 500°C for growth of (100) silicon (Lau *et al.*, 1981). In contrast, oxygen impurities significantly retard regrowth. More extensive regrowth data (Csepregi *et al.*, 1977; Kennedy *et al.*, 1977; Campisano, 1982) have indicated that low concentrations (less that about 1 atom per cent) of both n-type and p-type dopants enhance the regrowth rate, whereas impurities such as oxygen, nitrogen and carbon are notable retarders of regrowth rate. Recent results (Suni *et al.*, 1982; Lietoila *et al.*, 1982) have shown that multiple implants of equal (but low) concentrations of p-type and n-type impurities provide a compensation-like effect whereby the regrowth rate returns to that of intrinsic (impurity-free) silicon. We shall return to discuss such impurity-related effects in a later section.

Returning to Fig. 6, higher concentrations of In and As are shown to result in a drop in regrowth rate for (100) silicon. In fact, recent evidence (Williams and Elliman, 1980; Campisano and Barbarino, 1981) suggests that the regrowth rate attains a maximum and then slows down appreciably at concentrations close to or exceeding the particular equilibrium solubility limit for the impurity in silicon. This behavior has been attributed to high levels of strain at the amorphous-crystal interface, which arise from significant concentrations of impurities that are smaller (e.g. boron) or larger (e.g. As, In, Sb) than silicon.

The (111) regrowth data in the lower part of Fig. 6 illustrate some interesting differences compared with (100) silicon regrowth. For impurity-free silicon, (111) regrowth is much slower than that of (100) layers. Indeed, it has been shown (Csepregi et al., 1978) that all silicon orientations exhibit roughly similar regrowth activation energies, but (100) samples regrow about three times faster than (110) samples and about twenty-five times faster than the initial growth rate for (111) substrates. Moreover, the growth of (111) silicon is non-linear with anneal time and exhibits pronounced twinning along (111) planes, the twins occupying about 30-40% of the overall volume of the regrown layer (Lau et al., 1981).

For (111) silicon, small concentrations of impurities (e.g. the In in Fig. 6) may also enhance the regrowth rate, but the onset of retardation with increasing dose appears earlier for (111) than for (100) Si. This retardation effect is more catastrophic for (111) substrates in the sense that polycrystalline growth processes can often dominate epitaxy. Such effects are more readily apparent for even smaller concentrations of low-solubility impurities, such as the rare gases and Pb (Williams and Grant, 1976; Williams et al., 1977; Williams, 1980). The particularly poor epitaxy for these impurities has been attributed to nucleation of polycrystalline growth at implant precipitates or aggregates within the amorphous layer. These processes are more typical in the higher implant dose regime.

At higher implant doses (exceeding a few atomic per cent), more complex recrystallization processes can be apparent, even for (100) silicon. For ease of description, we distinguish between regrowth effects appropriate to (a) slow-diffusing implanted impurities, including all conventional dopants, which are effectively immobile in silicon at the normal regrowth temperatures of 500-600°C, and (b) fast-diffusing impurities such as Cu and Ag, which may have precipitated in the amorphous Si phase prior to recrystallization. Slow and fast diffusers are defined in terms of their diffusivity

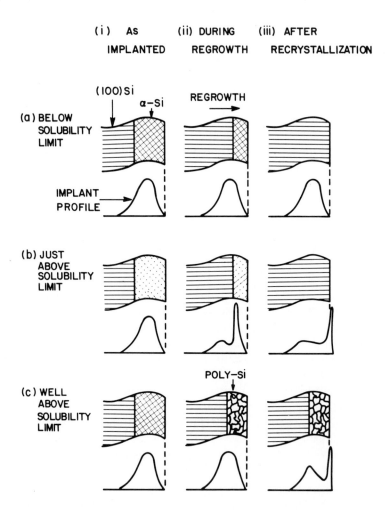

Fig. 7.   Schematic of typical regrowth sequence for ≤600°C annealing of ion implanted (100) Si. Three dose regimes are shown. From Williams and Short (1982).

in crystalline Si. There is no experimental knowledge at present of diffusion coefficients in amorphous Si. Indeed, the diffusion length of fast diffusers in crystalline Si, under the conditions of solid-phase regrowth, are less than 50 Å. Nevertheless, the data presented here indicate distinct differences between fast and slow diffusers, in terms of short-range diffusion and precipitation in amorphous Si. The typical regrowth behavior for type (a) implanted impurities is illustrated schematicaly in Fig. 7, for three dose regimes.

In the lowest dose regime, good quality epitaxy is obtained, no redistribution of impurities is observed during the growth process, and the impurities are almost totally incorporated onto substitutional lattice sites. This regime can occur even when the impurity concentration somewhat exceeds the maximum expected equilibrium solubility in Si. However, increased implant dose invariably leads to the behavior illustrated in Fig. 7b. In this case, the epitaxial regrowth rate proceeds at a much slower rate than in (a) and a fraction of the impurity is observed to segregate at the moving amorphous-crystal boundary during regrowth, to ultimately reside at the silicon surface following complete recrystallization. This particular redistribution behavior has been observed in silicon for In (Williams and Elliman, 1982; Fletcher et al., 1981a), Pb (Williams and Elliman, 1981), As (Williams et al., 1979), and Bi, Tl and Sb implanted impurities (Williams and Short, 1982). It is interesting that the fraction of impurity remaining in the bulk is observed to reside largely on substitutional sites. The implant dose at which "push out" is observed is species dependent, being related somewhat to the solubility limit of the impurity in silicon. The final regime in Fig. 7(c) illustrates typical regrowth behavior in (100) silicon at implant doses considerably in excess of the "push out" dose. During regrowth, epitaxy is retarded to such an extent that nucleation and growth of polycrystalline silicon within the near-surface layers may be the dominant recrystallization process. Following recrystallization, implanted impurities have been observed to diffuse through the polycrystalline surface layer, presumably along grain boundaries, to build up at the silicon surface. This behavior is typical of In, Pb, and Bi implants into (100) silicon (Williams and Short, 1982) and occurs at doses in excess of about 3×10^{15} cm^{-2}, or for implanted concentrations of the order of 4×10^{20} cm^{-3}, a value well above the equilibrium solubility limit for these impurities in silicon.

For type (b) implanted impurities (i.e. fast diffusers in silicon), the behavior represented in Fig. 7c is obtained for relatively low (often < 1 at %) implanted concentrations. This behavior has been observed for Cu, Ag and rare gas implants into (100) silicon (Campisano et al., 1980a,b; Williams and Grant, 1976; Revesz et al., 1978; Wittmer et al., 1978). As discussed by Williams (1982a), polycrystalline nucleation is thought to arise either from precipitates of the fast diffusing impurity species already present in the amorphous phase (type b), or as a result of slow regrowth and impurity segregation at the moving interface for the impurities of low diffusivity (type a). Indeed, gas bubbles have been observed in the amorphous phase for rare gas implants into silicon (Revesz et al., 1978), and these induce polycrystalline growth.

We have presented, in this section, various effects which can take place during recrystallization of amorphous implanted layers. Polycrystalline or

highly defective layers, resulting from recrystallization, are extremely difficult to remove even at annealing temperatures of greater than 1000°C (see
Chapter 8).

B. Crystallization of Gallium Arsenide

In contrast to the normally well-behaved epitaxial growth process associated
with low-dose implantation into silicon, solid-phase annealing of ion-
implanted GaAs proceeds via a more complex, multi-stage process. Early
studies (Mazey and Nelson, 1969; Carter et al., 1971) revealed that the removal of damage in GaAs occurred over the broad temperature range of
250-600°C. More recent data of Gamo et al. (1977), Williams and Harrison
(1981) and Kular et al. (1980) reveal the presence of two annealing stages
in the removal of amorphous implant damage in GaAs. The first stage occurs
sharply in the temperature range 125-230°C and is related to an amorphous-
to-crystalline transition with rather poor epitaxy. A second stage, in the range
400-600°C, usually succeeds in removing extended defects and more complex damage which has accompanied the poor epitaxy. However, more
detailed studies (Kular et al., 1980) have indicated that there are at least three
important annealing stages associated with the complete removal of damage.
These are the two previously mentioned and a third stage involving the con-
tinual improvement in electrical activity and mobility of dopant implants up
to 900°C (Eisen, 1980; Donnelly, 1981; Kular et al., 1980).

The poor-quality epitaxial regrowth of GaAs has precluded detailed
measurements of regrowth kinetics. However, the work of Williams and Austin (1980) indicates that good-quality crystalline GaAs (as measured by
channeling) can be obtained under carefully controlled implant and low-
temperature annealing conditions. For example, Fig. 8 indicates the annealing behavior of Ar^+ implanted (100) GaAs for two doses just sufficient to
create an amorphous surface layer at liquid nitrogen temperatures. For the
lower dose case in Fig. 8a, almost complete damage removal is obtained at
180°C. A slightly higher dose (Fig. 8b) does not anneal to good-quality crystal during epitaxial growth (at 250°C), and an anneal temperature of 600°C
is required to remove all the defects. This behavior suggests a dose dependence in which heavily damaged amorphous layers are harder to regrow via
a simple (stage 1) epitaxial process. Williams et al. (1980a), in attempting
to measure the regrowth kinetics, found that the rate of epitaxial growth at
temperatures below 200°C was very sensitive to small changes in the implant
dose close to the amorphous threshold dose, with the regrowth rate slowing
down as the dose increased. More recent and detailed low-temperature
annealing studies by Grimaldi et al. (1981a,b) have found that the crystal

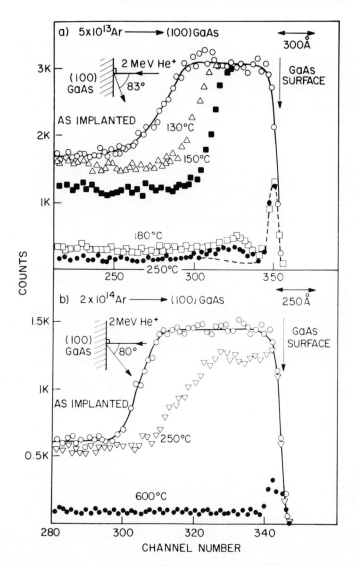

Fig. 8. Channeling spectra of epitaxial regrowth of amorphous layers on (100) GaAs: (a) planar movement of interface and (b) non-planar. From Williams and Austin (1980).

quality following stage 1 recovery depends strongly on the thickness of the amorphous layer generated by ion implantation, and less strongly on ion species, dose and implant temperature. Single-crystal growth, free of defects as detected by channeling, was only achieved for a very thin amorphous layer

($\leq$400 Å). In addition, Nissim *et al.* (1982) have indicated that only below a critical energy deposition density (during implantation) are amorphous layers able to be annealed successfully at temperatures below 400°C. Thus, although these results indicate the possibility of improved epitaxy, the most general behavior (particularly for room-temperature implants) is that annealing temperatures of >600°C are needed to remove remnant crystalline damage. Poor-quality solid-phase epitaxy is probably an intrinsic feature of binary materials. In particular, the poor epitaxy associated with ion-bombarded GaAs can be ascribed to local non-stoichiometry, as discussed by Williams (1982b). Dopant activation in GaAs therefore requires complex annealing steps (see Chapter 10).

C. Regrowth Models

Various models have been proposed to explain the dependence of epitaxial regrowth rates in Si on orientation and dopant type. These have been reviewed by Williams (1982a). A model recently proposed by Williams and Elliman (1983) incorporates the structural interface model of Spaepen and Turnbull (1979), which accounts for orientation-dependent growth, together with Fermi level and electronic considerations necessary to explain the compensation-like effect on regrowth. The essential elements of the model are as follows. The crystalline growth sites at the amorphous-crystalline interface are envisaged as kink-like steps on [110] ledges (as illustrated in the schematic representation in Fig. 9). It is proposed that the SPEG process is controlled by the motion of these kink-like growth sites BB' along [110] ledges AA'. In a manner analogous to dislocation motion (Hirsch, 1979, 1981), doping may enhance the epitaxial regrowth velocity by either increasing the concentration of charged kinks or reducing their migration energy. The effect of doping is to move the Fermi level, which will lead to an increase in the charged vacancy (Van Vechten and Thurmond, 1976) or kink concentrations. Fig. 9 shows regrowth via kink motion on the upper ledge AA': this may be envisaged as a cooperative process in which a moving kink recrystallizes many atoms before annihilation. The lower ledge illustrates pinning of kinks at a "strong" bond between certain impurity atoms and silicon. The solid lines joining the row of ledge atoms in Fig. 9 are not meant to represent the true bonding situation: atoms at kink sites may be either fully coordinated or possess dangling bonds, similar to dislocation models (Hirsch, 1981). The above model has several appealing features: (i) it can account for compensation-like regrowth effects; (ii) it is based upon a strong analogy with dislocation motion in silicon, where the doping effects are better understood; and (iii) it can readily incorporate the basic details of the Spaepen

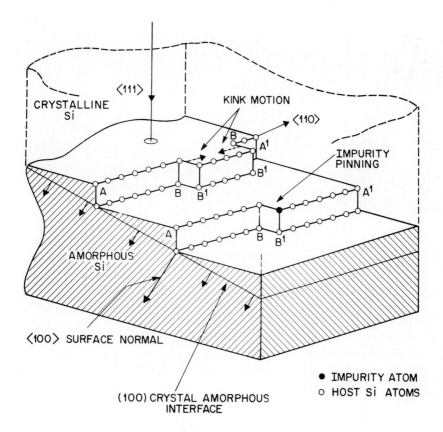

Fig. 9. Movement of kinks in epitaxial growth of amorphous Si on (100) Si. From Williams (1982a).

model for the structure of the crystalline-amorphous interface (Spaepen and Turnbull, 1979, 1982).

D. Metastable Solid Solutions

Ion implantation can incorporate impurities in solids at concentrations which greatly exceed maximum equilibrium values. However, in silicon, subsequent annealing to reconstitute the crystalline lattice structure may lead to impurity precipitation effects and a return to near-equilibrium solubility conditions. Indeed, in section III A, it was suggested that retarded regrowth

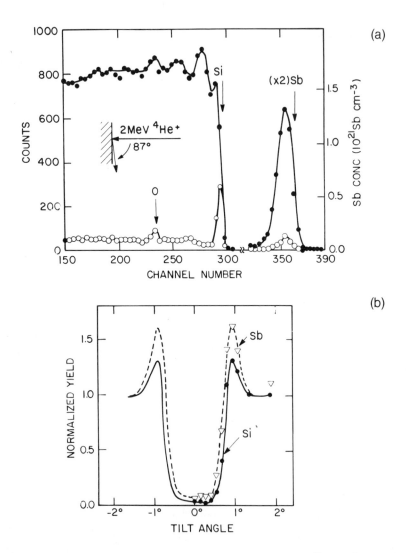

Fig. 10. (a) High resolution Rutherford backscattering spectra of 5×10^{15} Sb cm^{-2} implanted (100) Si after 600°C for 30 min. (b) Channeling angular scan for (a). From Williams and Short (1982).

rate, poor-quality epitaxial growth, and concentration-dependent precipitation effects may well be related to solid solubility limits for the implanted impurity in silicon. In terms of regrowth and implant redistribution, it has already been shown that a clear distinction can be made between fast-diffusing and slow-diffusing impurities in silicon. Similarly, for solid solubility, one may expect differences between fast diffusers, which can precipitate ahead of the advancing crystal-amorphous interface during epitaxy, and slow diffusers, which may remain randomly dispersed as the recrystallization front sweeps to the surface to incorporate them into the crystalline lattice. In the latter case, super-saturated solid solutions might be expected to accompany SPEG. Indeed, early studies of ion implantation and furnace annealing in silicon (e.g. Mayer *et al.*, 1970) gave clear indications of the possibility of forming super-saturated solid solutions via solid-phase recrystallization. More recent measurements have detailed the dependence of super-saturation on implant species, substrate orientation and annealing conditions (Williams *et al.*, 1977; Blood *et al.*, 1979; Williams *et al.*, 1980b; Josquin and Tamminga, 1978). Detailed measurements have clearly identified that highest solubilities are obtained for (100) silicon and for furnace anneal temperatures $\sim 600°C$ (Williams and Elliman, 1980, 1981, 1982; Campisano *et al.*, 1980a,b; Fletcher *et al.*, 1981a).

An example of super-saturation is illustrated in Fig. 10 for $600°C$ annealing of 5×10^{15} Sb cm^{-2} implanted (100) silicon. In this case, the high resolution channeling spectra of Fig. 10a indicate that $>94\%$ of the Sb atoms have been incorporated on, or close to, lattice sites, giving a peak substitutional Sb concentration of $\sim 1.3 \times 10^{21}$ cm^{-3}, which substantially exceeds the maximum equilibrium solid solubility limit of 7×10^{19} cm^{-3} (Trumbore, 1960). It is of interest to examine the detailed atom location of such metastable solid solutions using angular scan measurements about the $<100>$ axis (see Fig. 10b). These scans indicate only a slight narrowing of the Sb dip compared with that of Si, indicating that only a small fraction of the Sb atoms are displaced off Si lattice sites, even for this highly metastable solid solution.

In Table II we summarize some typical measurements of metastable solubility limits obtained from solid-phase epitaxy of (100) silicon. We have included solubility limits (Trumbore, 1960) and the differences in tetrahedral

TABLE II

Tabulations of equilibrium solubility limits, measured solubility limits, "push-out" dose and covalent radius mismatch with Si for the various implanted impurities.[a]

Species	Maximum equilibrium limit (cm^{-3})	Metastable solid-phase limit (cm^{-3})	"Push-out" dose (cm^{-2})	$\mid r_i - r_{si} \mid$ (Å)
As	1.5×10^{21}	9×10^{21}	$\geq 3 \times 10^{16}$	0.01
Sb	7×10^{19}	1.3×10^{21}	$\sim 7 \times 10^{15}$	0.19
In	8×10^{17}	5×10^{19}	10^{15}	0.37
Pb	$<5 \times 10^{17}$	8×10^{19}	$\sim 10^{15}$	0.37
Bi	8×10^{17}	9×10^{19}	$\sim 2 \times 10^{15}$	0.39

[a] From Williams and Elliman (1981)

covalent radius (Pauling, 1948) between the various implanted atoms and Si. The measured solubility limits are correlated with impurity push-out doses and impurity size. Such correlations are discussed more fully in a recent review (Williams, 1982a).

Having formed supersaturated solid solutions, it is interesting to examine their stability during subsequent heat treatment. As an example, subsequent annealing of metastable Sb solid solutions at temperatures between 600°C and 1000°C have resulted in a considerable drop in the substitutional Sb fraction for doses $>10^{15}$ cm^{-2}. Such results (Williams and Short, 1982) have suggested that the equilibrium substitutional solubility limit for Sb in Si in the temperature range 750-850°C is close to 2.2 × 10^{20} cm^{-3}, about a factor of three above the maximum equilibrium solubility reported by Trumbore (1960). It is suggested that precipitation of impurities from metastable solid solutions, as in the SPEG measurements, may be a more accurate method of determining equilibrium solubility limits. Accurate determinations of solubility limits in silicon and corresponding electrical activities are clearly important (see Chapter 9). At high dopant concentrations, solubility limits may not correspond exactly with electrical activity. For example, maximum measured concentrations of electrically active As in Si ($\sim$3 × 10^{20} cm^{-3}) are at least a factor of five lower than the measured solubility limit in the temperature range 850-950°C (Lietoila et al., 1981). However, both the measured solubility limit and the measured electrical activity are the same for Sb in Si (2.2 × 10^{20} cm^{-3}), as reported by Williams and Short (1982).

IV. LIQUID-PHASE CRYSTALLIZATION

A. Laser Melting and Recrystallization

Pulsed lasers provide a controllable means of melting thin surface layers of Si. The solidification process is demonstrated in the micrographs of Cullis (1982) (see Fig. 2 of Chapter 1). If the melt does not penetrate completely through both the amorphous layers and defects at the interface, polycrystallites or extended defects are formed on solidification. Once the melt completely engulfs all the defective material, perfect epitaxy results at solidification velocities of about 3 m sec^{-1}. Liquid-phase epitaxy using pulsed lasers is therefore a very efficient way of removing implantation damage. In fact, epitaxy can be achieved even with an oxide layer at the interface between an amorphous layer and underlying crystal (Bean et al., 1979). The practical depth of laser melting is limited by the amount of energy that can be deposited without vaporizing the surface. For pulsed lasers, the maximum depths that have been melted are typically $\sim$1 μm. This depth sets a practical limit on the thickness amenable to recrystallization by liquid-phase epitaxy. The use of pulsed lasers in Si processing technology has recently been reviewed by Hill (1982). The following section will be primarily concerned with the melting and solidification processes in Si. Numerous studies (e.g. Fletcher *et al.*, 1981b) have now shown that GaAs can be recrystallised by liquid-phase epitaxy using pulsed lasers (as reviewed by Williams, 1982b). However, no detailed studies have been made of the basic crystallization phenomena. Eisen (Chapter 10) and Baglin *et al.* (Chapter 11) review device applications in GaAs.

B. Heat Flow and Interface Velocities

A determining parameter in liquid-phase epitaxy is the velocity of the liquid-solid interface. In the case of conventional liquid-phase crystal growth (Czochralski, for example) the rate of extraction of the seed crystal from the melt is determined by the rate of extraction of latent heat through the seed. The temperature gradients are low and growth rates are typically 10^{-5} m sec^{-1}. The situation is diametrically opposite in laser melting of surfaces. The molten layers are very thin, typically 1000 Å, and the temperature gradients into the solid substrate can be enormous. The latent heat of crystallization can therefore be extracted very rapidly, and the layer will resolidify at high velocities. This behavior should be contrasted with solid-phase recrystallization, where the temperature gradients are essentially zero and the rate of regrowth depends upon the temperature dependence of bond breaking and the atomic configuration of the interface.

Heat-flow calculations (Baeri, 1982) of regrowth velocities are shown in Fig. 11 for ruby laser irradiation of Si at energies sufficient to produce a 1000 Å-thick molten layer. The regrowth velocity is a strong function of laser pulse width and laser absorption coefficient. The velocity will be faster for irradiation conditions where the energy is deposited more rapidly (i.e. short pulse length) or in smaller volumes (i.e. high absorption coefficient). The absorption coefficient is both a function of material and laser wavelength. The calculations were made for ruby ($\lambda = 0.694$ μm) irradiation of crystalline Si or crystalline Si with a 1000 Å amorphous overlayer. For the former case, the low absorption coefficient ($\alpha = 4 \times 10^3$ cm^{-1}) ensures that the regrowth velocity is almost independent of pulse length. This behavior does not apply for the amorphous case where $\alpha = 5 \times 10^4$ cm^{-1}. The absorption coefficient can be increased by frequency doubling the ruby wavelength to give UV radiation with $\alpha = 2 \times 10^5$ cm^{-1} in Si. The highest velocities are obtained for this strong coupling case. However, carrier diffusion, which increases the effective energy deposition length, produces an upper limit (dashed line) to

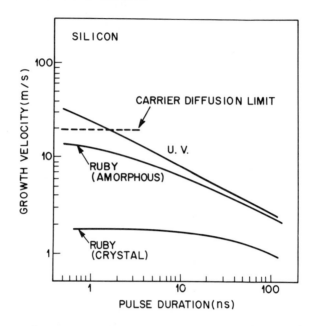

Fig. 11. Average liquid–solid interface velocity for the resolidification of a 1000Å-thick molten layer on Si as a function of laser pulse width. The two lower curves refer to ruby (0.694 μm) irradiations of a 1000Å amorphous layer on crystalline Si (upper) and crystalline Si only (lower). The upper curve refers to UV (0.347 μm) irradiation of crystalline Si. From Baeri (1982).

the velocity. At present it is experimentally possible with pulsed lasers to vary the regrowth velocities over the range of 1-20 m sec⁻¹ (Poate, 1982). The subject of heat-flow calculations and regrowth velocities has recently been reviewed by Baeri and Campisano (1982).

The fact that the resistivity of Si drops by a factor of thirty when melted has enabled Galvin *et al.* (1982) to measure the interface velocities directly. The conductance of the thin molten layer is measured as a function of time, thus giving melt-in and solidification velocities. The agreement between heat-flow calculations of interface regrowth velocities and these measurements is excellent for velocities ∿3 m sec⁻¹.

C. Segregation and Crystal Growth

At present it is not possible to observe crystallization phenomena at the rapidly moving interface. The segregation of impurities at the interface is, however, one of the more striking manifestations of rapid crystal growth. Fig.

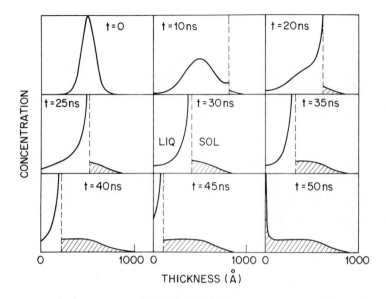

Fig. 12. Schematic of the motion of the liquid–solid interface (2 m sec⁻¹) and segregation of impurities with $\kappa' = 0.1$. Liquid state diffusivity is assumed to be 10^{-4} cm² sec⁻¹. From Baeri and Campisano (1982).

12 shows a computer simulation of the melting and solidification process with segregation of an impurity (Baeri and Campisano, 1982). The zero time curve shows the implanted distribution of the impurity in the solid. After 10 nsec, a layer which has been melted to a depth of 1000 Å has resolidified some 200 Å, with an interface velocity of 2 m sec⁻¹. The impurities are diffused in the liquid, with a diffusion coefficient of 10^{-4} cm² sec⁻¹, hence the broadening of the distribution. The impurity is assumed to have an interfacial segregation coefficient of $\kappa' = 0.1$, which is the ratio of the impurity concentration in the solid to that in the liquid at the interface. As time progresses, a zone-refined layer is pushed to the surface, and the final segregated profile is shown at 50 nsec. If, for example, the impurity has an interfacial segregation coefficient of unity, only profile broadening will be observed, without any segregation to the surface. Indeed, this is the case for As, B and P.

A series of experiments has been used to measure segregation phenomena by pulsed laser melting of Si implanted with very low-solubility dopants (Poate, 1982). Fig. 13 shows measurements of Bi implanted into (100) Si following laser melting using a calculated resolidification velocity of 1.8 m sec⁻¹ (Baeri *et al.*, 1981). The solid line represents a fit to the data assuming a unique interfacial segregation coefficient of 0.1. It is notable how well the theory fits the data. The theory assumes that the Bi atoms are frozen

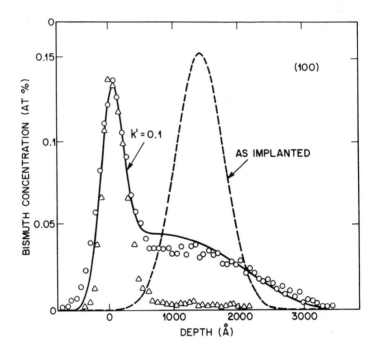

Fig. 13. Bismuth depth profiles in (100) Si for a regrowth velocity of 1.8 m sec^{-1}. Open circles are random yields and triangles are aligned yields. Smooth curves are κ' fits. From Baeri *et al.* (1981).

in the solid after the liquid-solid interface has passed. This assumption is perfectly reasonable considering the known quench rates and maximum solid-state diffusivities. The success of the fit gives confidence in the applicability of the classical model of impurity segregation at the liquid-solid interface. What is remarkable is the increase in value of the segregation coefficient over the equilibrium value of 7×10^{-4}.

As discussed previously, resolidification velocities are a function of laser parameters such as energy, pulse length and wavelength. The velocity will also depend upon the thermal conductivity of the substrate, which can be varied by changing the ambient temperature of the substrate. Segregation measurements as a function of interface velocity have been carried out for Bi (Baeri *et al.*, 1981) and In (Poate, 1982). Fig. 14 shows κ' vs. interface velocity for In in Si of different orientations. There is not only a strong velocity dependence, but also a strong orientation dependence. No data are shown for (111) samples at 7.5 m sec^{-1} since at this velocity numerous defects remain in the lattice and it is not possible to extract segregation coefficients. Below 5 m sec^{-1}, the (111) liquid-phase epitaxy is defect free (Cullis *et al.*, 1982a).

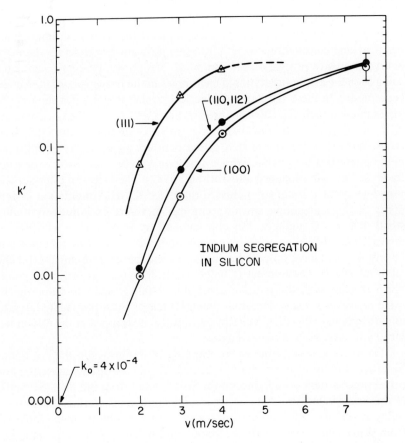

Fig. 14.   Interfacial segregation coefficients (κ') for In in Si as functions of liquid–solid interface velocity and substrate orientation. Dashed line indicates that the (111) regrowth becomes defective above 5 m sec[-1]. From Poate (1982).

What are the physical bases of these segregation phenomena? To first order, the observed velocity dependence can be explained in terms of competition between the velocity of the moving liquid-solid interface and diffusive motion of the impurities in the liquid away from the advancing interface. Impurities will be trapped if they reside at the interface for times greater than the intrinsic recrystallization time of the interface. Trapping can therefore occur when interface velocities exceed ~ 1 m sec[-1] and liquid-state diffusivities are $\sim 10^{-5}$ cm^2 sec[-1].

Various authors (Cahn *et al.,* 1980; Jackson *et al.,* 1980; Wood, 1980) have used different approaches to the kinetic theory of trapping in order to explain, for example, the velocity dependence of Fig. 14. It is not obvious how atomistic concepts or crystal-growth concepts can be developed in these theories. In particular, the strong orientation dependence and saturation of κ' can apparently only be incorporated in an *ad hoc* fashion. Gilmer (1983) has provided considerable insight into this problem by modeling the rapid Si crystal-growth process on the computer. The growth process is simulated using Monte Carlo computational techniques in the framework of the kinetic Ising model. In these simulations, identical crystal growth rates can only be maintained at high velocities on the (111) and (100) faces if the undercooling of the melt at the (111) face is assumed to be twice that at the (100) face. (Undercooling is the depression in temperature beneath the equilibrium melting temperature, 1685K, which is necessary to provide the driving force for crystal growth (Spaepen and Turnbull, 1982). The melt and interface will therefore be at a lower temperature than 1685K.) The orientation dependence of the segregation and trapping can therefore be intuitively understood in terms of undercooling; an increase in undercooling will give an increased condensation or trapping probability of impurities. Spaepen and Turnbull (1982) have proposed an atomistic model for trapping at (111) and (100) interfaces. The number of ledges controlling (111) growth is probably much smaller than the number controlling (100) growth. To maintain the same regrowth velocity, therefore, the (111) ledges must propagate laterally at much greater velocities. More impurities will be trapped at the (111) interface by these rapidly moving ledges.

There are several limits to the trapping of impurities in the crystalline Si lattice. Firstly, at the highest velocities, as we will discuss later, the epitaxial process desists and amorphous Si is formed from the melt. Secondly, at the lower velocities, there are thermodynamic and interfacial instability limits to the maximum amount of impurity that can be trapped. Table III, from White *et al.* (1979, 1980), compares equilibrium segregation coefficients

TABLE III

Comparison of equilibrium segregation coefficients (κ_0) and solubility limits (C_0) with laser-annealed segregation coefficients (κ') and maximum solubility (C_{max}).[a]

Dopant	κ_0	κ'	C_0 (cm^{-3})	C_{max} (cm^{-3})
B	0.80	~ 1.0		
P	0.35	~ 1.0		
As	0.30	~ 1.0	1.5×10^{21}	6.0×10^{21}
Sb	0.023	0.7	7.0×10^{19}	2.0×10^{21}
Ga	0.008	0.2	4.5×10^{19}	4.5×10^{20}
In	0.0004	0.15	8.0×10^{17}	1.5×10^{20}
Bi	0.0007	0.4	8.0×10^{17}	4.0×10^{20}

[a] From White *et al.* (1979, 1980)

(κ_0) and solubility limits (C_0) with the laser annealed segregation coefficients (κ') and the maximum solubilities (C_{max}) that can be incorporated in the lattice at velocities ~ 4 m sec^{-1}. Cahn et al. (1980) have calculated the thermodynamic limits to the amount of impurity that can be accommodated at the liquid-solid interface. Indeed, the As concentration is close to the thermodynamic limit. However, the amount of trapped In (C_{max}) is considerably less than the thermodynamic limit. The reason for this behavior is that, for the very insoluble impurities, the interface will become unstable and break down due to the phenomenon of constitutional super-cooling (Cullis et al., 1981, Narayan, 1981). Breakdown occurs for In at implantation concentrations of 3×10^{15} cm^{-2} (170 keV) and liquid-solid interface velocities of 2 m sec^{-1}. Besides the basic thermodynamic and interface instability limitations, there is also the fact that the lattice itself might be unstable because of the large strain. For example, large concentrations of B can be incorporated in the lattice, but cracking occurs (White et al., 1981) because of the high strain occurring whenever the local B concentration exceeds ~ 4 at. %.

It is interesting to compare the trapped concentrations obtained by solid-phase growth (Table II) with the liquid-phase data of Table III. In both cases, remarkably high concentrations of impurities can be trapped in the lattice. Indeed, there are some similarities between the liquid-phase and solid-phase processes. Trapping occurs at both the solid-phase and liquid-phase interfaces because of diffusional limitations in either the amorphous solid or liquid phase. But there the similarities stop. Diffusional effects dominate in the liquid phase to give, for example, the segregation profiles or interface instabilities. However, for most impurities in the amorphous phase, no diffusion is observable before recrystallization. The basic differences in the solid-phase and liquid-phase mechanisms are illustrated by the behavior for Pb and Bi. Both can be trapped at high concentrations in the solid phase, whereas only Bi can be trapped at measurable concentrations in the liquid phase. It is thought that for Pb the interface breaks down due to constitutional super-cooling before any significant concentration can be incorporated in the lattice (White et al., 1982). Similarities and differences in the solid-phase and liquid-phase trapping regimes are discussed by White et al. (1982) and Williams (1982a).

V. THERMODYNAMIC CONSIDERATIONS

A. Enthalpies of Crystallization and Melting Temperatures

The production and crystallization of amorphous Si has long been a preoccupation of ion-implantation research. But only recently has one of the central issues been addressed—the thermodynamic properties of the amorphous phase. This lack of work is somewhat surprising but probably originates from the simple fact that amorphous layers of sufficient thickness were not available for analysis. Moreover, the recent ability to rapidly heat and melt surface layers has generated considerable interest in the thermodynamic properties of amorphous, crystalline and liquid Si (a-Si, c-Si and l-Si). Much interest was created by the proposals of Spaepen and Turnbull (1979) and Bagley and Chen (1979) that a-Si should melt at approximately 300K beneath the crystalline melting temperature (T_{cl} = 1685K) because of the free energy difference beneath a-Si and c-Si. Their estimates were based on the assumption that the enthalpy of crystallization, ΔH_{ac}, of Si could be obtained from the value measured for Ge, scaled by the ratio of the melting temperature of c-Si and c-Ge.

The enthalpy of crystallization of deposited, a-Ge was measured by Chen and Turnbull (1969) using calorimetric techniques. Recently, Fan and Andersen (1981) have measured ΔH_{ac} for deposited a-Si. Surprisingly they found ΔH_{ac} = 9.9 kJ mole^{-1}, which is lower than the value of 11.5 kJ mole^{-1} for Ge reported by Chen and Turnbull (1969). However, there was quite a large spread in the reported values, presumably because of embedded impurities in the Si films. Recently, Donovan et al. (1983) have measured, for the first time, ΔH_{ac} for implanted Si, using thick layers similar to those shown in Figs. 2 and 3.

Fig. 15 shows the differential scanning calorimetry (DSC) measurements of the heat released when an amorphous layer of 1.8 μm on (100) Si was heated at a rate of 40K min^{-1}. The layer was formed by Xe bombardment at liquid nitrogen at four energies up to 3 MeV. The total integrated dose was 6.5 × 10^{14} cm^{-2}. The rate of heat release should scale with the interface velocity and, as discussed earlier, the temperature dependence of the interface velocity should have the Arrhenius form. The smooth line is a fit to the data of the equations $v = v_0 \exp(-Q'/kT)$ where v_0 = 1.77 × 10^{14} Å sec^{-1} and Q' = 2.24 eV. This fit is shown in Fig. 16, along with the earlier data of Csepregi et al. (1977). The excellent Arrhenius fits to the calorimetry data give confidence in the extraction of the ΔH_{ac} values of 11.9 ± 0.7 kJ mole^{-1}. This procedure could not be followed in the earlier work of Fan and Andersen (1981) on the deposited films because they did not recrystallize epitaxially, but rather by polycrystalline formation.

It is surprising that the value of ΔH_{ac} for Si is approximately the same as that for Ge. The atomistic origin of ΔH_{ac} is thought to be bond-angle distortion in the amorphous, random network. The structures of a-Si and a-Ge are isomorphous and, therefore, they might be expected to have the same amount of bond-angle distortion. Thus, ΔH_{ac} would be expected to scale with the elastic properties which, to first order, should scale with the melting tem-

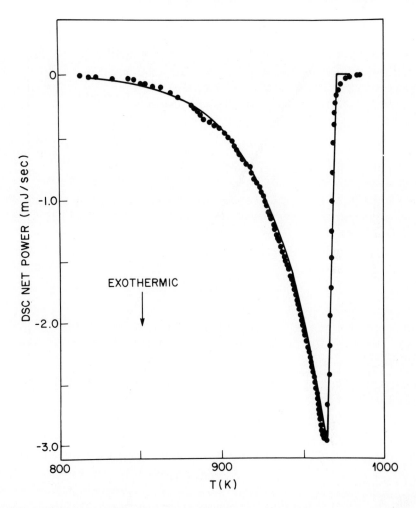

Fig. 15. Differential scanning calorimeter output (net power released) for the amorphous (1.8 μm) Si-crystalline Si transformation. Scan rate of 40 K min^{-1}. Smooth line is Arrhenius fit shown in Fig. 16. From Donovan *et al.* (1983).

peratures. The approximate equality of the values of ΔH_{ac} is therefore a puzzle.

Fig. 17 shows calculations by Donovan *et al.* (1983) of the Gibbs-free energy (ΔG) of *l*-Si and *a*-Si referenced to *c*-Si. Heat capacity data for *a*-Si do not exist and the lines a(1) and a(2) represent respectively $\Delta C_p = 0$ and, more realistically, ΔC_p having the same functional form measured by Chen and Turnbull (1969) for Ge.

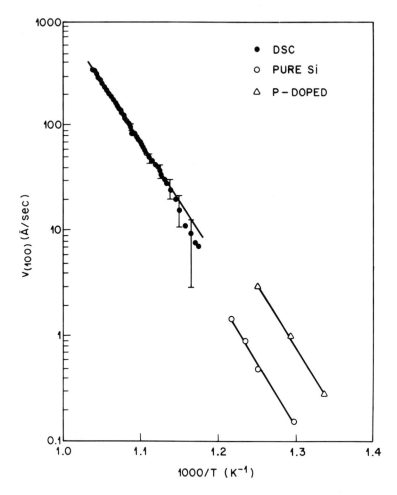

Fig. 16.   Velocity of the (100) Si interface moving into amorphous Si. The data of Csepregi *et al.* (1977) are also shown. From Donovan *et al.* (1983).

The fundamental difference in bonding (covalent or metallic) and coordination number (4 vs. 11-12) between *a*-Si and *l*-Si strongly suggests that the intersection of the amorphous and liquid lines represents a first-order phase transition, so that T_{al} can be considered as the melting temperature of amorphous Si. Line a(1) can be regarded as giving a lower limit to T_{al} of 1335K with $\Delta H_{al} = 37.9$ kJ mole^{-1}. Line a(2) is probably a more realistic estimate, with $T_{al} = 1460$K and $\Delta H_{al} = 37.8$ kJ mole^{-1}. Indeed, Baeri *et al.* (1980) directly measured ΔH_{al} by rapidly melting *a*-Si using a pulsed electron beam

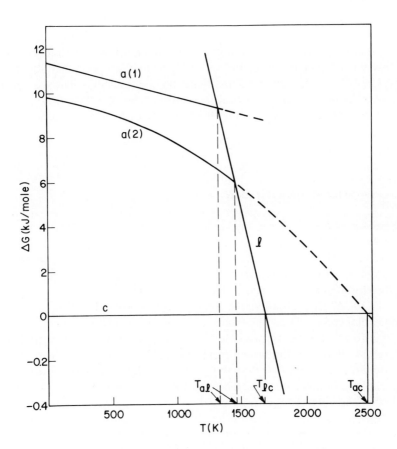

Fig. 17.   Difference in Gibbs free energy between the crystalline phase (*c*), the amorphous phase, *a*(1) and *a*(2), and the liquid phase (*l*). See text for explanation. From Donovan *et al.* (1983).

as the heating source. They found ΔH_{al} be 34.3 ± 4 kJ mole^{-1}, in very good agreement with the values obtained from the calorimetric measurements. Moreover, they observed that the *a*-Si melted and crystallised at low electron energies, with the formation of unusual layered microstructures. From heat-flow calculation of the deposited electron energy, T_{al} was estimated to be 1170K, with considerable uncertainty.

It would appear from these calculations and measurements that the melting temperature of *a*-Si is depressed some 250K beneath the crystalline melting temperature. Such a reduction in a melting temperature is quite remarkable. Recently, however, Kokorowski *et al.* (1981), using a dynamic reflectivity technique, have estimated that a-Si can be heated to within 50K of T_{cl}, with no change in the kinetics of crystallization. It seems that, if their estimates are correct, the a-Si did not melt and, in fact, must be super-heated. If this is not the explanation and $T_{al} \approx T_{cl}$, as they propose, then the differences in ΔG must become very small near the melting point. The solid-phase kinetics should thus slow drastically because of the decreased driving force. Since the kinetics do not change, the amorphous Si must be super-heated (Turnbull, 1982).

B. Laser-Induced Amorphization

There is now firm evidence that amorphous Si can be formed from the melt by laser quenching (Liu $et\ al.$, 1979; Tsu $et\ al.$, 1979; Cullis $et\ al.$, 1982b). These important observations were the first demonstrations that amorphous Si could be formed by ultra-rapid quenching. Fig. 18 shows high resolution, Rutherford backscattering and channeling spectra of amorphous Si formed by UV (0.347 μm) radiation, 0.5 J cm^{-2}, on (100) Si held at 77K. The amorphous film recrystallizes epitaxially when heated at 550°C. Epitaxial recrystallization at 550°C implies that the films are free of impurities and, therefore, that the formation from the melt is not impurity stabilized. Regrowth rates are slower than those measured for amorphous films formed by implantation (Poate, 1982). More experiments are required to ascertain whether the differences in rates are due to intrinsic structural differences.

Spaepen and Turnbull (1982) have pointed out that it is thermodynamically possible to form amorphous Si in the melt when the degree of undercooling exceeds the difference of $T_{cl}-T_{al}$. In other words the amorphous phase will freeze out in the melt. Undercooling is a strong function of the interface velocity. At present, however, the functional form of undercooling vs. interface velocity in Si is not known. Recent experiments by Cullis $et\ al.$ (1982b) and Thompson $et\ al.$ (1983) indicate that the amorphous phase forms on (100) Si when the interface velocity exceeds 15 m sec^{-1}. From the previous discussions, therefore, it would appear that the undercooling is 250K when the interface velocity is 15 m sec^{-1}.

The laser-melting experiments are summarized schematically in Fig. 19. At the lower velocities, the (100) solidification is characterized by good epitaxy and with velocity-dependent segregation coefficients which can be explained in terms of undercooling effects. At sufficient undercooling, the amorphous phase can freeze out in the melt. The behavior is similar for (111) solidification, except that the undercooling effects are enhanced and the epitaxy becomes defective before the onset of amorphization.

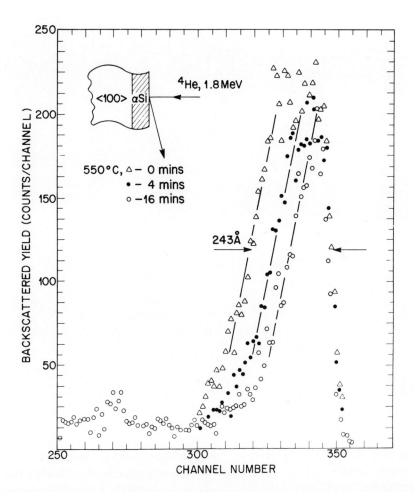

Fig. 18. High-resolution channeling spectra of laser-quenched amorphous Si on (100) Si after annealing at 550°C. From Poate (1982).

VI. AMORPHIZATION AND CRYSTALLIZATION PERSPECTIVES

This chapter has dealt with the use of energetic ion and laser beams to study the amorphization and crystallization of semiconductors. The mechanisms of energy deposition are very different for heavy ions or photons. The collision cascades produced by ions are violent and localized phenomena on the atomic scale, with remarkably short lifetimes $< 10^{-11}$ sec. Individual

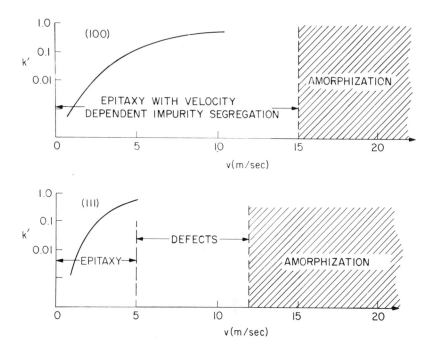

Fig. 19. Schematic of crystallization and amorphization phenomena in Si as a function of interface velocity. From Poate (1982).

cascades can produce amorphous zones which will overlap to produce continuous layers at high doses. Our macroscopic understanding of this amorphization regime is empirically quite good, but the scenario is blurred on the atomic scale. Nevertheless, these amorphous layers, because of their bulk and interface cleanness, are proving excellent vehicles for studying solid-state crystallization processes.

There are two areas where the implanted layers are providing important solid-phase information. Firstly, the epitaxial growth process can be quantitatively studied, and it appears that the movement of the interface can only be understood in terms of both the interface atomic structure and the electronic configuration. Secondly, foreign atoms implanted in amorphous layers can be trapped in the advancing crystal at very high concentrations, thus allowing the study of metastability and, perhaps more importantly, the study of solubility limits.

The need to master and understand the annealing of implantation damage has provided a strong technological and scientific driving force. The phenomenology of solid-state furnace annealing is clearly well understood, but the relationships between dynamic and bulk annealing are subtle and can produce unusual microstructures. A novel annealing regime has emerged in the past five years—pulsed laser melting of surface layers. In many ways laser melting is a great simplifier, as all memory of pre-existing defects can be erased by melting. It has, however, opened new regimes of crystal growth. Epitaxy and segregation can be studied at interface velocities approximately five orders of magnitude greater than those occurring in conventional liquid-phase epitaxy. Moreover, at interface velocities ~ 15 m sec^{-1}, the amorphous phase forms from the melt. A complete understanding of this process will provide important clues to the thermodynamic properties of amorphous and crystalline Si. It will be intriguing to see whether these developments in rapid quenching from the melt will aid in the interpretation of amorphous zones produced by heavy ion bombardment.

ACKNOWLEDGEMENTS

We are indebted to Larry Howe and Jagdish Narayan for supplying Figures 1 and 5.

REFERENCES

Ahmed, N. A. G., Carter, G., Christodoulides, C. E., Nobes, M. J., and Titov, A. (1980). *Nucl. Instrum. Methods* **168**, 283.
Appleton, B. R., and Celler, G. K., eds. (1982). "Laser and Electron Beam Interactions with Solids." North Holland, New York.
Baeri, P. (1982). *In* Appleton and Celler (1982), p. 151.
Baeri, P., and Campisano, S. U. (1982). *In* Poate and Mayer (1982), p. 75.
Baeri, P., Foti, G., Poate, J. M., and Cullis, A. G. (1980). *Phys. Rev. Lett.* **45**, 2036.
Baeri, P., Foti, G., Poate, J. M., Campisano, S. U., and Cullis, A. G. (1981). *Appl. Phys. Lett.* **38**, 800.
Bagley, B. G., and Chen, H. S. (1979). *In* Ferris *et al.* (1979), p. 97.
Baranova, E. C., Gusev, V. M., Martynenko, Y. V., and Hailbullin, I. B. (1975). *Rad. Effects* **25**, 157.
Bean, J. C. and Poate, J. M. (1980). *Appl. Phys. Lett.* **35**, 280.
Bean, J. C., Leamy, H. J., Poate, J. M., Rozgonyi, G. A., van der Ziel, J., Williams, J. S., and Celler, G. K. (1979). *In* Ferris *et al.* (1979), p. 487.
Beanland, D. G. and Williams, J. S. (1978). *Rad. Effects* **36**, 25.
Blood, P., Brown, W. L., and Miller, G. L. (1979). *J. Appl. Phys.* **50**, 173.
Cahn, J. W., Coriell, S. R., and Boettinger, W. J. (1980). *In* White and Peercy (1980), p. 89.
Campisano, S. U. (1982). Private communication.

Campisano, S. U., and Barbarino, A. E. (1981). *Applied Physics* **25**, 153.

Campisano, S. U., Rimini, E., Baeri, P., and Foti, G. (1980a). *Appl. Phys. Lett.* **37**, 170.

Campisano, S. U., Foti, G., Baeri, P., Grimaldi, M. G., and Rimini, E. (1980b). *Appl. Phys. Lett.* **37**, 719.

Carter, G., Grant, W. A., Haskell, J. D., and Stephens, G. A. (1971). *In* "Ion Implantation" (L. T. Chadderton and F. H. Fisen, eds.), p. 261. Gordon and Breach, London.

Chadderton, L. T., and Eisen, F. H. (1971). *Rad. Effects* **14**, 271.

Christel, L. A., Gibbons, J. F., and Sigmon, T. W. (1981). *J. Appl. Phys.* **52**, 7143.

Chen, H. S., and Turnbull, D. (1969). *J. Appl. Phys.* **40**, 4212.

Corbett, J. W., Karins, J. P., and Tan, T. Y. (1981). *Nucl. Instrum. Methods* **182/183**, 457.

Csepregi, L., Mayer, J. W., and Sigmon, T. W. (1975). *Phys. Letters* **54A**, 157.

Csepregi, L., Kennedy, E. F., Gallagher, T. J., Mayer, J. W., and Sigmon, T. W. (1977). *J. Appl. Phys.* **48**, 4234.

Csepregi, L., Kennedy, E. F., Mayer, J. W., and Sigmon, T. W. (1978). *J. Appl. Phys.* **49**, 3906.

Cullis, A. G. (1982). *In* Poate and Mayer (1982), p. 147.

Cullis, A. G., Hurle, D. T. J., Webber, H. C., Chew, N. G., Poate, J. M., Baeri, P., and Foti, G. (1978). *Appl. Phys. Lett.* **38**, 642.

Cullis, A. G., Webber, A. C., and Chew, N. G. (1982a). *In* Appleton and Celler (1982), p. 131.

Cullis, A. G., Webber, A. C., Chew, N. G., Poate, J. M., and Baeri, P. (1982b). *Phys. Rev. Lett.* **49**, 219.

Dennis, J. R., and Hale, E. B. (1978). *J. Appl. Phys.* **49**, 1119.

Donnelly, J. P. (1981). *Nucl. Instr. Meth.* **182/183**, 553.

Donovan, E. P. (1982). PhD Thesis, Harvard University.

Donovan, E. P., Spaepen, F., Turnbull, D., Poate, J. M., and Jacobson, D. C. (1983). *Appl. Phys. Lett,* **42**, 698.

Eer Nisse, E. P. (1973). *In* "Ion Implantation in Semiconductors and Other Materials" (B. L. Crowder, ed.), p. 531. Plenum Press, New York.

Eisen, F. H. (1980). *In* White and Peercy (1980), p. 309.

Eisen, F. H., and Welch, B. (1971). *Rad. Effects* **7**, 143.

Fan, J. C. C., and Anderson, H. (1981). *J. Appl. Phys.* **52**, 4003.

Fan, J. C. C., Geis, M. W., and Tsaur, B. Y. (1981). *Appl. Phys. Lett.* **38**, 365.

Ferris, S. D., Leamy, H. J., and Poate, J. M., eds. (1979). "Laser–Solid Interactions and Laser Processing–1978". AIP Conference Proceedings No. 50, New York.

Fletcher, J., Narayan, J., and Holland, O. W. (1981a). *Inst. Phys. Conf. Ser.* **60**, 295.

Fletcher, J., Narayan, J., and Lowndes, D. H. (1981b). *In* "Defects in Semiconductors" (J. Narayan and T. Y. Tan, eds.), p. 421. North Holland, New York.

Fulks, R. T., Russo, C. J., Hanley, P. R., and Kamins, T. I. (1981). *Appl. Phys. Lett.* **39**, 150.

Galvin, G. J., Thompson, M. O., Mayer, J. W., Hammond, R. B., Paulter, N., and Peercy, P. S. (1982). *Phys. Rev. Lett.* **48**, 33.

Gamo, K., Inada, T., Mayer, J. W., Eisen, F. H., and Rhodes, C. G. (1977). *Rad. Effects* **33**, 85.

Gat, A. (1981), *IEEE Elect. Dev. Lett.* **2**, 85.

Gat, A., and Gibbons, J. F. (1978). *Appl. Phys. Lett.* **32**, 142.

Gibbons, J. F., Hess, L. D., and Sigmon, T. W. (eds.) (1981). "Laser and Electron-Beam Solid Interactions and Materials Processing". North Holland, New York.

Gilmer, G. H. (1983). *In* "Laser–Solid Interactions and Transient Thermal Processing" (J. Narayan, W. L. Brown, & R. L. Lemons, eds.) p. 249. North Holland, New York.

Grimaldi, M. G., Paine, B. M., Maenpaa, M., Nicolet, M.-A., and Sadana, D. K. (1981a). *Appl. Phys. Lett.* **39**, 70.

Grimaldi, M. G., Paine, B. M., Nicolet, M.-A., and Sadana, D. K. (1981b). *J. Appl. Phys.* **52**, 4038.

Harrison, H. B., Grigg, M., Short, K. T., Williams, J. S., and Zylewicz, A. (1982). *In* Appleton and Celler (1982), p. 771.

Hill, C. (1982). *In* Poate and Mayer (1982), p. 479.

Hirsch, P. B. (1979). *J. de Phys.* **40**, C6-117.

Hirsch, P. B. (1981). *In* "Defects in Semiconductors" (J. Narayan and T. Y. Tan, eds.), p. 257. North Holland, New York.

Jackson, K. A., Gilmer, G. H., and Leamy, H. J. (1980). *In* White and Peercy (1980), p. 104.

Howe, L. M., and Rainville, M. H. (1981). *Nucl. Instrum. Methods* **182/183**, 143.

Howe, L. M., Rainville, M. H., Harigan, H. K., and Thompson, D. A. (1980). *Nucl. Instrum. Methods* **170**, 419.

Josquin, W. J. M. J. and Tamminga, Y. (1978). *Applied Physics* **15**, 73.

Kennedy, E. F., Csepregi, L., Mayer, J. W., and Sigmon, T. W. (1977). *J. Appl. Phys.* **48**, 4241.

Kinchin, G. H., and Pease, R. S. (1955). *Rep. Prog. Phys.* **18**, 2.

Kokorowski, S. A., Olson, G. L., Roth, J. A., and Hess, L. D. (1982). *Phys. Rev. Lett.* **48**, 498.

Kular, S. S., Sealy, B. J., Stephens, K. G., Sadana, D. K., and Booker, G. R. (1980). *Solid State Electronics* **23**, 831.

Lau, S. S., Von Allmen, M., Golecki, I., Nicolet, M. A., Kennedy, E. F., and Tseng, W. F. (1979). *Appl. Phys. Lett.* **35**, 327.

Lau, S. S., Tseng, W. F., and Mayer, J. W. (1981). *In* "Handbook on Semiconductors" (S. P. Keller, ed.), Vol. 3, Chapter 7. North Holland, Amsterdam.

Lietoila, A., Gold, R. B., Gibbons, J. F., Sigmon, T. W., Scovell, P. D., and Young, J. M. (1981). *J. Appl. Phys.* **52**, 230.

Lietoila, A., Wakita, A., Sigmon, T. W., and Gibbons, J. F. (1982). *J. Appl. Phys.* **53**, 4399.

Liu, P. L., Yen, R., Bloembergen, N., and Hodgson, R. T. (1979). *Appl. Phys. Lett.* **34**, 864.

Mayer, J. W., Eriksson, L., Picraux, S. T., and Davies, J. A. (1968). *Can. J. Phys.* **45**, 663.

Mayer, J. W., Eriksson, L., and Davies, J. A. (1970). "Ion Implantation in Semiconductors." Academic Press, New York.

Mazey, D. J., Nelson, R. S., and Barnes, R. S. (1968). *Phil. Mag.* **17**, 1145.

Mazey, D. J., and Nelson, R. S. (1969). *Rad. Effects.* **1**, 229.

McMahon, R. A. and Ahmed, H. (1979). *In* "Laser and Electron Beam Processing of Electronic Materials" (G. L. Anderson, G. K. Celler and G. A. Rozgonyi, eds.), p. 130. Electrochemical Society, Princeton.

Moore, J. A., Carter, G., and Tinsley, A. H. (1975). *Rad. Effects* **25**, 49.

Morehead, F., Jr., and Crowder, B. L. (1970). *Rad. Effects* **6**, 27.

Nakata, J., and Kajiyama, K. (1982). *App. Phys. Lett.* **40**, 686.

Narayan, J. (1981). *In* "Microscopy of Semiconducting Materials 1981"(Inst. Phys. Conf. Series No. 60) (A. G. Cullis and D. C. Joy, eds.), p. 101. Institute of Physics, London.

Narayan, J., and Holland, O. W. (1982). *Appl. Phys. Lett.* **41**, 239.

Nissim, Y. I., Christel, L. A., Sigmon, T. W., Gibbons, J. F., Magee, T. J., and Ormrod, R. (1982). *J. Appl. Phys.* **52**, 6228.

North, J. C., and Gibson, W. M. (1971). *In* "Ion Implantation" (F. H. Eisen and L. T. Chadderton, eds.), p. 143. Gordon and Breach, London.

Pauling, L. (1948). "The Nature of the Chemical Bond." Cornell University Press, Ithaca, New York.

Poate, J. M. (1982) *In* Appleton and Celler (1982), p. 121.

Poate, J. M., and J. C. Bean (1982). *In* Poate and Mayer (1982), p. 247.

Poate, J. M., and Foti, G., eds. (1982). "Surface Modification and Alloying." Plenum, New York.

Poate, J. M., and Mayer, J. W., eds. (1982). "Laser Annealing of Semiconductors." Academic Press, New York.

Regolini, J. L., Gibbons, J. F., Sigmon, T. W., and Pease, R. F. W. (1979). *Appl. Phys. Lett.* **34**, 410.

Revesz, P., Wittmer, M., Roth, J., and Mayer, J. W. (1978). *J. Appl. Phys.* **49**, 5199.

Sigmund, P. (1969). *Appl. Phys. Lett.* **14**, 114.

Spaepen, F., and Turnbull, D. (1979). *In* Ferris *et al.* (1979), p. 73.

Spaepen, F., and Turnbull, D. (1982). *In* Poate and Mayer (1982), p. 15.

Suni, I., Goltz, G., Grimaldi, M. G., Nicolet, M. A., and Lau, S. S. (1982). *Appl. Phys. Lett.* **40**, 269.

Swanson, M. L., Parsons, J. R., and Hoelke, C. W. (1971). *Rad. Effects* **9**, 249.

Thompson, D. A. (1981). *Rad. Effects* **56**, 105.

Thompson, M. O., Mayer, J. W., Cullis, A. G., Webber, H. C., Chew, N. G., Poate, J. M. and Jacobson, D. C. (1983). *Phys. Rev. Lett.* **50**, 896.

Thompson, P. A., Golanski, A., Hagen, H. K., Howe, L. M., and David, J. A. (1980). *Rad. Effects* **50**, 125.

Trumbore, F. (1960). *Bell Syst. Tech. J.* **39**, 205.

Turnbull, D. (1982). *In* "Metastable Materials Formation by Ion Implantation" (S. T. Picraux and W. J. Choyke, eds.), p. 103. North Holland, New York.

Van Vechten, J., and Thurmond, C. H. (1976). *Phys. Rev.* **B14**, 3539.

Walker, R. S., and Thompson, D. A. (1978). *Rad. Effects* **37**, 113.

Whan, R. E., and Arnold, G. W. (1970). *Appl. Phys. Lett.* **17**, 378.

White, C. W., and Peercy, P. S. (eds.) (1980). "Laser and Electron Beam Processing of Materials." Academic Press, New York.

White, C. W., Pronko, P. P., Wilson, S. R., Appleton, B. R., Narayan, J., and Young, R. T. (1979). *J. Appl. Phys.* **50**, 3261.

White, C. W., Wilson, S. R., Appleton, B. R., and Young, F. W., Jr. (1980). *J. Appl. Phys.* **51**, 738.

White, C. W., Appleton, B. R., Stritzker, B., Zehner, D. M., and Wilson, S. R. (1981). *In* Gibbons *et al.* (1981), p. 59.

White, C. W., Zehner, D. M., Campisano, S. U., and Cullis, A. G. (1982). *In* Poate and Foti (1982), p. 155.

Williams, J. S. (1980). *In* "Laser and Electron Beam Processing of Electronic Materials," p. 249. (G. L. Anderson, G. K. Celler and G. A. Rozgonyi, eds.). Electrochemical Society, Princeton.

Williams, J. S. (1982a). *In* Poate and Foti (1982), p. 198.

Williams, J. S. (1982b). *In* Poate and Mayer (1982), p. 383.

Williams, J. S., and Austin, M. W. (1980). *Appl. Phys. Lett.* **36**, 994.

Williams, J. S., and Elliman, R. G. (1980). *Appl. Phys. Lett.* **37**, 829.

Williams, J. S., and Elliman, R. G. (1981). *Nucl. Instrum. Methods* **183**, 758.

Williams, J. S., and Elliman, R. G. (1982). *Appl. Phys. Lett.* **40**, 226.

Williams, J. S., and Elliman, R. G. (1983). *Phys. Rev. Lett.* (in press).

Williams, J. S., and Grant, W. A. (1976). *In* "Application of Ion Beams to Materials" (G. Carter, J. S. Colligon and W. A. Grant, eds.), p. 31. Institute of Physics, London.

Williams, J. S., and Harrison, H. B. (1981). *In* Gibbons *et al.* (1981), p. 209.

Williams, J. S., and Short, K. T. (1982). *In* "Metastable Phases by Ion Implantation" (S. T. Picraux and W. J. Choyke, eds.) p. 131. North Holland, New York.

Williams, J. S., Christodoulides, C. E., Grant, W. A., Andrew, R., Brawn, J. R., and Booth, M. (1977). *Rad. Effects* **32**, 55.

Williams, J. S., Brown, W. L., Leamy, H. J., Poate, J. M., Rodgers, J. W., Rousseau, D., Rozgonyi, G. A., Shelnutt, J. A., and Sheng, T. T. (1978). *Appl. Phys. Lett.* **33**, 542.

Williams, J. S., Brown, W. L., and Poate, J. M. (1979). *In* Ferris *et al.* (1979). p. 399.

Williams, J. S., Austin, M. W., and Harrison, H. B. (1980a). *In* "Thin Film Interfaces and Interactions" (J. E. E. Baglin and J. M. Poate, eds.), p. 137. Electrochemical Society, Princeton.

Williams, J. S., Christodoulides, C. E., and Grant, W. A. (1980b). *Rad. Effects* **48,** 157.

Wilson, W. D., Haggmark, L. G., and Biersack, J. P. (1977). *Phys. Rev. B 15,* 2458.

Winterbon, K. B., Sigmund, D., and Sanders, J. B. (1970). *Kgl. Danske Vid. Selskab Mat. Fys. Medd.* **37,** 14.

Wittmer, M., Roth, J., Revesz, P., and Mayer, J. W. (1978). *J. Appl. Phys.* **49,** 5207.

Wood, R. F. (1980). *Appl. Phys. Lett.* **37,** 302.

CHAPTER 3

Application of the Boltzmann Transport Equation to Ion Implantation in Semiconductors and Multilayer Targets

J. F. GIBBONS AND L. A. CHRISTEL

Stanford Electronics Laboratories
Stanford University
California, USA

I. INTRODUCTION

The application of ion implantation to device fabrication often involves processing in which surface coatings are present on the target substrates. Questions of interest that arise in such cases are:

1. What is the range distribution of the primary projectiles in the coated (or multilayer) target?

ION IMPLANTATION
AND BEAM PROCESSING
ISBN 0 12 756980 4

2. What are the range distributions of the atoms that are recoil-implanted from the surface coatings into the target?
3. What is the distribution of damage in the multilayer target?

The answers to all of these questions can be obtained when the momentum distribution of the primary projectile is known as a function of depth in the multilayer target. For example, if an As ion is implanted into a multilayer $Si_3N_4-SiO_2-Si$ target, then a knowledge of the As momentum distribution with distance is sufficient to calculate both the recoil energy and angle for each Si, N, and O recoil that is produced in a slab of width Δx_p at the position x_p. A knowledge of the As momentum distribution is also sufficient to predict the entire As concentration profile in the multilayer target, including in particular, the relative concentration of As ions on the two sides of each surface.

In compound semiconductors, it is important to know whether the energy deposited into atomic processes leads to disruption of local stoichiometry. Details of damage distributions and stoichiometric disturbances in semiconductors can also be calculated from a knowledge of the deposited energy distributions and momentum distributions associated with the energy loss of the primary projectile.

It is, of course, possible to calculate energy distributions for semi-infinite targets using an LSS-type moments method (Winterbon et al., 1970) or a direct construction technique (Brice, 1975). However, these methods are not readily applicable to a multilayer target, and it is therefore natural to resort to the Boltzmann transport equation, where the evolution of the momentum distribution with distance is a quantity that may be calculated directly.

Use of the Boltzmann equation to calculate the momentum distribution for both the primary and recoil particles is, in principle, straightforward when each layer of the target is assumed to be a random stopping medium. However, even for this case, the analysis requires several simplifying assumptions to be made in order to construct numerical solutions in particular situations. Fortunately, results show good agreement with experiments in which such comparison is possible, and the analysis provides a useful basis for additional calculations.

In this chapter, the Boltzmann transport equation is applied to the following ion implantation situations:

(a) the calculation of range and recoil distributions in multilayer targets; and
(b) calculations of damage distributions and stoichiometry disturbances in semiconductors.

II. RANGE DISTRIBUTIONS IN MULTILAYER TARGETS

A. Transport Equation and Assumptions

In a transport equation (TE) approach (Smith and Gibbons, 1976; Christel *et al.*, 1980), quantities of interest are determined by calculating in a stepwise fashion the momentum distributions of both primary and recoil particles as a function of distance z from the target surface. It is assumed that the target is amorphous or aligned in a random direction and possesses translational symmetry in all directions parallel to its surface. Thus, only two components of momentum, or equivalently an energy and a direction cosine, are necessary to define a particle's state of motion. Let $F(\vec{p},z)\,d\vec{p}$ be the number of particles (integrated over time) with momentum in the region $d\vec{p}$ about $\vec{p}$ which cross unit area perpendicular to the direction of incidence at depth z. There will be one such distribution function of each projectile type. The spatial evolution of each distribution is governed by the Boltzmann transport equation:

$$\delta F(\vec{p})/\delta Z = N \int [F(\vec{p}')\,d\sigma(\vec{p}' \to \vec{p})/\cos\theta_{p'}] - [F(p)\,d\sigma(\vec{p} \to \vec{p}')/\cos\theta_{p}] + Q(\vec{p}) \tag{1}$$

Here, for simplicity, we assume a single element target with number density N. The total differential scattering cross-section $d\sigma(\vec{p} \to p')$ represents a differential area presented to an incident ion by each target atom. Any ion which enters this area with momentum $\vec{p}$ is scattered to momentum $\vec{p}'$. A particle which scatters to a momentum below some fixed limit is considered to have stopped and is removed from the distribution. In this way, the range profiles of particles are generated. The factors of $\cos\theta$ result from the fact that a particle moving at an angle θ with respect to the z axis travels a distance $dz/\cos\theta$ as the entire distribution moves the distance dz. The quantity Q is a generation term which (for recoil distributions) allows particles to be created from rest.

The distribution functions are assumed known at the surface plane $z = 0$. Recoil distributions are identically zero there, and the momentum distribution of the primary ion is taken to be a delta function:

$$F(\vec{p},0) = \Phi\delta(\vec{p} - \vec{p}_0) \tag{2}$$

where Φ is the total dose (cm^{-2}) and $\vec{p}_0$ is the (unique) momentum of ions in the incident beam. With these initial conditions, the transport equation is integrated numerically to determine the distributions at all depths $z > 0$.

Crossing a material interface during the integration, as occurs in the case of a multilayer target, necessitates changing only the number density and cross-section to quantities appropriate to the new material. No changes in the momentum distributions occur, because such distributions are continuous functions of z for any target composition. Such an approach is thus easily applied to targets of practical interest.

To apply the TE effectively to problems in ion implantation, some additional assumptions must be made. These assumptions are not inherent in the TE approach but arise from our limited knowledge of the scattering process itself and are typically made in all methods. In particular, we assume that:

1. The scattering cross-section $d\sigma$ is the sum of an elastic nuclear part $d\sigma_n$ and an inelastic electronic part $d\sigma_e$.
2. Scattering consists of a series of independent binary events so that contributions from elements in a multi-element target may be simply summed.
3. Electronic stopping acts only as an energy-dependent drag force which removes energy continuously from the distribution.
4. Only nuclear events generate recoils or cause significant angular deflections.
5. Classical two-body mechanics may be used to describe the angular deflections of both incident and recoil particles.
6. For each nuclear event involving energy transfer T (assumed to be much greater than the binding energies of lattice atoms), a particle of energy T is created in the appropriate recoil distribution consistent with assumption (5).

The nuclear cross-section is taken to be of the form (Lindhard *et al.*, 1968):

$$d\sigma_n(t) = (\pi a^2/2) \left[f(t^{1/2}) dt / t^{3/2} \right] \tag{3}$$

where $a = 0.8853 \, a_0 \, (Z_1^{2/3} + Z_2^{2/3})^{-1/2}$
$\quad\quad t = TE(M_2/4M_1)(a/Z_1 Z_2 e^2)^2$
$\quad\quad E = $ initial ion energy
$\quad\quad T = $ energy transferred to recoil
$\quad Z_1, M_1 = $ ion atomic number and mass
$\quad Z_2, M_2 = $ recoil atomic number and mass
$\quad\quad a_0 = $ Bohr radius, 0.529 Å

The scattering function $f(t^{1/2})$ depends on the choice of interatomic potential. We use an analytic form (Winterbon et al., 1970):

$$f(t^{1/2}) = (\lambda t^{(1/2)-m})/[1 + (2\lambda t^{1-m})^q]^{1/q} \tag{4}$$

The constants $\lambda = 1.309$, $m = 0.333$, and $q = 0.667$ were originally a fit to an interatomic potential based on the Thomas-Fermi model of the atom and have been used in most work to date. Kalbitzer et al. (1978) proposed that the parameters $\lambda = 2.54$, $m = 0.25$, $q = 0.475$ would provide a better fit to a large collection of experimental data taken under conditions where nuclear stopping dominates (i.e., when the LSS-normalized energy $\varepsilon < 1$). We believe that the Kalbitzer cross-section is better at low energy transfers but that, near $\varepsilon = 1$, values closer to the Thomas-Fermi cross-section should be used. A cross-section with these characteristics was proposed by Wilson et al. (1977) and has been found to yield the best agreement between calculated and experimental results.

The one parameter nuclear cross-section (Eqn. 3) specifies only how the magnitude of a particle's momentum is changed as it generates a recoil. In accord with assumption (V), the directions in which the incident and recoil particles travel after the interaction as measured from the incident ion's initial trajectory are given by

$$\Phi' = (1 - \tau)^{1/2} + (1/2)(1 - \mu)\,\tau(1 - \tau)^{-1/2} \tag{5}$$
$$\Phi'' = (\tau/\gamma)^{1/2}$$

where $\tau = T/E$
$\mu = M_2/M_1$
$\gamma = 4M_1M_2/(M_1 + M_2)^2$

Here, Φ' and Φ'' refer to the incident and recoil particles, respectively, and γ is the maximum fractional energy transfer. Since nuclear collisions are assumed to be elastic, the energy of the recoil is just T. Thus, the equations (3) and (5) completely describe nuclear scattering events.

Because they cause no angular deflections, electronic losses may be accounted for by a stopping power of the form

$$S_e(E) = \int T\,d\sigma_e(T) = KE^{1/2} \tag{6}$$

Experimental values of the constant K for some ions in silicon are available from the data of Eisen (1968). Where such data are absent, the theoretical expression (Lindhard et al., 1963):

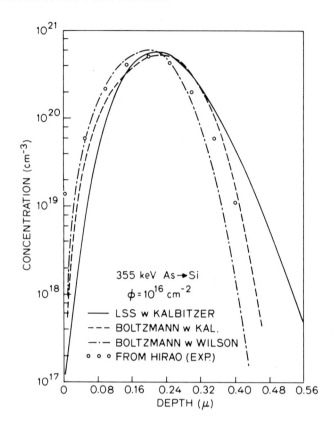

Fig. 1. Comparison of LSS and TE calculations and experimental results for the range distribution of 355 keV As implanted into silicon to a dose of 10^{16} cm^{-2}. The cross-section used for each calculation is indicated in the key.

$$K = 0.0793Z_1^{1/6} \pi a^2 \{ C_\varepsilon^{1/2}[Z_1Z_2(M_1 + M_2)^3/ZM_1^3M_2]^{1/2} \} \tag{7}$$

where $C_\varepsilon = [M_2/(M_1 + M_2)][a/Z_1Z_2e^2]$
and $Z = (Z_1^{2/3} + Z_2^{2/3})^{3/2}$
is used.

In Fig. 1, TE calculations using both the Kalbitzer and Wilson cross-sections are compared with a Pearson type IV distribution generated from LSS moments for a dose of 10^{16} As cm^{-2} at 355 keV. Also shown are experimental data of arsenic implanted into single crystal silicon substrates which were misaligned by 8° from the (111) direction (Hirao *et al.*, 1979). For direct comparison, the Kalbitzer cross-section was used in the LSS calculation.

Under these conditions ($\varepsilon \approx 0.5$), we expect nuclear scattering to be the dominant stopping mechanism and hence sensitivity to the nuclear cross-section is most effectively examined. The figure shows that if the Kalbitzer cross-section is used, the TE and LSS calculations agree well near the peak of the distribution. However, the LSS profile is more skewed, and both the TE and LSS calculations yield profiles that are somewhat deeper than the experimental data would suggest. By comparison, if the Wilson cross-section is used, the TE calculation is seen to agree quite well with experiment. The disagreement which occurs in the deepest part of the distribution is most likely due to channeling effects.

B. Recoil Implantation

A natural consequence of the calculation outlined above is the source density, $Q(\vec{p},z)$, for oxygen (or silicon) recoil atoms produced in energetic collisions. An As-O collision involving energy transfer T produces a recoiling oxygen atom with energy T traveling in a direction θ, where

$$\cos\theta = (T/\gamma E)^{\frac{1}{2}} \tag{8}$$

and $\gamma = 4M_{As}M_O/(M_{As} + M_O)^2$. By following the subsequent penetration of the oxygen atom, we can construct the distribution of recoil-implanted oxygen atoms.

Recoils may be divided into three types:

1. *Primary recoils,* which are produced with moderate to high energy (> 3 keV) directly by primary ions. These have the greatest range and are the only contribution to the recoil distribution at depths greater than a few hundred angstroms.

2. *Secondary recoils,* which are produced with moderate energy by other recoils. These enhance the surface concentration.

3. *Cascade recoils,* which are produced at very low energy by cascade processes very near the interface. These have ranges of only tens of angstroms but are produced in the greatest number and may enhance the near-surface concentration by orders of magnitude. Cascade recoils may be neglected in the calculation of recoil range distributions but must be accounted for when considering the total number (cm^{-2}) of recoil atoms crossing an interface.

The effect of recoiled oxygen on the annealing properties of arsenic-implanted SiO_2 on Si has been recently investigated by Hirao *et al.* (1979).

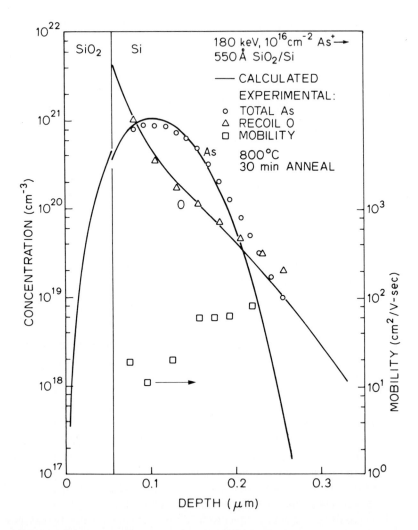

Fig. 2. Comparison of a TE calculation and experimental SIMS results for the recoil oxygen distribution resulting from an implantation of As into 550 Å of SiO_2 on silicon to a dose of 10^{16} cm^{-2}.

In this study, arsenic was implanted at 180 keV into a structure of 550 Å SiO_2 on Si to a dose of 10^{16} cm^{-2}. The oxygen recoil distribution in silicon was measured with SIMS. We have calculated the same distribution and the two results are compared in Fig. 2. Agreement between the calculated and experimental profiles is very good except at the greatest depths, where background oxygen begins to dominate the experimental signal. The recoil distribution is characterized by a very high surface concentration, which decreases rapidly to a region of nearly constant slope. At the greatest depths, the distribution falls off more rapidly again. All recoil range distributions resulting from implantation through thin films have these features in common.

TE calculations have been performed for the common silicon dopants B, P, and As implanted into silicon substrates coated with 500, 750, and 1000 Å of SiO_2 (Christel *et al.*, 1981). For each ion and film thickness, four incident ion energies were selected. These energies were chosen so that the projected range R_p and projected standard deviation σ_p of the primary ion range distribution (in SiO_2) satisfied one of the four conditions

$$R_p = t_{ox} - \sigma_p \tag{9a}$$
$$R_p = t_{ox} \tag{9b}$$
$$R_p = t_{ox} + \sigma_p \tag{9c}$$
$$R_p = 2t_{ox} \tag{9d}$$

where t_{ox} is the oxide thickness.

The results indicate that the largest surface concentration is obtained for that incident ion energy that results in the projected range R_p being roughly equal to the oxide thickness. In the central region of each distribution, the concentration profile $C(x)$ can be well approximated by an exponentially decaying function of the form

$$C(x) = Ae^{-x/L} \tag{10}$$

where A and L are two parameters which characterize the distribution and x measures the distance from the SiO_2–Si interface. Such an exponential function has been fitted to the central region of each calculated distribution.

It is found that, to a good approximation, the parameters A and L are given by

$$A = (1000 \text{ Å}/\gamma t_{ox} \text{ [Å]}) \, \Phi_0 \text{ [cm}^{-2}\text{]} \, 8.7 \times 10^4 \text{ g } (R_p/t_{ox}) \tag{11}$$

where

$$g(R_p/t_{ox}) = \exp \{[-\ln(R_p/t_{ox})]^2/0.51\}$$

and

$$L[\text{Å}] = 3.75 \, \gamma E_0 \text{ (keV)} \tag{12}$$

Here, Φ_0 is the incident dose, E_0 is the energy of the incident ions, and γ is the kinematic factor:

$$\gamma = 4M_1M_2/(M_1 + M_2)^2 \tag{13}$$

where M_1 and M_2 are the ion and recoil atomic mass, respectively.

With these relations, oxygen recoil distributions resulting from implants under general conditions can be simply estimated. The incident ion and energy E_0, as well as the oxide thickness t_{ox} and implanted dose Φ_0, are assumed known. The ion atomic mass M_1 is used in Eqn. (13) (with $M_2 = 16$) to determine γ. The decay length L is then calculated from Eqn. (12). To determine the prefactor A, the mean projected range R_p of the incident ion in SiO_2 must be known, and this can be obtained from published tables (Gibbons et al., 1975). The prefactor is then determined from Eqn. (11), and the approximate concentration profile of recoiled oxygen in silicon (for depths not too near the interface) is given by Eqn. (10). It should be noted, however, that, as a result of the cascade recoils, the concentration of recoiled oxygen very near the interface will be significantly greater than the exponential approximation would suggest.

C. Total Recoil Yields

A quantity of interest which is related to the recoil range distributions just discussed is known as the recoil yield. This is defined as the ratio of the total number of recoiled atoms in the substrate to the number of incident ions. Thus, the recoil yield is obtained by integrating the recoil distribution and dividing by the incident dose. Since the recoil distribution is a maximum at the interface, the integral of the distribution, and hence the recoil yield, will be dominated by those recoil atoms which cross the interface with the lowest energies. These recoils are the cascade recoils which result not from direct collisions involving primary ions but from secondary and higher order collisions involving recoils which have been generated earlier in the film.

When considering recoil range distributions, as in the previous section, the recoils considered are only those which are created with an energy above some threshold (about 3 keV). When one is interested in the total yield, the calculations are extended to include all recoils which originate from a collision by any atom with an energy above the threshold. Thus, the only recoils which are neglected are recoils which are produced by atoms moving with energies less than the threshold. The lowest energy recoils are assumed to be moving in all directions with equal probability.

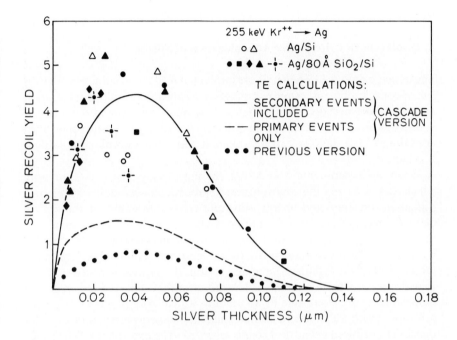

Fig. 3. Experimental and calculated data for the silver recoil yield as a function of silver film thickness for implants of 255 keV krypton. From Christel *et al.* (1981).

The results of TE calculations using both the previous method of section IIB (primary recoils only) and cascade methods involving all recoils (solid curve) are shown in Fig. 3. These calculations are compared with experimental data of the silver recoil yield resulting from krypton implantation into Ag on Si and Ag–SiO$_2$–Si multilayer targets (Christel *et al.*, 1981). Also shown is a calculation obtained by using the cascade method but neglecting any collisions not involving a primary krypton atom (dashed curve). It can be seen from the figure that the cascade method offers a significant improvement in the ability to predict the experimental recoil yield. In addition, it is evident that the secondary and higher order recoil events play a very significant role in determining the total recoil yield. It should also be noted that even the cascade method with secondary events neglects some recoil generation and thus may still be expected to underestimate the true recoil yield. This is verified by the results. Evidently, the cascade method accounts for essentially all of the recoil yield except near the yield peak, where the calculated results are about 20% lower than the experimental results seem to indicate.

III. DAMAGE DISTRIBUTIONS IN SEMICONDUCTORS

A. Displacement Criterion for Amorphization of Silicon

The damage produced when ions are implanted into semiconductors is a subject of considerable importance in practical applications of the implantation process. It is especially useful to know how many ions must be implanted in order to drive the surface region of the crystal amorphous, since improved annealing of the damage can be obtained when the amorphous condition is achieved.

From an experimental standpoint, the most easily determined quantity which characterizes the amorphization process, given implantation conditions of ion mass and energy, substrate temperature, etc., is the critical dose, Φ_c, necessary to form a continuous amorphous layer. The dependence of Φ_c on temperature and ion mass has been semi-quantitatively modeled by Morehead and Crowder (1970). In this model, each ion impinging on the target produces a cylindrical damage region, the radius of which is determined primarily by the ion mass. The radius of this damaged region is then reduced in a very short time by an amount which corresponds to a vacancy diffusion length which has an ordinary activation energy temperature dependence. The reduced cylindrical core is assumed to be amorphous. When such damage regions completely fill the area of the target, amorphization is assumed to have occurred. According to this model, the critical dose decreases with increasing ion mass and is constant at low temperatures (e.g. liquid N_2). At higher temperatures, Φ_c increases rapidly with temperature until at some temperature (which is ion dependent) no amorphous layer can be formed. This upper temperature limit is lowest for the lightest ions (306K for boron and 600K for antimony). A modification of this basic model was published by Gibbons (1972), who assumed that amorphous material may, in addition, be produced by the overlap of damaged, non-amorphous regions associated with individual damage clusters. This model explains the dose dependence of damage and the approach to amorphicity in light ion cases where the model of Morehead and Crowder is inapplicable.

Vook (1972) found that the curves of critical dose versus temperature obtained by Morehead and Crowder (1970) for each of the ions boron, phosphorus and antimony could be collapsed into a single universal curve if one considered not the dose itself but the amount of energy density deposited into atomic processes. This energy density was taken to be the dose multiplied by the quantity νR_p, where ν is the total energy deposited into atomic processes (per ion) (Brice, 1975) and R_p is the projected range of the ion (Gibbons et al., 1975). Such a procedure leads to the conclusion that, when the amount of energy density deposited into elastic atomic processes exceeds a certain threshold, a continuous amorphous layer is formed. Experimental evidence reviewed by Gibbons (1972) and Vook (1972) indicates that for silicon this critical energy density lies in the range of 6–10 × 10^{20} keV cm^{-3} for substrates which are held at low temperatures during implantation so as to ensure that all defects produced remain as stable damage.

Although this is a useful criterion for the production of an amorphous layer in silicon, such estimates suffer somewhat from an inability to account for the *spatial* distribution of the energy deposited into atomic processes. An approximation is typically made by assuming that the total energy deposited into atomic processes (determined, for example, by the calculations of Brice, 1975) is uniformly distributed between the surface and the projected range R_p of the ion. Both the calculations of Brice (1975) and our own TE calculations (Christel *et al.*, 1980) clearly indicate that the damage is not uniformly distributed but is a maximum at a depth slightly less than R_p. Thus, the simple energy density model discussed above cannot, for example, predict the extent of a buried amorphous layer which is known to be produced by implantation of light ions into low temperature substrates. To make such predictions, a more detailed knowledge of the spatial distribution of damage, such as the number of lattice displacements which occur at each depth, is necessary. Relating the critical dose and critical energy density to the number of lattice displacements produced is more difficult, because the recoil phenomena involved are extremely complex.

In this section an attempt is made to ascertain what fraction of the silicon lattice must be displaced in order to cause the transition from the single crystal to the amorphous state. Although the above discussion indicates that this transition has been empirically characterized in terms of deposited energy density (Gibbons, 1972; Vook, 1972), only crude estimates of the fractional lattice displacement which induces the transition have been given. Swanson (1971) considered the difference in free energy between the crystalline and amorphous states for Ge (0.11 eV/atom) and concluded that the transition might occur when 2–4% of the lattice is displaced. This should be considered a lower bound, since a highly damaged lattice may be considerably metastable to the amorphous transition. Kinchin and Pease (1955) obtained an expression valid at low energies for the number of atoms $N(E)$ displaced when energy E is deposited into atomic processes:

$$N(E) = E/2E_d \qquad (14)$$

where E_d is the displacement energy, i.e. the energy required to remove an atom from its lattice position (typically 15–20 eV). Sigmund (1969) gave a more detailed argument and modified Eqn. (14) by a factor of 0.8. Vook (1972) used Sigmund's result, together with the experimentally determined

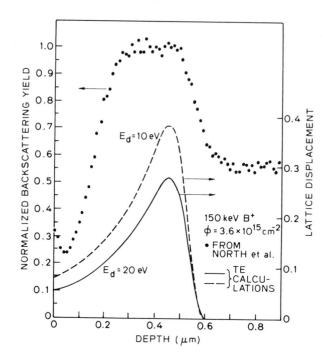

Fig. 4. Comparison of the experimental Rutherford backscattering and channeling (RBS) results of North and Gibson (1971) and a TE calculation which shows the correlation between the experimentally observed edges of the buried amorphous layer and the calculated fractional displacement of the silicon lattice for an implantation of 3.6 × 10¹⁵ cm⁻² 150 keV B into silicon held at liquid nitrogen temperature.

energy density criterion, and concluded that about 30–40% of the lattice must be displaced before the transition occurs. The order-of magnitude range of these estimates indicates that a good deal of uncertainty remains regarding this aspect of the amorphization process.

With the TE calculations (Christel *et al.*, 1980), it is possible to determine fairly accurately the fraction of the lattice which is displaced at each depth during ion implantation. In the calculations, coupled transport equations are numerically integrated in order to yield the momentum distributions of both primary and recoil particles as a function of depth. This information, in conjunction with the differential elastic scattering cross-section proposed by Wilson *et al.* (1977), is used to determine the number of silicon recoils produced per unit volume at each depth. Dividing the number of recoils produced by the atomic density of silicon (5×10^{22} cm⁻³) yields the fractional displacement of the lattice. The results of these calculations correlate well with the extent of implantation-induced amorphous layers which have been measured experimentally by channeling and backscattering of MeV He particles, if one assumes that about 10% lattice displacement results in amorphous silicon. In the next section we compare such calculations with experimental results.

In Fig. 4 we present the experimental results of North and Gibson (1971) which were obtained by channeling and backscattering of 2 MeV He particles for the disorder distribution resulting from implantation of 150 keV boron into silicon held at liquid nitrogen temperature. The depth scale was determined following the procedure given by Feldman and Rodgers (1970). The backscattering spectrum obtained with the sample aligned in the $<110>$ direction is normalized channel by channel to a spectrum obtained when the sample is oriented in a random direction. Thus, a value of 1.0 indicates complete randomness of the sample, and this is taken to imply that the sample is amorphous at that depth. The position of the edges of the buried amorphous layer produced by the implantation are taken to be the points at which the normalized yield drops to half the lowest yield outside the amorphous region (yields of about 0.62 for the left edge and 0.77 for the right edge). Thus, the amorphous region in this case is observed to lie between 0.15 and 0.55 μm.

Shown with the experimental data in Fig. 4 is the result of a TE calculation for the fractional displacement of the lattice under the same implant conditions, assuming displacement energies E_d of 10 eV and 20 eV. Comparison of the calculated curves with the experimental results indicates that the fractional lattice displacement at both edges of the amorphous layer is about 8.5% for $E_d = 20$ eV and about 12.5% for $E_d = 10$ eV. Thus, in this case it appears that about 10% lattice displacement results in amorphous silicon.

The results of TE calculations indicate that the number of displaced atoms is proportional to the energy deposited into atomic processes. In Fig. 5 we compare the TE calculation with the results of Brice (1975) for the energy deposited into atomic processes under the same conditions as in Fig. 4. For this case, in which the ion range distribution is highly skewed, it can be seen that the assumption by Brice of Gaussian intermediate range distributions results in significant differences when compared to the TE calculation, in which the energy deposition is determined more directly. The dotted line in Fig. 5 indicates the level of damage necessary to create an amorphous layer. This was obtained using the energy density criterion that 10^{21} keV cm^{-3} results in amorphous silicon. Note that at a normalized depth of 1.2 the TE calculation yields better agreement between the observed and predicted edge of the amorphous layer. If the energy density criterion is combined with the 10% atomic displacement criterion, it can be seen that on average, 200 eV of deposited energy into atomic processes results in one displacement; i.e., the average silicon recoil receives about 200 eV.

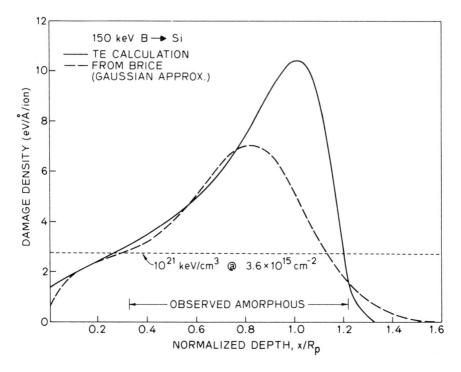

Fig. 5. Comparison of a TE calculation and a calculation from Brice (1975) for the energy density deposited into elastic collision processes under the same conditions as in Fig. 4.

In Figs. 6 and 7 we present similar results for room temperature implantations of Si^+ into silicon at 100 and 200 keV, respectively. In these cases, the channeling spectra are not normalized, but the height of the most heavily damaged region is equal to the random yield, and again the extent of the amorphous layer is evident. The results of TE calculations are shown on the same graphs for comparison. In this case, it appears that for $E_d = 20$ eV, a lattice displacement of about 14% is necessary before amorphous silicon results. This is roughly 60% increase in the apparent fractional displacement necessary to amorphize silicon for substrates at room temperature, compared with substrates at liquid nitrogen temperature, and is consistent with the observed temperature dependence of damage for phosphorus implantation into silicon (Vook, 1972). Thus, if the room temperature data are extrapolated back to the case in which the substrate is held at liquid nitrogen temperature, it is possible to again conclude that about 10% lattice displacement

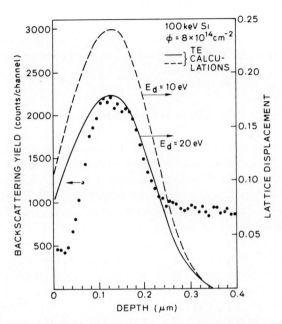

Fig. 6. Comparison of experimental RBS results and TE calculations for 8×10^{14} cm^{-2} 100 keV Si into Si at room temperature.

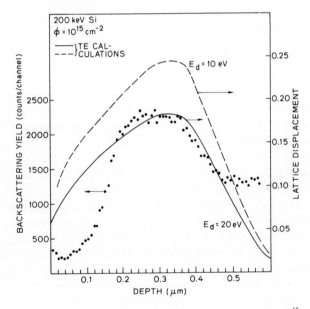

Fig. 7. Comparison of experimental RBS results and TE calculations for 10^{15} cm^{-2} 200 keV Si into Si at room temperature.

is necessary before the amorphous transition is induced. It appears, therefore, that the 10% displacement criterion is rather independent of ion species and energy as long as the substrate is held at sufficiently low temperatures.

B. Stoichiometric Disturbances in Compound Semiconductors

When ions are implanted into compound semiconductors such as GaAs, the different charges and masses associated with the constituents of the compound imply that the collision cross-section, maximum energy transfer, and recoil range distribution corresponding to each type of lattice atom may be vastly different. (For example, lighter atoms have greater ranges than heavier atoms of the same energy.) As a result, after implantation, the compound lattice will not only be damaged but, in addition, will be left with a non-uniform stoichiometric distribution. The proper annealing of such a disturbed lattice may be hindered if the correct stoichiometry cannot be regained by diffusion processes. Such stoichiometric disturbances can be easily calculated using the TE method.

The major interest here is the imbalance in normal stoichiometry of the substrate; i.e., the excess concentration of one substrate element over the other. This information is obtained in two steps. Consider the practical case of gallium arsenide. The calculations yield directly four concentration profiles; namely, gallium and arsenic vacancy distributions (from the origin points of high energy recoils) and gallium and arsenic recoil distributions (from the final stopping points of the same recoils). Since for every recoil there exists a vacancy, the integrals of the vacancy and recoil distributions for one type of atom are equal. However, *locally*, the magnitudes of the distributions may be unequal. We expect vacancy concentration to exceed recoil concentration at shallow depths and vice versa at greater depths. The first step is thus to subtract the vacancy distribution from the recoil distribution for each atom type so as to obtain what we refer to as a *net displaced atom* distribution. Hence, we obtain a distribution of net displaced gallium and a distribution of net displaced arsenic. A negative value of net displaced gallium at any point, for example, indicates that the concentration of gallium at that point is below the bulk concentration of gallium in GaAs.

A non-zero value of the net displaced gallium distribution, however, does not necessarily imply a stoichiometric imbalance at that point. If the net displaced arsenic distribution is of the same value as the corresponding gallium distribution, then there is still one arsenic atom for every gallium atom; i.e., perfect stoichiometry. Thus, the second step is to subtract the net displaced arsenic distribution from the net displaced gallium distribution in order to

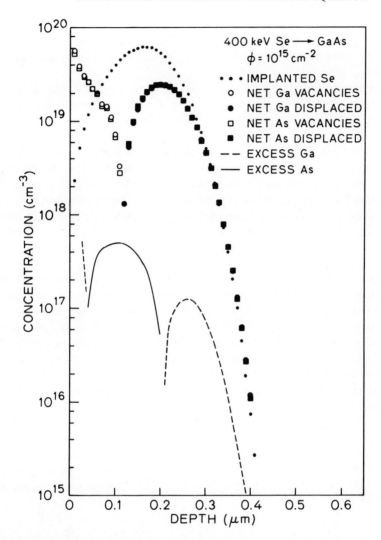

Fig. 8. TE calculation of the stoichiometric distribution in GaAs implanted with 400 keV Se to a dose of 10^{15} cm^{-2}.

obtain the net excess atom distribution, which is a true measure of the stoichiometric imbalance. A positive value indicates excess gallium; a negative value excess arsenic.

An example of such a calculation is shown in Fig. 8, where the results for an implantation of 400 keV Se into GaAs are presented. At shallow depths, an excess of arsenic is present, while at greater depths, an excess of gallium exists. In addition, it can be seen that these effects occur in concentrations which are of the same order of magnitude as the implanted ion concentration, indicating that complications in the proper activation and annealing of such compounds may arise.

As discussed briefly in Chapter 2 (III,B), in a solid-phase annealing process such as furnace or cw laser annealing, the proper reconstruction of the damaged lattice is dependent on the availability of elements of the lattice in the correct proportions near the interface between damaged and recrystallized regions. In a compound in which a significant stoichiometric disturbance exists, some elements of the compound must diffuse hundreds of angstroms in order to satisfy the requirements of the epitaxially growing lattice. If the solid phase, diffusion coefficients of the lattice elements are small and do not allow such long-range diffusion over reasonable time and temperature conditions, then one cannot expect the successful solid-phase annealing of such a compound. In such cases, it may be necessary to attempt a liquid phase regrowth mechanism; e.g., pulsed laser annealing.

The effects of implantation on the stoichiometry of compound semiconductors have been investigated for nine ion/target combinations by using the TE approach (Christel and Gibbons, 1981). In all cases, it is observed that an excess concentration of the heavier element exists at shallow depths, while an excess concentration of the lighter element exists at greater depths, the transition point being somewhat shallower than the peak of the implanted ion distribution. The effects are greatest when the mass ratio of the constituent elements of the compound is high and when the mass of the implanted ion is large. The proper annealing of such damaged compounds will depend on the magnitude of the disturbance as well as the solid phase or liquid phase diffusion coefficients of the elements involved (and their vacancies). In some cases, it may be practically impossible to attain a solid phase epitaxial regrowth—in which case, a pulsed laser anneal (as discussed in Chapter 2, sect. IV) may be the most promising method for regrowth and dopant activation.

IV. SUMMARY

As the foregoing calculations and comparisons with experimental data show, the Boltzmann transport equation provides a very comprehensive treatment of the general ion implantation problem. The primary ion distribution in a multilayer target can be calculated directly and is found to be in good agreement with experiments. At the same time, the transport equation predicts the spatial distribution of recoils and thus provides the theoretical information needed to determine (i) the fractional atomic displacement necessary for amorphization of silicon, and (ii) the degree of stoichiometric imbalance that is produced when energetic ions are incident on a target having more than one type of host atom. It therefore seems likely that the Boltzmann transport equation will be used increasingly for ion implantation problems in compound semiconductors and for a variety of silicon processing applications, particularly where thin surface coatings are present on the sample surface.

REFERENCES

Brice, D. K. (1975). *J. Appl. Phys.* **46**, 3385.
Brice, D. K. (1975). "Ion Implantation Range and Energy Deposition Distributions", Vol. 1, Plenum, New York.
Christel, L. A., and Gibbons, J. F. (1981). *J. Appl. Phys.* **52**, 5050.
Christel, L. A., Gibbons, J. F., and Mylroie, S. (1980). *J. Appl. Phys.* **51**, 6176.
Christel, L. A., Gibbons, J. F., and Mylroie, S. (1981). *Nucl. Instrum. Methods* **182/183**, 187.
Crowder, B. L. (1970). *J. Electrochem. Soc.* **117**, 671.
Crowder, B. L., and Morehead, F. F. (1969). *Appl. Phys. Lett.* **14**, 313.
Eisen, F. (1968). *Can. J. Phys.* **46**, 561.
Feldman, L. C., and Rodgers, J. W. (1970). *J. Appl. Phys.* **41**, 3667.
Gibbons, J. F. (1972). *Proc. IEEE* **60**, 1062.
Gibbons, J. F., Johnson, W. S., and Mylroie, S. W. (1975). "Projected Range Statistics in Semiconductors." Wiley, New York.
Hirao, T., Inoue, K., Takayanagi, S., and Yaegashi, Y. (1979a). *J. Appl. Phys.* **50**, 193.
Hirao, T., Fuse, G., Inoue, K., Takayanagi, S., Yaegashi, Y., and Ichikawa, S. (1979b). *J. Appl. Phys.* **50**, 5251.
Kalbitzer, S., and Oetzmann, H. (1978). *In* "Ion Beam Modification of Materials" (J. Guylai *et al.*, eds.). Hungarian Acad. Sci., Budapest.
Kinchin, G. H., and Pease, R. S. (1955). *Rep. Prog. Phys.* **18**, 2.
Lindhard, J., Scharff, M., and Schiøtt, H. (1963). *Mat. Fys. Med. Dan. Vid. Selsk.* **33**, 1-39.
Lindhard, J., Nielsen, V., and Scharff, M. (1968). *Mat. Fys. Med. Dan. Vid. Selsk.* **36**, 14.
Moorehead, Jr., and Crowder, B. L. (1970). *Rad. Effects* **6**, 27.
North, J. C., and Gibson, W. M. (1971). *In* "Ion Implantation" (F. H. Eisen and L. T. Chadderton, eds.), p. 143. Gordon and Breach, London.
Sigmund, P. (1969). *Appl. Phys. Lett.* **14**, 114.
Smith, D. H., and Gibbons, J. F. (1976). *In* "Ion Implantation in Semiconductors, 1976" (F. Chernow *et al.*, eds.). Plenum Press, New York.
Swanson, M. L. (1971). *Rad. Effects* **9**, 249.
Vook, F. L. (1972). "Radiation Damage and Defects in Semiconductors." Institute of Physics, London.
Wilson, W. D., Haggmark, L. G., and Biersack, J. P. (1977). *Phys. Rev.* **B 15**, 2458.
Winterbon, K. B., Sigmund, D., and Sanders, J. B. (1970). *Kgl. Danske Vid. Selskab Mat. Fys. Medd.* **37**, 14.

CHAPTER 4

High Energy Density Collision Cascades and Spike Effects

J. A. DAVIES

Atomic Energy of Canada Limited Research Company
Chalk River, Ontario, Canada

I. INTRODUCTION

As discussed in previous chapters, when an energetic ion penetrates a solid, it gives up its kinetic energy via two processes: (i) electronic excitation; and (ii) elastic nuclear collisions with target atoms. The latter process produces a series of energetic atomic recoils; i.e., a collision cascade. As long as the nuclear collision cross-section is sufficiently small, each successive event can be described by a simple binary collision between the moving ion and a

ION IMPLANTATION
AND BEAM PROCESSING
ISBN 0 12 756980 4

stationary target atom. Under such conditions, the spatial distribution of deposited energy can be described by a linear Boltzmann transport equation (as discussed in Chapter 3). However, the cross-section for nuclear collisions increases strongly with increasing atomic number of the projectile (Z_1) and substrate atom (Z_2) and also with decreasing projectile energy E. Hence, as ($Z_1 Z_2 / E$) is increased, the nuclear collision cross-section eventually becomes so large that the assumptions appropriate to the linear cascade model are no longer satisfied. This is the so-called high-density cascade regime, in which some sort of collective effect or energy spike provides a more realistic model.

Simple estimates show that, for most heavy ion implantations, the final deposited energy density (if shared equally among all atoms within the cascade volume) corresponds to a very significant increase in thermal motion. Consider, for example, a 100 keV ion with a mean range of 200 Å implanted at room temperature. The total cascade volume contains less than 10^5 atoms, and hence the final deposited energy density exceeds 1.0 eV/atom. Since the total cascade propagation time is too short ($\sim 2 \times 10^{-13}$ s) for normal quenching mechanisms to remove significant energy, and since 1.0 eV/atom is comparable to the heat of melting of most substrates, it is obvious that the final stages of the cascade no longer involve stationary target atoms.

Sigmund (1974) suggested that a thermal spike mechanism might be utilized to handle these high-density cascades. Indeed, the anomalously large damage levels observed in many semiconductor implantations (Section III,A) are certainly consistent with the formation (and subsequent rapid quenching) of a pseudo-liquid region around each heavy ion track.

The thermal spike concept is an extremely old one. It was proposed originally by Brinkman in the 1950s, then discarded, and now has been resurrected again. Many people are still vehemently opposed to the concept. They point out (quite correctly) that the quenching times are often too short and the cascade dimensions too small for Maxwell–Boltzmann statistics to apply; also, the coupling between atomic motion and electronic excitation is too slow for a true equilibrium to be achieved. Indeed, a few picoseconds after implantation, two completely different "temperatures" are probably necessary: one to describe the vibrational motion of the target atoms and a second one for the electronic excitation. (For example, it is possible to have "hot" atoms and "cold" electrons within the same cascade, or vice versa.) But this merely illustrates the complexity of the problem. Obviously, we cannot directly apply ordinary thermodynamic arguments or thermal conductivity equations to such a non-equilibrium situation. However, because we cannot quantitatively describe a phenomenon does not make it disappear.

The important point to be emphasized here is that, in most implantations, the energy density around the end of each ion track is far too high (i.e. several eV/atom) for ordinary binary collision theory to apply and that some sort of collective "hot spot" occurs for at least a few picoseconds after the ion comes to rest. Indeed, an energy density of 1 eV/atom is very comparable to that involved in the pulsed laser and electron-beam annealing studies discussed in Chapters 2, 7 and 11; however, because of the much smaller dimensions, the rate of quenching of such high density cascades may be $\sim 10^3$ times faster.

In this chapter, the theoretical basis for estimating the mean deposited energy density Θ within an individual cascade will be described briefly in terms of various experimental parameters. The experimental evidence for spike effects in three widely differing systems will then be examined: (i) radiation damage in heavy ion bombardment of Si and Ge; (ii) sputtering of heavy metals (Au, Pt, Ag) by heavy ions; and (iii) sputtering of ice and frozen gases by MeV helium ions. Finally, the relevant thermal spike parameters will be considered for each system in order to provide a basis for assessing the extent to which thermal arguments may be appropriate.

II. COLLISION CASCADE CONCEPTS

There are several different criteria for defining the onset of spike behavior. For example, whenever Θ for the cascade exceeds some critical value Θ_c for a phase change to occur (typically ~ 1 eV/atom for melting, or 3–4 eV/atom for evaporation), then the possibility of some sort of *thermal* spike effect exists. Alternatively, when the nuclear stopping power $(dE/dx)_N$ per atomic plane exceeds the threshold displacement energy E_d, then a continuous network of defects is created; this would be termed a *displacement* spike. Again, in insulators, when the electronic stopping power $(dE/dx)_e$ exceeds some critical value, then a continuous network of ionized atoms, i.e. an *ionization* spike, may occur. An extensive review of energy spikes and the various models for representing them (thermal spike, shock wave, displacement or ionization spike, etc.) has recently been prepared by Thompson (1981). The basic dependence on various bombardment parameters, such as E, Z_1 and Z_2 turns out to be similar for all these models; i.e., in all cases, the deposited energy density Θ must exceed some critical value, which is typically of the order of a few eV/atom.

The deposited energy density Θ within each individual cascade can easily be varied by more than four orders of magnitude; namely, from less than 10^{-3} eV/atom to 10 eV/atom, or even higher. Quantitative estimates of Θ may be obtained from the description of the collision cascade, based solely on collisional (stopping) processes, in Lindhard *et al.* (1963). They separated the

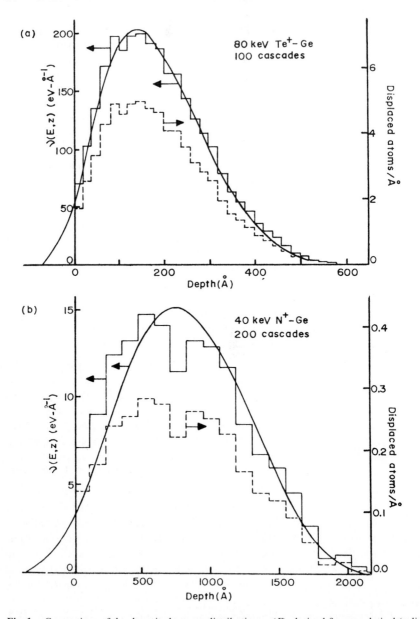

Fig. 1. Comparison of the deposited energy distributions, $v(E)$, derived from analytical (solid curve) and Monte Carlo (histogram) methods. (From Walker and Thompson, 1978.) Note the large change in depth scale between the upper and lower figures, indicating that the heavier ion (Te^+) is producing a much larger θ than the N^+ cascade. The displaced atom distribution (dashed histogram) is also included.

energy–loss mechanisms into two types: nuclear (recoil) loss $\nu(E)$ and electronic excitation $\eta(E)$, with $\nu(E) + \eta(E) = E_{ion}$. Using this description, Winterbon et al. (1970) developed analytical procedures based on the transport equation that predict quite well the mean dimensions (depth, transverse and longitudinal straggling, etc.) of the collision cascade, and comprehensive tabulations have subsequently been prepared (Winterbon, 1975). An alternative procedure is to use Monte Carlo techniques to simulate individual collision cascades and then to average the results from several hundred such cascades.

The excellent agreement (Fig. 1) between these analytical and Monte Carlo predictions indicates that one can predict with some confidence the average dimensions of the collision cascade. In the "displacement spike" model, one would also be interested in the displaced atom distribution resulting from such a cascade; this requires additional assumptions to be made about the threshold displacement energy (E_d) and the extent to which vacancy/interstitial recombination affects the final distribution within the cascade. However, in the (thermal) spike context, we need to consider only the deposited (nuclear recoil) energy distribution, $\nu(E)$, and so avoid these complications.

In estimating the appropriate value of Θ for an *individual* cascade, it is extremely important to distinguish between the average depth distribution of $\nu(E)$ resulting from a large number of cascades (see Fig. 1) and the distribution produced within a single cascade. The latter quantity can only be obtained by Monte Carlo simulation. Several examples are shown in Fig. 2, with the corresponding *average* distribution envelopes included for comparison. When the incident ion is heavier than the substrate (e.g. the Bi^+-implanted Si case), the resulting deposited energy distribution is seen to be distributed fairly uniformly throughout the $\nu(E)$ envelope. In this case, the average $\nu(E)$ distribution provides a reasonable approximation to the individual cascade behavior. However, at the other extreme of mass ratio (e.g. N^+-implanted Si), the individual cascade occupies only an extremely small fraction of the corresponding $\nu(E)$ envelope, and hence Θ in each individual cascade will be much larger than that calculated from the volume of the overall $\nu(E)$ envelope.

The magnitude of this volume correction factor (V_R) has been evaluated by Walker and Thompson (1978) as a function of mass ratio, M_1/M_2, where M_1 is the mass of the projectile, and M_2 the mass of the substrate atoms. For the Bi^+-implanted Si case of Fig. 2, where $M_1 \gg M_2$, the appropriate volume reduction factor is ~ 0.7 (i.e. not much less than unity), but for the N^+-implanted Si case the corresponding reduction is almost a factor of 100. Obviously, whenever $M_1 \lesssim M_2$, the calculated value of the deposited energy density Θ within each cascade is increased enormously by this effect; in such

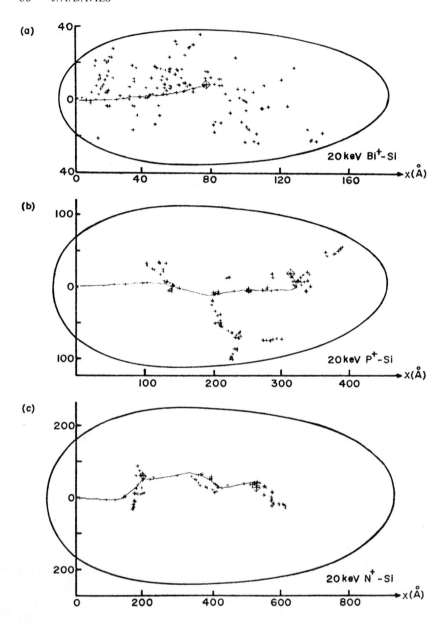

Fig. 2. Relationship between individual (Monte Carlo) cascade dimensions and the average distribution obtained from the transport equation. The elliptical curves represent the $v(E)$ contour at 10% of $v(E)_{max}$. The primary ion trajectory is indicated by a continuous line and those cascade atoms receiving more than E_d are denoted by $+$. From Walker and Thompson (1978.)

cases, there may also be considerable local variations in Θ from one region of the cascade to another; i.e., so-called sub-cascades.

Taking the above considerations into account and using power–law approximations (with exponent m) to the Thomas–Fermi potential to simplify the calculations, Sigmund (1974) and Winterbon (1981) provided a convenient set of graphs and computer tabulations for all combinations of Z_1, Z_2 and E from which Θ and other cascade parameters of interest may be evaluated. For example, within the $m = \frac{1}{3}$ power law regime (i.e. for $\varepsilon \lesssim 0.2$), Sigmund (1974) showed that $\Theta = G_3 N^2/E$, where N is the target number density in atoms Å^{-3}, E is the incident energy in keV and G_3 depends only on M_1 and M_2. Within the $m = \frac{1}{2}$ regime (valid for reduced energy, ε, values $\gtrsim 0.2$); Θ exhibits an even stronger reciprocal E dependence; i.e., $\Theta = G_2 N^2/E^2$. Graphical representation of G_2 and G_3 as a function of M_1 and M_2 has been given by Sigmund (1974).

To illustrate this very strong E dependence, Sigmund (1974) took a typical medium–mass case (Te^+-implanted Ag) and evaluated the mean deposited energy density as a function of the incident energy (Fig. 3). Also included in Fig. 3 is Sigmund's estimate of the subsequent quenching rate t_q, which is based on a high–pressure kinetic gas model for estimating the appropriate thermal conductivity value in such a "hot", short-lived spike.

Provided Z_1 and Z_2 are almost equal, very simple scaling laws may be developed for estimating Θ. For example, within the $m = \frac{1}{3}$ power law approximation, the ion range (R) expressed in g cm^{-2} depends only weakly on Z (i.e. $R \propto Z^{1/6}$); the resulting expression for Θ is then directly proportional to ($\rho^2 Z^{1/2}/E$), where ρ is the target density in g cm^{-3}. Evidence for this very strong dependence on target density is clearly seen in Table I.

For the selected cases in Table I, $\nu(E)$ is always significantly greater than $\eta(E)$. Hence, the initial energy deposition is predominantly into atom recoil motion; i.e., the cascade spike consists of "hot" atoms and (relatively) "cold" electrons. However, for light, high-energy ions such as MeV He, $\nu(E)/E = 10^{-3}$ and $\eta(E)/E = 1.0$; i.e., the energy is deposited almost exclusively into electronic excitation. In such a case, the resulting spike consists essentially of "cold" atoms and "hot" electrons. In the following section, evidence for both types of spike effect are presented and discussed.

III. EXPERIMENTAL EXAMPLES OF SPIKE EFFECTS

The thermal spike concept is a fairly old and controversial topic and, over the past twenty-five years, a wide variety of experimental results has been

TABLE I
Dependence of the mean deposited energy density (θ) on energy (E), density (ρ) and atomic numbers (Z_1 and Z_2).

E (keV)	Z_1	Z_2	ρ (g cm^{-3})	θ (eV/atom)
100	Si	Si		0.001
10	Si	Si	2.5	0.1
10	Au	Si		1.0
10	Au	Au	19.3	25.0
10	Au	Bi	9.8	6.0

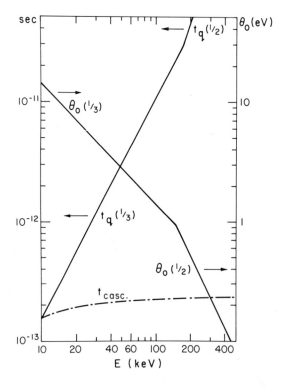

Fig. 3. Initial deposited energy density, θ_0, versus incident energy E for Ag bombarded with Te$^+$ ions: for the power-law exponent $m = \frac{1}{2}$ and $m = \frac{1}{3}$ regimes. t_{casc} is the cascade propagation time and t_q is the time to quench θ_0 to half its initial value. From Sigmund (1974).

attributed to it. In many cases, more recent work has shown that other processes were responsible for the observed behavior. In recent years, however, rather compelling evidence of significant spike effects has been found in at least three diverse experimental studies.

A. Implantation Damage in Semiconductors

In ion-implanted semiconductors such as Si and Ge, the observed damage level (usually determined as the number of displaced atoms per cascade, N_D) at low temperature can be almost an order of magnitude *greater* than that predicted from linear collision cascade theory, especially for heavy ions such as Tl (Fig. 4). Note that the high-energy portion of each curve bends over to approximately the same slope as the N_{kp} line, which gives the linear cascade calculation via a Kinchin-Pease model. This indicates that the rate of damage created at high energy agrees well with collision cascade theory and that the enhanced value of N_D is entirely due to the low-energy portion of each ion track, where the deposited energy density becomes extremely high. The reciprocal slope $(dv(E)/dN_D)$ of the curves in Fig. 4 is a measure of the effective energy required to create each displaced atom. Obviously, at high $v(E)$, this must correspond closely to the displacement energy E_d (14 eV in Si), since all the curves become approximately parallel to the N_{kp} line. But, at low $v(E)$ and high Z_1 (i.e. high Θ), the reciprocal slope is seen to fall rapidly and, in the case of Tl, it actually approaches the heat of melting for Si (0.7 eV).

In a closely related electron microscopy study, Howe and Rainville (1981) have found that at sufficiently high Θ (i.e. > 0.5 eV/atom) each implanted ion produces an observable amorphous blob whose radius is in excellent agreement with that derived from the RBS measurement of N_D. This strongly suggests that each high density cascade is initially a molten zone which is subsequently quenched rapidly enough to remain amorphous.

In this context it should be noted that the solidification rate resulting from the extremely rapid quenching of the small cascade volume is of the order of 100 Å in $\sim 10^{-12}$ sec; i.e., 10^3–10^4 m sec⁻¹. As discussed in Section IV of Chapter 2, the rate of epitaxial regrowth observed in a typical pulsed laser annealing experiment is only ~ 5 m sec⁻¹. Furthermore, experiments outlined in Chapter 2 indicate that amorphous layers are formed when the solidification interface moves faster than about 15 m sec⁻¹. Hence, the extremely rapid quenching of a collision cascade spike would be expected to produce a non-epitaxial (i.e. amorphous) region in Si or Ge.

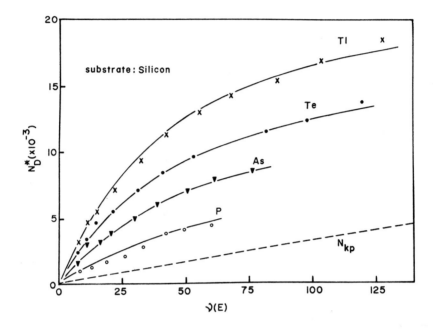

Fig. 4. The total observed number of displaced atoms, N_D, per cascade versus $v(E)$ in silicon at 35K, as determined by the RBS/channeling technique. The dashed line N_{kp} is the damage level predicted by linear cascade theory via the Kinchin-Pease relation. From Thompson and Walker (1978).

Further evidence that Θ is the dominant parameter controlling Si implantation damage in high-density collision cascades is shown by the molecular ion studies in Table II (Mitchell *et al.*, 1974; Davies *et al.*, 1975). In each case, the molecular ion bombardment (with As_2^+ or $C_6H_6^+$) exhibits significantly larger $N_D/v(E)$ values than the corresponding monatomic ion (As^+ or C^+), even though the incident velocities (energies/atom) are identical. Hence, the increase in the value of Θ, which is caused by simultaneously injecting two (or, in the case of C ions, six) identical cascades into the same cascade envelope, produces much more than a linear increase in damage level. Furthermore, one can also choose an appropriate heavier ion (50 keV Bi^+ and 57 keV Ga^+, respectively), for which the incident energy E and the deposited energy density Θ within the cascade are both essentially identical to the corresponding values for the two molecular ions. As can be seen in Table II, the observed damage production efficiency $N_D/v(E)$ in each case agrees extremely closely with the corresponding molecular ion result, showing clearly that Θ is the main experimental parameter controlling the observed damage level.

B. Sputtering of Metals

Simple collision cascade theory predicts that the observed sputtering yield should increase linearly with Θ_s, the energy density deposited in the surface region of the cascade. Strong deviations from this linear dependence have been reported, firstly by Andersen and Bay (1973) in a series of comparisons of diatomic versus equal-velocity monatomic ion bombardments (e.g. 50 keV Te_2^+ versus 25 keV Te^+), and more recently by Thompson (1981) in an extensive sputtering study of Ag, Au and Pt targets as a function of Θ_s (Fig. 5). Two clearly resolved regions of behavior are observed: at low energy densities, the linear dependence predicted from collision cascade theory agrees well with the data, but at higher Θ_s values, the data in each case exhibit a sharp transition to a much stronger than linear dependence, indicating the onset of some sort of collective process, such as a thermal spike.

C. Frozen-Gas Erosion by MeV Ions

The third and final example of spike effects involves a completely different energy regime—the sputtering of frozen gases by MeV light ions such as $^4He^+$. Here, the ratio $v(E)/\eta(E)$ is extremely small ($\sim 10^{-3}$), and the sputtering yield due to atomic collision processes is usually negligible. In metals, the energy deposited via electronic excitation, $\eta(E)$, is rapidly dissipated

TABLE II

Total number (N_D) of displaced Si atoms per incident ion (300K) for various incident ions of incident energy E. The values of the nuclear energy component $v(E)$, and the ratio $N_D/v(E)$ are also tabulated.

Ion	E (keV)	$v(E)$ (keV)	N_D (atoms)	$N_D/v(E)$ (atoms/keV)
As^+	25	17	1306	77
As^+_2	50	34	4504	132
Bi^+	50	33	4300	130
C^+	8.8	5.5	9	2
$C_6H_6^+$	57	34	842	25
Ga^+	57	37	1081	29

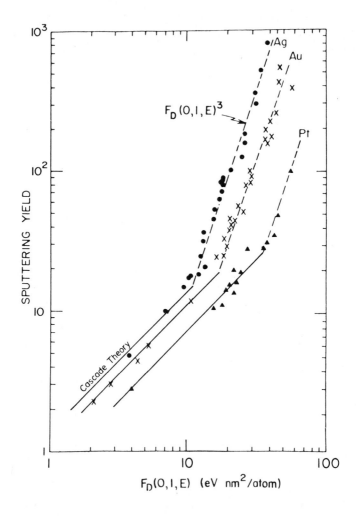

Fig. 5. Sputtering yields for Ag, Au and Pt bombarded with various monatomic and poly-atomic ions as a function of the surface deposited energy density F_D (i.e. θ_s) obtained by Monte Carlo calculations. From Thompson (1981). It should be noted that the abscissa scale in his review paper contained a numerical error of 10^4 and we thank Dr Thompson for supplying this corrected figure.

throughout the lattice and so does not contribute significantly to any spike effects. However, in certain non-metallic materials such as frozen gases, ice and UF_4, very large sputtering yields are observed (Table III), and these yields generally increase approximately as the *square* of the total deposited energy density. Presumably, in these electrically insulating materials, the

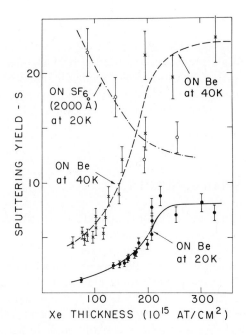

Fig. 6. Thickness and substrate dependence of the sputtering yields S for 1.0 MeV He[+]-implanted Xe. From Ollerhead *et al.* (1980).

TABLE III

Sputtering yields (S) for MeV ^{4}He ions on various targest at ~ 20K.

Target (~ 20K)	S (atoms/ion)	Reference
Xe	10	Ollerhead *et al.* (Chalk River)
Kr	20	Ollerhead *et al.* (Chalk River)
Ar	100	Bottiger *et al.* (Aarhus)
Ice (H_2O)	10	Brown *et al.* (Bell Labs.)
CO_2	100	Brown *et al.* (Bell Labs.)
N_2	300	Pirronello *et al.* (Catania)
UF_4 (4 MeV $^{16}O^+$)	4	Tombrello *et al.* (Cal. Tech.)
Various metals	10^{-3}	

$\eta(E)$ contribution is not as rapidly dissipated and perhaps contributes to some sort of spike effect.

In the case of the rare gases (Xe, Kr and Ar), the observed sputtering yields exhibit a strong dependence on the thickness of the frozen gas and also on the thermal conductivity of the underlying substrate (Fig. 6). This behavior is interpreted by Ollerhead *et al.* (1980) as strong evidence that the sputtering is due to some sort of thermal spike process.

An extensive account of the widespread experimental data now available on frozen-gas erosion is contained in Section II of Chapter 5, together with a detailed discussion of the various spike models that may be involved. From the various examples presented above, it is clear that different ion bombardment systems can, under certain conditions, exhibit large non-linear spike effects.

IV. THERMAL SPIKE CONCEPTS

Even when Θ within the collision cascade far exceeds the characteristic threshold for some specific process (melting, evaporation, etc.), there are still several criteria to be met before a simple thermal spike concept will have quantitative significance. Firstly, the cascade dimensions must be large enough for statistical dynamics to apply. For example, the diameter of a 10 keV Au^+ in Au cascade is only ~ 20 Å, and hence would contain less than 500 target atoms. A second, closely related requirement is that the thermal gradient across the spike should be reasonably small. In the above Au^+ case, where the initial value of Θ (~ 25 eV/atom) is roughly 10^3 greater than that of the surrounding substrate, the initial "thermal" gradient would be enormous; i.e. almost a factor of 10 per lattice spacing. Finally, the quenching time constant $t_q = R/4k$ (where R is the ion range, as before, and k is the thermal diffusivity of the target) must be longer than the time required for electron/phonon coupling (i.e. $\gtrsim 10^{-11}$ sec). Otherwise, the spike will require two different "temperatures" to describe it properly, one for the electron system, and a quite different one for the atomic motion. Under such circumstances, the choice of an appropriate k value to describe the "thermal diffusivity" presents a severe problem.

A comprehensive review of the theoretical basis for treating these high-density cascade effects, including the relative merits of various spike models, has recently been published by Thompson (1981). Generally speaking, quantitative treatment of such spike effects in terms of simple thermal diffusivity is not possible, since the above criteria are rarely fulfilled within the small dimensions of a typical collision cascade. However, in order to give some insight into the problems involved, the approximate magnitude of the various spike parameters (size, temperature gradient, quench rate, etc.) for each of the experimental systems in Section III were estimated, assuming the validity of Boltzmann statistics and bulk thermal diffusivity concepts. The results are summarized in Tables IV and V.

TABLE IV

Non-linear cascade damage parameters for Si and Ge. $\nu(E)/E$ is the fraction of the initial energy lost in nuclear processes, ΔH is the enthalpy of melting, k is the diffusivity, r_{max} is the "thermal" calculation of the spike radius, t_q is the quenching time constant, dT/dx is the temperature gradient and r_{exptl} is the experimentally observed radius of the damaged zones.

	Si	Ge
Ion beam	30 keV	30 keV
	Bi^+_2	Bi^+_2
$\nu E/E$	0.8	0.8
ΔH (eV/atom)	0.7	0.6
$k(cm^2\ sec^{-1})$	0.23	0.15
r_{max} (Å)	56	65
t_q (10^{-12} s)	0.4	0.7
dT/dx (K/Å)	30	20
r_{exptl} (Å)	51	65

TABLE V

Non-linear sputtering cascade parameters for solid targets of Au, Xe, H_2O and UF_4. The symbols are defined in the caption of Table IV with $S_{cascade}$, $S_{thermal}$ and $S_{observed}$ being the sputtering yields for cascade calculations, thermal calculations and experimental values, respectively.

Target	Au	Xe	H_2O (ice)	UF_4
Ion beam	90 keV	1 MeV	1 MeV	4 MeV
	Sb^+_3	He^+	He^+	$^{16}O^+$
$\nu(E)/E$	0.8	0.005	0.003	0.004
ΔH (eV/atom)	1	0.06	0.2	2.0
k ($cm^2\ s^{-1}$)	0.7	0.002	0.01	0.01
r_{max} (Å)	80	100	30	20
t_q (10^{1-12} s)	0.3	150	2	1
dT/dx (K/Å)	100	1	10	200
$S_{cascade}$ (atoms/ion)	40	0.02	0.001	0.01
$S_{thermal}$ ($\alpha\pi r^2 tq$)	0.01	20	0.01	<0.005
$S_{observed}$ (atoms/ion)	600	10	10	4

In the case of the enhanced implantation damage in semiconductors (Table IV), a reasonable upper limit to the size of the "molten spike" has been established by dividing the available nuclear energy $\nu(E)$ by the enthalpy of melting ΔH (eV/atom). (Note that these ΔH values also include the integrated heat capacity from the substrate temperature to the melting point.) The resulting spike radius (r_{max}) agrees remarkably well with r_{exptl}; i.e.

the radius of the amorphous zone measured by electron microscopy (Howe and Rainville, 1981). In both Si and Ge, using standard thermal diffusivity data, the estimated magnitude of the time (t_q) to reduce Θ to half its initial value is less than 10^{-12} sec. This is far too short for electron-phonon equilibration to occur. However, since most of the energy is deposited directly into atomic motion, t_q is probably long enough to create a random liquid-like distribution of atoms. It should be emphasized that 10^{-12} sec is still far too short for significant diffusive mixing to occur within the spike volume, since, even for a hot liquid, the diffusion length would not exceed 1-10 Å.

In treating enhanced sputtering (Table V), the approximate surface area of the spike is estimated by dividing the initial stopping power $(-dE/Ndx)$ of the incident beam by the enthalpy of melting ΔH. These ΔH values also include the integrated value of the heat capacity from the substrate temperature to that at which the vapor pressure becomes ~ 1 atmosphere. For MeV ions, where the main component of dE/dx is electronic excitation, this estimate of r_{max} may be far too large unless some mechanism exists for converting electronic excitation into thermal motion more rapidly than the quench rate, t_q. In the case of Xe (and the other inert gases), however, the resulting estimate for t_q ($\sim 10^{-10}$ sec) is probably large enough for significant electron-phonon equilibration ($\sim 10^{-11}$ sec) to occur. It is interesting to note that this is also the only case in which the calculated amount of evaporation ($S_{thermal}$) from the spike is comparable in magnitude to the observed sputtering yield. For all the other cases in Table V, t_q is so short and the thermal gradients are so large that simple thermal diffusivity concepts would certainly not apply. Nevertheless, all the experimental sputtering yields in Table V are many orders of magnitude greater than the $S_{cascade}$ values predicted by linear collision cascade theory, indicating that spike effects of some sort must be dominant in every case.

It is intriguing to note that simple thermal spike considerations would predict the sputtering yield in Xe to be at least a factor of 10^3 greater than that in ice or in UF_4—yet the measured S values are almost identical (Table V). Clearly, there must be a much more energy-efficient spike mechanism involved in the latter two materials, perhaps a coulomb "explosion" mechanism due to the high ionization density along the incident ion trajectory, as suggested by Brown et al. (1980). This mechanism and other possible contributing factors are discussed in detail by Brown in section II of chapter 5.

For metal targets such as Au, one has the further complication of selecting an appropriate value for the thermal diffusivity, k. Since t_q is far too short for electron-phonon equilibration to occur, and since $\nu(E)$ is the dominant energy deposition process in this case, we should probably replace the metallic thermal diffusivity value of 0.7 cm sec^{-1} by a k value that is more typical of an insulator (i.e. $\sim 10^{-2}$ cm^2 sec^{-1}). This would increase considerably the estimated spike contribution to the sputtering yield (i.e. by ~ 1 atom/ ion), but this is still almost a factor of 10^3 less than $S_{observed}$.

V. CONCLUSIONS

Widespread experimental evidence exists showing that significant spike effects occur whenever the deposited energy density within the collision cascade approaches the eV/atom level. Unfortunately, the quenching time t_q is usually far too rapid for the electron-phonon equilibrium to be established. Hence, the choice of an appropriate thermal diffusivity value and even the validity of Maxwell-Boltzmann statistics will present severe problems in attempting to develop a quantitative treatment of such spike effects.

REFERENCES

Andersen, H. H., and Bay, H. L. (1973). *Rad. Effects.* **19**, 139.
Brown, W. L., Augustyniak, W. M., Brody, E., Cooper, B., Lanzerotti, L. J., Ramirez, A., Evatt, R. and Johnson, R. E. (1980). *Nucl. Instrum. Methods.* **170**, 321.
Davies, J. A., Foti, G., Howe, L. M., Mitchell, J. B., and Winterbon, K. B. (1975). *Phys. Rev. Letters* **34**, 1441.
Howe, L. M., and Rainville, M. H. (1981). *Nucl. Instrum. Methods* **182/183**, 143.
Lindhard, J., Nielsen, V., Scharff, M., and Thomsen, P. V. (1963), *Kgl. Danske Vid. Selsk. Mat. Fys. Med.* **33**, No. 10.
Mitchell, J. B., Davies, J. A., Howe, L. M., Walker, R. S., Winterbon, K. B., Foti, G., and Moore, J. A. (1974). *In* "Ion Implantation in Semiconductors" (S. Namba, ed.), pp. 493-500. Plenum Press, New York.
Ollerhead, R. W., Bøttiger, J., Davies, J. A., L'Ecuyer, J., Haugen, H. H., and Matsunami, N. (1980). *Rad. Effects.* **49**, 203.
Sigmund, P. (1974). *Appl. Phys. Lett.* **25**, 169 (and an erratum in volume **27**, 52).
Thompson, D. A., (1981) *Rad. Effects.* **56**, 105.
Thompson, D. A., and Walker, R. S. (1978). *Rad. Effects.* **36**, 91.
Walker, R. S., and Thompson, D. A. (1978), *Rad. Effects.* **37**, 113.
Winterbon, K. B. (1975). "Ion Implantation Range and Energy Distributions, Vol. 2, Low Energy." Plenum Press, New York.
Winterbon, K. B., Sigmund, P., and Sanders, J. B. (1970), *Kgl. Danske Vid. Selsk. Mat. Fys. Medd.* **37**, No. 14.

CHAPTER 5

Implantation of Insulators: Ices and Lithographic Materials

W. L. BROWN

Bell Laboratories
Murray Hill, New Jersey, USA

ION IMPLANTATION
AND BEAM PROCESSING
ISBN   0 12 756980 4

I. INTRODUCTION

Ion implantation in all solids produces atomic displacements, defects and sputtering (Mayer *et al.*, 1970). These processes result from so called collision cascades that are initiated by collisions of an incident ion with the nuclei of the solid (the nuclear stopping power). In insulators, new phenomena, which are completely absent in metals and almost absent in semiconductors, occur. These phenomena arise from electronic excitation of the solid by the ion (the electronic stopping power). Electronic excitation, of course, occurs around the track of an energetic ion in all materials. However, in metals, this primarily results in excitation of conduction band electrons which then rapidly share their energy with other electrons. Thus, the energy density drops too low to be capable of rearranging the atoms in the solid. In semiconductors, the electrons and holes formed in ionization are sufficiently mobile to diffuse away from their point of creation and again dilute the energy density. In large band gap semiconductors, it is possible for recombination of a single electron–hole pair to result in atomic motion (Lang and Kimerling, 1974; Kimerling, 1978), but this route for recombination has a very low probability.

In insulators, the energy of ionization is large, often larger than the energy required to displace atoms or molecules. Furthermore, the energy remains localized around the track of the incident ion because the resultant positive ions have low mobility and their space charge restrains the electrons. Details of the dynamics of this localized region of electronic excitation are poorly understood. However, there is a growing body of information on the experimental consequences; for example, the ion-induced erosion of insulating films and the formation of molecular fragments, new molecules and new molecular structures. Two aspects of this work will be considered in the following sections: ion induced erosion of condensed gas films and ion beam lithography.

II. ION EROSION OF CONDENSED GAS FILMS

A. Ions, Ices and Astrophysics

Interplanetary space is full of ions: the solar wind, which blows continually outward from the sun (Holzer, 1979); solar cosmic rays, which are emitted in bursts associated with eruptions in the solar corona (Fisk, 1979); and ions trapped in the magnetic fields of planets (Kennel and Coroniti, 1979; Siscoe, 1979), which are analogous to the radiation belts of earth. An artistic view of these sources is shown in Fig. 1. Interplanetary space also contains a great deal of ice (Lekosfsky, 1975) on the surfaces of planets and their moons

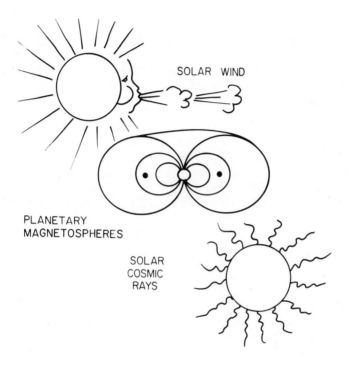

Fig. 1.   An artistic view of sources of energetic ions in the solar system, illustrating solar wind, solar cosmic rays, and trapped radiation belt particles.

(Pilcher *et al.*, 1974; Lekosfsky, 1977; Broadfoot *et al.*, 1979; Smith *et al.*, 1981), in comets (Whipple, 1950, 1977) and in tiny ice grains (Delsemme and Miller, 1971; Delsemme and Wagner, 1970). Water ice is the most pervasive, but ices of CO_2, SO_2 and CH_4 are also found. Inevitably these ices are exposed to at least some of the ions. Curiosity concerning the possible consequences of this interaction led to a series of experiments which have shown the dominant effect of electronic energy loss in the erosion of ice films by ions. Some of these results are discussed below.

B. Ion Erosion of H_2O Films

The energy dependence of H_2O ice erosion by hydrogen and helium ions at 78K is shown in Fig. 2. The yield, Y, is defined as the number of molecules lost from a film per incident ion. The yields have maxima at ~ 100 keV/

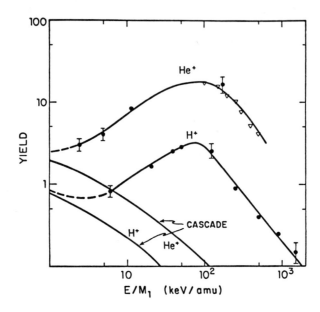

Fig. 2. Experimental erosion yields (molecules lost/incident ion) of H_2O ice at 78K for He^+ and H^+ ions of different energies. Calculated curves are also shown based on expectations of the collision cascade theory of sputtering. After Brown *et al.* (1980a).

atomic mass unit (amu), which is the region of the maximum of the electronic stopping power. At these energies, Y is about 100 times larger than would be expected if it arose from normal collisional sputtering, which involves the nuclear, not the electronic, stopping power. Calculated curves (Sigmund, 1969) for the cascade (nuclear stopping) case are also shown in Fig. 2. Ionization processes are clearly of dominant importance.

When data such as those of Fig. 2 are plotted against the electronic stopping power $(dE/dx)_e$, rather than against energy per amu, the results fall along a line of slope 2 (Fig. 3). The data points for hydrogen ions define this line over a factor of 400 in Y. The data for helium ions deviate in a systematic way around this line. These deviations arise from a combination of the non-equilibrium charge state of the incident ion and the velocity dependence of the diameter of the region of ionization around the ion track. A thorough discussion of these two effects is given in Johnson and Brown (1982). There are two data points in Fig. 3 for carbon and oxygen ions at 1.5 MeV and a set of points obtained by Cooper for fluorine ions at energies up to 25 MeV (Cooper, 1982; Seiberling *et al.*, 1982). These points also deviate from the line defined by the hydrogen data. The systematic deviations in the case of fluorine have the same character as those for helium, although their origin

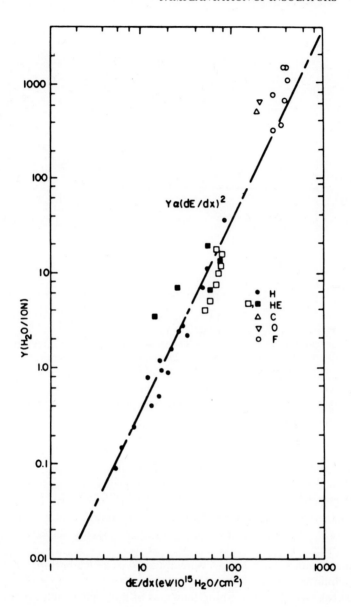

Fig. 3. The erosion yield of H_2O ice at low temperatures plotted as a function of the electronic stopping power of incident ions, H, He, C, O, F. The line has a slope of 2. After Brown *et al.* (1980a).

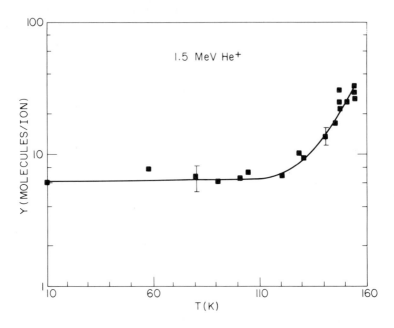

Fig. 4. Temperature dependence of the erosion yield of H_2O ice for 1.5 MeV He^+ ions. At the highest temperatures the beam-induced erosion data have been corrected for the rate of loss of ice by normal sublimation. After Brown *et al.* (1980b).

has not yet been studied as thoroughly. The overall $(dE/dx)_e$ dependence of yield is nevertheless relatively well expressed as $(dE/dx)_e^2$.

Fig. 4 shows results for the temperature dependence of the erosion of H_2O ice by 1.5 MeV He ions. Below 110K the yield is constant within the reproducibility of the measurements. Above 110K, Y rises smoothly by a factor of about four to the maximum temperature at which measurements can be made before sublimation of the ice. The stopping power dependence of the added yield at high temperatures is not quadratic and may even be linear in (dE/dx), suggesting that a second process is playing an increasingly important role.

The data of Figs. 2, 3 and 4 were obtained using Rutherford backscattering techniques on thin films of ice deposited from the vapor phase onto a cold substrate. The diminishing thickness of these films with ion bombardment provides values of the erosion yield. Recently, initial measurements have been made by using a quadruple mass spectrometer to examine the species that are ejected from the film in the erosion process. Results for masses 4, 20, and 32 are shown in Fig. 5 for 1.5 MeV He^+ erosion of heavy water (D_2O) ice. Note that D_2O rather than H_2O was used in order to reduce the background in the mass spectrometer. At low temperatures, the yield is

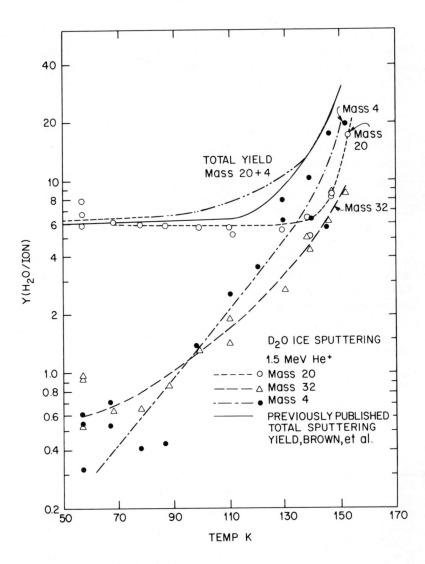

Fig. 5. Temperature dependence of the erosion products for 1.5 MeV He$^+$ ions on D$_2$O ice. The yield of Mass 20 (D$_2$O) is temperature independent over a very broad range. Mass 4, D$_2$, and 32, O$_2$, have a strong temperature dependence. The solid curve has been normalized to the Rutherford backscattering measurements of Fig. 4 at T = 120K (Brown *et al.*, 1980b), assuming that the temperature independent part of Fig. 4 is dominated by H$_2$O. After Brown *et al.* (1982).

dominated by mass 20 (D_2O), which is temperature independent below $\sim 110K$. Mass 4 (D_2) and mass 32 (O_2), however, show continuously increasing yields over the whole temperature range. An absolute calibration was not available in these measurements, so the contributing yield of D_2 (O_2 was assumed to be half as large) was normalized to the data of Fig. 4 at 120K. The resultant total yield curve is in moderate agreement with the solid line defined by the Rutherford backscattering data (Fig. 4). In making this normalization, it was assumed that the added yield at high temperature is associated with fragmentation of the ice and the formation of H_2 and O_2 molecules, these new molecules having sufficient mobility at high temperatures to escape from the ice.

C. Erosion of Other Frost Layers

The effects of electronic energy deposition discussed for ice films are found in all other condensed gas films on which experiments have been carried out. Table I lists the erosion yield due to 1.5 MeV He^+ ion bombardment on a series of rare gas and molecular gas frosts. The list is in order of increasing temperature of sublimation, here chosen to be the temperature at which the

TABLE I
Erosion of rare gas and molecular gas frosts by 1.5 MeV He^+

Frost	Y	T_M (K)	Institution	T_v (K)	H_v (eV/mole)	S_{cal}
Ne	2700	7	Bell	8	0.020	0.7
N_2	240	4	Catania	25	0.077	0.3
CO	250	7	Bell	28	0.088	0.3
Ar	30	7	Bell	29	0.083	0.3
	43	6	Aarhus			
O_2	120	7	Bell	30	0.095	0.3
CH_4	120	7	Bell	34	0.10	0.2
Kr	20	7	Bell	39	0.12	0.4
Xe	7	25	Chalk River	54	0.16	0.4
CO_2	120	7	Bell	81	0.27	0.11
NH_2	140	7	Bell	96	0.33	0.07
SO_2	17	10	Bell	106	0.37	0.08
H_2O	7	7	Bell	153	0.52	0.04
	6	25	Chalk River			

Y—the erosion yield in molecules/incident ion.
T_M—the measurement temperature.
T_v—the temperature at which the equilibrium vapor pressure is 10 torr.
H_v—the heat of sublimation.
S_{cal}—the expected values of sputtering yield based on collisional sputtering.

equilibrium vapor pressure is 10^{-7} torr. The table includes the expected values of sputtering yield, S_{cal}, based only on collisional sputtering and calculated from Sigmund's relationship (Sigmund, 1969). This depends dominantly on the ratio of the nuclear stopping power in the frost to the surface binding energy of the atomic or molecular species. The surface binding energies are assumed in this calculation to be just the heats of sublimation. In all cases, the measured yield exceeds the cascade sputtering expectation by at least two orders of magnitude. The measured values do not, however, decrease monatomically in the table, as might be expected if the result depended only on the electronic stopping power and the surface binding energy. The four rare gas solids are at least in order, but the molecular gas solids are not.

The temperature dependence of the erosion yield for different frosts also shows quite different behavior. The results for Ar (Besenbacher *et al.*, 1981), CO_2 (Brown *et al.*, 1982; Johnson *et al.*, 1983) and SO_2 (Lanzerotti *et al.*, 1982) are shown in Fig. 6 in comparison with the curve for H_2O (reproduced from Fig. 4). Argon shows the simplest result—a constant erosion yield with temperature until just below the sublimation temperature and then a sudden rise. Sulfur dioxide has a dependence similar to that of H_2O—a constant yield at low temperature but gradually rising, in this case above $\sim 60K$, to the maximum measurement temperature. The yield for CO_2 shows considerable "structure" above a low temperature constant value—two quite sharp upward steps at about 35K and 50K. These differences reinforce the conclusion drawn for H_2O, that fragmentation of the molecules in the molecular-gas solids must play an important part in the higher-temperature erosion yields.

D. Models of the Process

In cascade sputtering (as discussed in Chapter 6), atoms are set in motion by direct collisions of the incoming ion or in further collisions of these primary knock-ons with other atoms and molecules in the cascade that develops. Escape from the surface (i.e. sputtering) occurs when the atoms at the surface receive large enough outward directed energies to overcome the surface binding. In contrast, the electronic energy loss of a penetrating ion puts energy into ionization and excitation of electronic states, not into motion of the atoms. In this case, ejection of material from the surface requires conversion of electronic energy into atomic motion. The question of how this occurs is still not settled, and the process may not be the same for all systems. Three models of the phenomena are discussed below. The first two attempt to describe the temperature independent region of Y at low temperatures; the third, the temperature dependence seen for molecular solids.

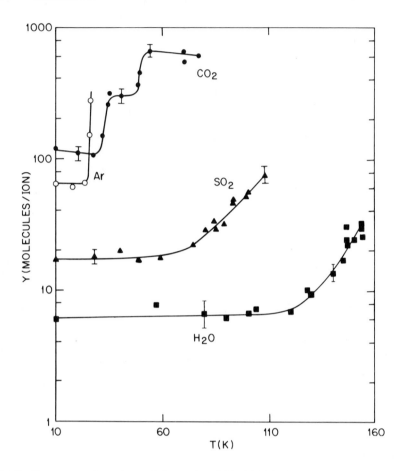

Fig. 6. Temperature dependence of the erosion yield of H_2O ice in comparison with that of SO_2, CO_2, and Ar. Erosion is by 1.0 MeV He^+ ions for Ar ice and 1.5 MeV He^+ ions for the three molecular ices. The Ar data are from Besenbacker *et al.* (1981).

1. Thermal Spike

The thermal spike description of erosion does not address the question of how the electronic energy is transformed into motion of the atoms; it assumes that such transfer occurs rapidly and locally along the track of the ion. The atomic motion is characterized by a local temperature which can be characterized as a function of time and radial position in cylindrical geometry, as illustrated in Fig. 7a. The cylinder grows in radius and decreases in temper-

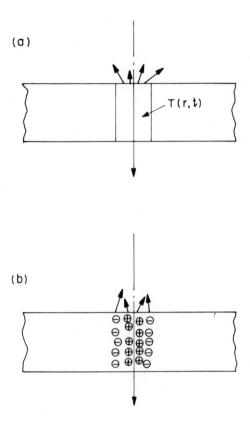

Fig. 7. Two models for temperature independent erosion: (a) thermal spike leading to fast transient sublimation; and (b) coulomb acceleration and ejection.

ature with time because of thermal conduction. Where the hot cylinder inter-sects the surface, sublimation takes place (Brown *et al.*, 1980a, Ollerhead *et al.*, 1980; Seiberling *et al.*, 1980). It has been shown on quite general grounds that the net effect, in a thermally activated process such as sublimation, is proportional to the square of the initial thermal energy per unit length along the ion track (Vineyard, 1976; Johnson and Evatt, 1980). This is in agreement with the $(dE/dx)_e^2$ dependence observed for H_2O ice, and also for frosts of Ar (Besenbacher *et al.*, 1980), CO_2 (Johnson *et al.*, 1983) and SO_2 (Lanzerotti *et al.*, 1982). There are several aspects of this model which need cautious con-sideration, however. First, the quadratic dependence on the heat input is valid only in the limit of a delta function of heat input in time and radius. In a finite situation, the central temperature (at $r = 0$) must be much higher than that given by $kT = H_v$ (where H_v is the heat of sublimation); therefore the sublimation rate is no longer exponential with temperature. This is equivalent to requiring that the electronic energy be transformed to heat both rapidly and locally. If the transfer is slow compared to thermal conduction times or takes place over a large region, the quadratic dependence no longer holds (Johnson and Evatt, 1980). If $\sim 20\%$ of the total electronic energy loss is rapidly available as heat at the core of the track, this would be sufficient to produce the erosion yields observed at low temperature for H_2O, CO_2, SO_2 and Argon (Johnson and Brown, 1982). Whether such a transfer actually occurs is still uncertain, but two possible mechanisms by which it might take place have been proposed (Johnson and Inokuti, 1982; Ritchie and Claussen, 1982).

A second point of caution is associated with the cylindrical approximation. If the primary ionization events along an ion track are not close together compared with the radial size of the ionization cascade that forms around each event, they are poorly approximated as a single cylindrical region. A spherical hot region close to the surface (the first of a string of such regions spaced along an ion track) will not yield a $(dE/dx)_e^2$ erosion dependence (Johnson and Brown, 1982). For MeV protons (the lowest points in Figs. 2 and 3) the average spacing of ionization events is 15–20 Å along the ion track, which is comparable to and perhaps larger than the distance over which the electronic energy loss is spread radially by secondary electrons. Nevertheless, these low $(dE/dx)_e$ points are well accounted for by the quadratic line. It would be useful to push these measurements to still higher proton energies in order to see if and where the results deviate from the quadratic line.

2. Coulomb Ejection

A different (coulomb ejection) model of what may be happening in the erosion of frozen gases by ions is illustrated schematically in Fig. 7b. Immediately following the passage of a fast ion through the insulating solid there is a separation of charge. Secondary electrons are generally thrown outward from the ion track and produce a shell of negative charge surrounding a positive core (Fleischer et al., 1975). The electrostatic fields in this space charge region can be very large. The energy in the coulomb field can become a significant fraction of the total electronic stopping energy (Johnson and Brown, 1982) when the charge densities are high (from MeV heavy ions for example). The coulomb forces are strong enough to set the ions in motion. This picture has also been used to describe the formation of etchable tracks in insulating minerals by the passage of very fast heavy ions: that is, disruption of the crystalline material by a "coulomb explosion" (Fleischer *et al.*, 1975). At the surface, the fringing fields of the space charge will have outward components which tend to result in the ejection of particles (Fig. 7b). This coulomb ejection model also results in an erosion yield which is dependent on $(dE/dx)_e^2$ (Brown *et al.*, 1980a; Haff, 1976; Stieger and Noggle, 1962). This relationship is most simply evident from the fact that the space charge energy is proportional to the square of the charge density, which in turn is linear in $(dE/dx)_e$.

The coulomb ejection model presents one major problem: the separation of negative and positive charge is highly transient unless the electrons are trapped in the form of negative ions. If the electrons remain free, they will return to the core of the track much more quickly than the 10^{-14} seconds in which ions can gain sufficient energy from the field to be able to escape the surface. Deep trapping seems unlikely in such a short time. However, if the electrons are not trapped at their outer radial positions, they will oscillate back and forth through the positively charged core (Johnson and Brown, 1982). They will thus continue to provide, on average, a shell of negative charge outside the positive core, until such time as they have dissipated the space charge energy through collisions with the atoms (Ritchie and Claussen, 1982).

The concern about non-cylindrical geometry which was discussed in connection with the thermal spike might arise in the coulomb ejection case as well. However, in the limit of low charge density, the ejection process retains a $(dE/dx)_e^2$ dependence. The probability of two ionization events occurring near the surface, one producing an ion close enough to the surface to be ejected and the second producing an ion close enough to the first to provide a repulsive force for its ejection, is quadratic in the linear probability of ionization, hence to $(dE/dx)_e^2$ (Johnson and Brown, 1982).

Quantitative predictions of the magnitude of erosion yields arising from coulomb ejection are quite uncertain but the parameters of the simplest formation at least seem reasonable (Brown *et al.*, 1980a).

3. New Molecule Formation and Release

In addition to temperature independent erosion at low temperatures, molecular solids show strong increases in erosion at higher temperatures. These seem certain to be associated with the breakup of the original molecules, and the formation of new molecules and their release from the surface. The electronic excitation of a molecular solid by a fast ion results in the breaking of many intramolecular bonds, in addition to ionization of the molecular units themselves. These electronic excitations can decay again to their initial ground states, but they are also transiently susceptible to the formation of different bonds than those which existed originally. Such processes lie within the field of radiation chemistry and biology (Hart and Platzman, 1961). Fragmentation and new molecule formation are clearly responsible for the O_2 and D_2 molecules observed in He^+ irradiation of D_2O ice (see Fig. 5 and Sect. II,B).

At low temperatures, new molecules may be formed in an ice matrix, for example, and be incapable of escaping from the solid. Measurements on CO_2 have illustrated this case. Low temperature bombardment with He^+ ions produces erosion (as discussed in Sect. II,C). Warm-up (without further irradiation) gives substantial additional erosion, as species formed at low temperatures (presumably O_2 and CO) are able to escape from the film (Johnson et al., 1983).

The formation processes of more complex molecules, as well as less complex ones, have recently been observed. In a frost condensed from a half-and-half gas phase mixture of CO_2 and D_2O, warm-up after irradiation at low temperatures resulted in release of formaldehyde at temperatures near to the sublimation temperature of D_2O (Pirronello et al., 1982).

It is possible that release of new molecules can even contribute to the measured low-temperature erosion yield. They may be formed to a steady state concentration in the near surface of an ice and subsequently released by another ion; for example, in a thermal spike or by coulomb ejection. This field is rich with variations that suggest a wide range of experiments which can be carried out to test the kinetics of the processes more directly.

E. Relationship of Ion Erosion to Electron and Photon Stimulated Desorption and to Laser Processing of Materials

Ion induced erosion of ice films has points in common with electron and photon stimulated desorption (ESD and PSD) from insulating surfaces. In the latter cases, choice of electron and photon energy allows excitation of particular electronic states, usually ionization of a particular core electron. This might be a 1s electron in the O^- ion of TiO_2. Auger filling of the core hole may further increase the positive charge state of this atom, rendering it positive in an environment of nearest-neighbor Ti^+ ions (Knotek and Feibelman, 1978). It is desorbed (ejected) by coulomb repulsion. The desorption yields in these cases are low but so is the ionization density—at most one ionization event per incident electron or photon. It would be interesting to carry out experiments on similar materials with ions, to see if there exists a non-linear relationship that would allow extension of this single-atom coulomb repulsion to the regime in which ice erosion has been measured. Alternatively, ESD or PSD experiments might be done on ice layers under conditions similar to those used in ion erosion.

The erosion of ices also has a point of common interest with laser process-ing of materials. Although the particular materials are quite different, the question of energy transfer is similar. A great deal of attention has been given to the case of silicon excited by nano-second or pico-second pulsed laser beams. The energy, as in the case of fast ions, is coupled into electronic exci-tation (ionization to produce holes and electrons and to increase their ener-gies within the valence and conduction bands). The speed of transfer of the electronic excitation to heat and then to the melting of a surface layer has been determined to be $<10^{-11}$ sec (Bloembergen et al., 1982). This is in rather good agreement with theoretical estimates of electron-photon scattering in silicon (Yoffa, 1980). In the laser case, the geometry is one-dimensional: the depth of excitation is small compared to the beam diameter. The thermal conduction time constants are nano-seconds to hundreds of nano-seconds. These are very long compared with the time for cooling a single cylindrical region 10 or 20 Å in radius (as in the thermal spike model of erosion discussed in section D above). So far, no meaningful experiment has been devised for simulating ion results with laser excitation of ices, and the issue of energy transfer remains a crucial one.

III. ION BEAM LITHOGRAPHY

Lithography is the general term for producing two-dimensional patterns that define the geometry of successive processing steps in modern electronic tech-nology (Bowden, 1979, Bowden and Thompson, 1979). Fig. 8 illustrates the two general classes of lithographic materials, generally called "resists". These are analogous to emulsions in photographic processing. They are called re-sists because they resist some processing step and limit processing to areas where they are absent. A negative resist is one which radiation renders in-soluble (in some solvent) so that after development the resist remains where it was irradiated. A negative polymer resist is typically one that cross-links under radiation to form bigger, less soluble molecules. A positive resist has the other sense: where radiation falls, the resist is more soluble. As shown in Fig. 8, this corresponds to polymer scission under radiation, the smaller fragments being more soluble than the original chain.

A. Lithography at less than 1000 Angstroms

Almost all lithography in the semiconductor industry is still done with optical exposure of resists working at resolutions $\gtrsim 1$ micron. Diffraction is one limi-tation to this resolution. Electron beam lithography is not limited by diffrac-tion and is being used in an increasing number of installations for making

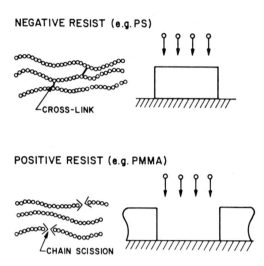

Fig. 8.   Lithography using polymer resist films. A typical negative resist cross-links under exposure to ionizing radiation and is insoluble in a solvent developer where it has been exposed. A typical positive resist undergoes scission by ionizing radiation and is more soluble where exposed.

masks which are then used to produce optical lithographic patterns directly in a resist on a device wafer (Brewer, 1980). Demonstration patterns using E-beam lithography have been made at resolutions <1000 Å, but there is an intrinsic problem in working routinely to such dimensions—the proximity effect (Chang, 1975; Greenich, 1974; Parish, 1978). Lateral scattering of electrons passing through the thickness of a resist, energetic secondary electrons produced in the resist and backscattering of electrons from the substrate underneath broaden the region of exposure beyond that of the incident beam. This makes the exposure of one feature of a pattern dependent upon the nearness (the proximity) of a neighboring feature. Thin resists and low atomic number resists and substrates minimize the problem but do not eliminate it.

The proximity effect has led to consideration of ion beams for lithography for cases in which very fine dimensions are needed. The lateral scattering and the backscattering of ions is much less than for electrons. In addition, ions of practical energies move much more slowly than the 20 to 40 keV electrons used in electron beam lithography, and thus generate only low energy secondary electrons which stop close to the ion track ($\sim$20 Å). It is the narrowness of this region of electronic excitation around the path of an ion passing through an ice film that leads to the possibility of a thermal spike or of

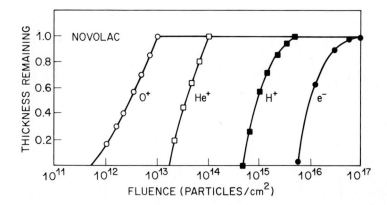

Fig. 9.   Exposure curves for novolac (a negative resist) radiated by electrons, H^+, He^+, and O^+ ions. After Hall *et al.* (1979).

coulomb ejection. Proximity effects are expected for ion beams only at dimensions $\lesssim 100$ Å.

B. Non-linear Exposure

There is another limitation in electron beam exposure of resists—sensitivity (Bowden, 1979). In order to obtain high sensitivity to reduce required exposure time, very elegantly tailored polymer materials which may sacrifice robustness or good adherence have been developed. Ions deposit a great deal more energy per unit of path length than electrons, and hence should expose resists at much lower fluences. Fig. 9 shows that this is the case. Novolac, a negative resist, was exposed as shown with 20 keV electrons and 1.5 MeV H^+, He^+ and O^+ ions (Hall *et al.*, 1979). The fluences required for exposure decrease with increasing ion mass, since this corresponds to increasing stopping power. More than three orders of magnitude in fluence separate the two extreme curves.

If the 50% exposure points (the fluence at which half the thickness of the Novolac remains after development) are plotted against the linear stopping power of the particles, the result is that of Fig. 10 (Hall *et al.*, 1979). The simplest expectation would be for a decrease in required fluence proportional to the increase in stopping power. This is the case comparing protons and electrons in the figure, but for the higher stopping power ions, the exposure fluence falls more rapidly than $(dE/dx)^{-1}$. Between He^+ and O^+ the relationship is $\sim (dE/dx)^{-2}$. This non-linearity in resist response has led

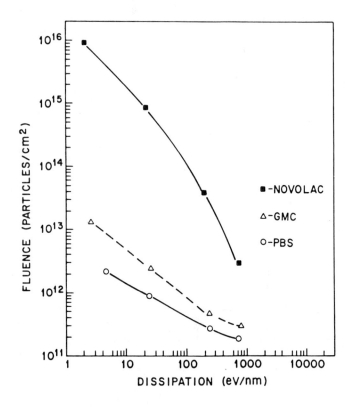

Fig. 10.   The fluence required for half exposure of novolac (from Fig. 9), GMC, and PBS, plotted against the electronic energy loss of electrons, H^+, He^+, and O^+ ions. After Hall *et al.* (1979).

to the conclusion that at high dE/dx, ionization events in neighboring molecules enhance the probability of polymer cross-linking (Hall *et al.*, 1979). Cooperative effects dominate the exposure process.

Not all polymer resists show this effect. Some have sublinear rather than superlinear dependence on dE/dx. PBS and GMC are two such cases, as shown in Fig. 10. These are resists developed to have high sensitivity for electron beam exposure. Notice that they are about a thousand times more sensitive to electrons than Novolac. In these cases the high dE/dx of ions represents overkill (Hall *et al.*, 1979). Triggering a molecule to cross-link (PBS) or scission (GMC) requires only one ionization event per molecule, and ions in general provide more. It is interesting that for O^+ ions, the exposure sensitivities of all three resists differ by only an order of magnitude. It seems that the ionization density is so high in the track of such an ion that almost any molecular rearrangement that is chemically feasible will take place. Even for relatively low ionization density He ions in H_2O ice, the formation of O_2 and H_2 molecules (as discussed in Section II,D,3) is evidence of the high chemical activity in the track of an ion.

So far there have been no measurements of erosion of organic resists caused by ion bombardment. At the fluences required for exposure it is unlikely that substantial changes in thickness are produced. It would, however, be interesting to look for new molecule production and release. There is a general tendency for organic materials to lose hydrogen under ion bombardment. This tendency is familiar in the cracking of organic materials on target surfaces in any accelerator system. In the case of methane frost (Johnson *et al.*, 1982), bombardment causes loss of carbon, but the loss of hydrogen is over four times larger, so that the stoichiometry of the methane films changes to that of CH_2 and, under more extended bombardment, to even lower hydrogen content.

C. Implanted Resists

Ion beams can expose conventional optical and electron resists but they also provide a different type of resist exposure. Many polymer and inorganic materials can be used as negative resists by implanting them with appropriate low energy metal ions. In a subsequent reactive ion etching of the resist layer in a suitable plasma, the implanted ions form non-volatile compounds which act as an *in situ* mask. Unimplanted regions are etched away. This has been demonstrated with indium ions implanted into SiO_2 and etched in a fluorocarbon plasma and also with thick organic polymers, indium implanted and developed in an oxygen plasma (Venkatesan *et al.*, 1981; Kuwano *et al.*, 1980; Yamazuki, *et al.*, 1980). Implantation doses required are relatively high for the layer to be an effective mask, 5×10^{15} to 1×10^{16} ions cm^{-2}: five to ten monolayers. This is not surprising since a continuous chemical barrier is required for resist action.

D. Inorganic Resists

Another class of resist for ion beam exposure is the inorganic system $GeSe_2$–Ag_2Se (Yoshikawa *et al.*, 1976; Tai *et al.*, 1979). A thin layer (~ 100 Å) of Ag_2Se covers a $GeSe_2$ film (Chen and Tai, 1980). Exposing the resist to radiation causes silver to diffuse into the $GeSe_2$ film. The remaining Ag_2Se is chemically stripped away, and the film is subsequently developed in a solvent in which silver doped $GeSe_2$ is insoluble. The lithographic pattern is thus in negative relief. The system has the interesting feature that the silver diffusion is not limited to the depth to which the exposing radiation penetrates. As long as the radiation passes through the $Ag_2Se-GeSe_2$ interface, silver is able to diffuse throughout the whole $GeSe_2$ thickness (Wagner et al., 1981).

It has been found that both the nuclear and the electronic stopping power of ions are active in this resist (Wagner et al., 1981). Presumably, defects formed by the radiation provide for silver diffusion, though the mechanism has not yet been established in any detail. Neither the structure of the defects nor the process by which they are formed in either the electronic or the nuclear stopping regime is understood. Since $GeSe_2$ is an insulator, it is interesting to speculate that a coulomb repulsion mechanism may be responsible. If only shallow silver diffusion is required, the sensitivity of the $GeSe_2-Ag_2$ Se resist to 20keV heavy ions is $\sim 5 \times 10^{13}$ cm^{-2}. Sensitivity enhancement beyond this is possible with obliquely deposited films (Balasubramanyam et al., 1981; Venkatesan, 1981).

E. Methods of Ion Beam Lithographic Exposure of Resists

All lithographic exposure, with light, electrons, X-rays, or ion beams, takes place in either a serial or parallel mode. A scanning, focused beam provides serial exposure. Flooding a mask with radiation over its entire area provides parallel exposure. Focused electron beams are currently providing serial exposure (Brewer, 1980) for formation of masks in some semi-conductor laboratories and factories. Commercial lithography on actual device wafers uses parallel optical exposure through masks in contact or projection printing. Parallel contact printing using X-rays is under development (Zacharias, 1981). Ion beam lithography is at an even earlier point on its learning curve, but both serial and parallel modes are being explored.

1. Finely Focused Ion Beams

New, high-brightness ion sources have provided the possibilities of serial exposure of resists using finely focused ion beams. One such system is illustrated in Fig. 11. The source is a liquid metal ion source (Clampitt and Jefferies, 1978), in this case using liquid gold on a tungsten needle. Applying a positive voltage on the needle with respect to an aperture, the electric field forces overcome the surface tension forces of the liquid gold and pull it into a cone. A mathematically stable shape in which electric field and surface tension forces just balance is a Taylor cone (Taylor, 1964). However, the electric field at such a mathematical tip is infinite: in actuality ion emission occurs,

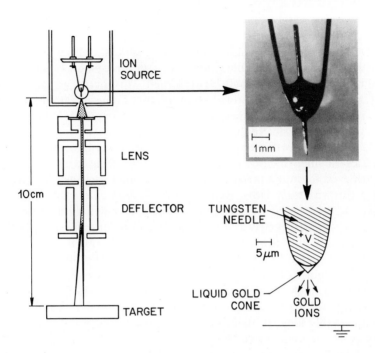

Fig. 11. A focused ion beam system using a liquid gold metal ion source. The formation of the liquid metal cone of gold which leads to ion emission requires a potential of a few KV between the tip and an aperture. The final ion energy in this system is approximately 30 keV. After Wagner *et al.* (1981).

the tip is slightly blunted and currents of 1 to 100 microamperes are emitted (Wagner and Hall, 1979). The effective source size is about 100 Å in diameter, and the source can run steadily with low noise for many hours. Liquid metal is supplied to maintain the liquid at the tip by capillary flow along the needle from a reservoir, in this case a ball of molten gold. Sources of this kind have been made for a number of different ions: gold, gallium and indium are the most common. In all cases, the vapor pressure at the melting point of the source materials must be low enough to avoid vacuum breakdown, and the liquid metal must wet but not react with the material of the needle.

The total system shown in Fig. 11 is only 10 centimeters from source to target. Focusing of ions from the source is chromatic aberration limited, the source having a typical energy spread of 5 to 10 eV (Swanson *et al.*, 1979) and being operated typically at 10 to 40 keV. Seliger, and his associates at Hughes (Seliger *et al.*, 1979), have reported focused spot sizes from such a system approximately 400 Å in diameter. They report a current density in the focused spot of approximately 1 A cm^{-2}.

Even higher current density in a focused spot is. in principle. available from another type of field ionization source. in this case an H_2^+ source developed by Hanson and Siegel (1979) at Cornell. This source. which runs at 4K in H_2 gas with a carefully formed arrangement of tungsten atoms at its emitting tip. has a higher brightness and a lower energy spread. Ion beams from such a source have not yet been focused.

As in all serial writing systems. writing speed is a critical issue. Fig. 12 ilustrates the finely focused ion beam case for two focused current densities. one achieved for liquid metal ion sources. the other projected for the H_2^+ ion source (Brown et al., 1981). Resists with two different sensitivities are included. As the focused spot diameter decreases. the writing time for a given total area goes up inversely as the square. However. for small spots the practical writing time runs into a shot noise limit. This is simply the fact that there must be enough ions in one spot to avoid the statistical probability of failing to expose a spot. For a Poission distribution. about 200 ions per pixel (area exposed in a single shot) is an acceptable minimum. As Fig. 12 indicates. the writing time for direct exposure of all or a large fraction of a silicon wafer is unacceptably long. It might be feasible to write critical features only in this way. but it seems more likely that the lithographic capability of finely focused ion beams will be primarily used for making fine masks which will be printed in some parallel exposure mode. for example by X-rays or by ion beams (as described below).

2. Parallel Ion Exposure Systems

Two parallel ion exposure systems are being studied—projection lithography and channeled beam lithography. The first is the work of Sacher Technik (Stengl et al., 1979) in Vienna. It involves a stencil mask (a mask with holes in it). a broad ion beam exposing the mask. and a lens system to demagnify the beam that passes through the mask by a factor of 10. The possibilities for such a system are intriguing. but the ion lens required to provide high resolution over a 5 mm × 5 mm focused field is a challenge: so too is the fabrication of suitable stencil masks.

Channeled ion lithography is another parallel exposure approach. It is a special type of contact printing being studied at Hughes Research laboratory (Rensch et al., 1979) and is illustrated in Fig. 13. A metal mask is prepared on a thin single crystal silicon substrate. Ions flood the mask in a direction parallel to the crystal axis in the substrate. Where the mask is open. ions penetrate through the substrate. Multiple scattering in this passage is

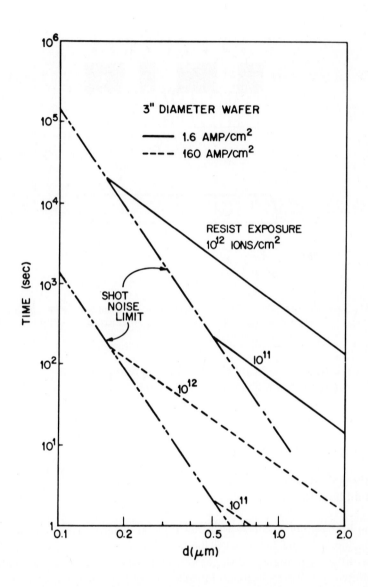

Fig. 12.   Lithographic writing times for a 3-inch diameter wafer with a finely focused ion beam as a function of focused spot diameter. Two focused ion current densities and two resist sensitivities are assumed. In the shot-noise region a minimum of 200 ions per pixel is required. After Brown *et al.* (1981).

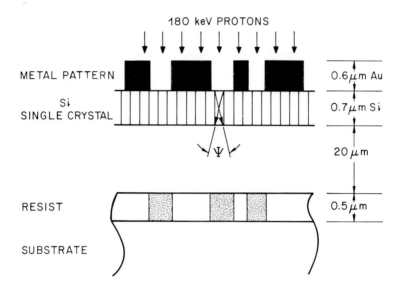

Fig. 13. Channeled ion lithography. Channeling of the ion beam reduces multiple scattering on emergence from the thin single crystal mask support. After Rensch *et al.* (1979).

greatly reduced by ion beam channeling. The resolution of the system is set by the emerging beam angle and the distance to the resist to be exposed. It should be feasible to obtain 0.1 micron resolution at 20 microns (as shown). The mask fabrication is a major challenge in this case. Thermal expansion owing to the energy of the stopped incident beam must not distort the mask no matter what the pattern of the metal features is.

F. Multi-level Resists

In ion lithography, a thin resist is desirable in order to avoid the necessity of developing stable, high-energy ion beams. However, in device fabrication, many different lithographic stages are required in order to define features in different processing steps, and the surface will in general have a complex vertical topography. A thin resist will not cover "hills" and "valleys" satisfactorily. A multi-level resist scheme, devised for other exposure systems, is illustrated in Fig. 14. The 2–3 micron resist smooths out all the surface features. The upper resist is all that needs to be exposed. Reactive ion etching can linearly transfer the pattern through the thick resist to the substrate.

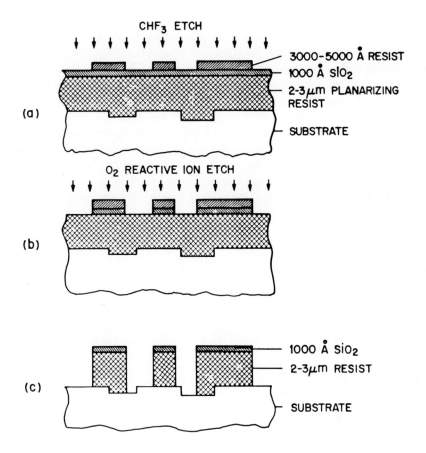

Fig. 14. Schematic of a multilevel resist for ion beam lithography. Penetration and exposure of only the uppermost resist layer is required. After Moran and Mayden (1979).

IV. CONCLUSIONS

The study of the change in the properties of insulating solids caused by bombardment by energetic ions opens an array of questions concerning the mechanisms that are active. It also leads to consideration of the consequences of these interactions in areas as diverse as astrophysics and solid state technology. The sensitivity of solids to electronic as well as nuclear energy input from an ion beam is a challenge of particular interest because it involves mechanisms of transfer of the energy of electronic excitation and ionization to the motion of the nuclei of the solid. The non-linearity of the response of solids to the deposited electronic energy density points to the importance of spatial correlation between individual excitation or ionization events. The non-linearities may be due to collective phenomena such as thermal or ionization spikes, but this has not yet been well established.

Original molecular structures of insulating solids are altered by the passage of ions, and new molecules are formed. For interplanetary ices exposed to energetic ions, erosion and fragmentation are important to a variety of astrophysical problems. For insulating solids, both organic and inorganic, that serve as resists in the lithography of electronic device fabrication, both ion exposure sensitivity and intrinsic spatial resolution are highly attractive aspects of a possible future technology. The whole field is in an early stage of exploration and speculation. It demands both more experiments and more thorough theoretical consideration.

REFERENCES

Balasubramanyam, K., Karapiperis, C., Lee, C. A., and Ruoff, A. L. (1981). *J. Vac. Sci. Techncl.* **19**, 18.

Besenbacker, F., Bǿttiger, J., Graversen, C. G., and Hansen, J. (1981). *Nucl. Instrum. Methods* **191**, 221.

Bloembergen, N., Kurtz, H., Liu, J. M., and Yen, R. (1982). *In* "Laser and Electron Beam Interaction with Solids" (B. R. Appleton and G. K. Celler, eds.). North Holland, New York.

Bowden, M. J. (1979). *CRC Critical Reviews in Solid State and Materials Sciences.* **8**, 223.

Bowden, M. J., and Thompson, L. F. (1979). *Solid State Technology* **22**, 72.

Brewer, G. R. (1980). "Electron-Beam Technology in Microelectronic Fabrication." Academic Press, New York.

Broadfoot, A. L., *et al.* (1979). *Science* **204**, 979.

Brown, W. L., Augustyniak, W. M., Brody, E., Cooper, B. H., Lanzerotti, L. J., Ramirez, A. L., Evatt, R., and Johnson, R. E. (1980a). *Nucl. Instrum. Methods* **170**, 321.

Brown, W. L., Augustyniak, W. M., Lanzerotti, L. J., Johnson, R. E., and Evatt, R. (1980b). *Phys. Rev. Lett.* **45**, 1632.

Brown, W. L., Venkatesan, T., and A. Wagner (1981). *Solid State Technology.* **24**, 60.

Brown, W. L., Augustyniak, W. M., Simmons, F., Marcantonio, K. J., Lanzerotti, L. J., Johnson, R. E., Boring, J. M., Riemann, C. J., Foti, G., and Pirronello, V. (1982). *Nucl. Instrum. Methods* **198**, 1.

Chand, T. H. P. (1975). *J. Vac. Sci. Technol.* **12**, 1271.

Chen, C. H., and Tai, K. L. (1980) *Appl. Phys. Lett.* **37**, 605.

Clampitt, R., and Jefferies, D. K. (1978). *Nucl. Instrum. Methods* **149**, 739.

Cooper, B. H. (1982). Ph.D Thesis, California Institute of Technology.

Delsemme, A. H., and Miller, D. C. (1971) *Planet and Space Sci.* **19**, 122.

Delsemme, A. H., and Wagner, A. (1970). *Planet and Space Sci.* **18**, 709.

Fisk, L. A. (1979). *In* "Solar System Plasma Physics" (C. F. Kennel, L. J. Lanzerotti and C. N. Parker, eds.) Vol. 1, p. 177. North Holland, New York.

Fleischer, R. L., Price, R. P., and Walker, R. M. (1975). "Nuclear Tracks in Solids Principles and Applications." Univ. Calif. Press, Berkeley.

Greeneich, J. S. (1974). *J. Appl. Phys.* **45**, 5264.

Haff, P. K. (1976). *App. Phys. Lett.* **29**, 473.

Hall, T. M., Wagner, A., Thompson, L. F. (1979). *J. Vac. Sci. Technol.* **16**, 1889.

Hanson, C. R., and Siegel, B. M. (1979). *J. Vac. Sci. Technol.* **16**, 1874.

Hart, R. J., and Platzman (1961). *In* "Mechanisms in Radiobiology" (M. Errera and A. Forssberg, eds.), Vol. 1, p. 93. Academic Press, New York.

Holzer, T. E. (1979). *In* "Solar System Plasma Physics" (C. F. Kennel, L. J. Lanzerotti, and C. N. Parker, eds.) Vol. 1, p. 101. North Holland, New York.

Johnson, R. E., and Brown, W. L. (1982). *Nucl. Instrum. Methods* **198**, 103.

Johnson, R. E., and Evatt, R. (1980). *Rad. Effects* **52**, 197.

Johnson, R. E., and Inokuti, M. (1982). *Nucl. Instrum. Methods* **206**, 289.

Johnson, R. E., Lanzerotti, L. J., Brown, W. L., Augustyniak, W. M., and Mussil, C. (1983). *Astron and Astrophys.* (in press).

Kennel, C. F., and Coroniti, F. V. (1979). *In* "Solar System Plasma Physics" (C. F. Kennel, L. J. Lanzerotti and C. N. Parker, eds.) Vol. 2, p. 105. North Holland, New York.

Kimerling, L. C. (1978). *Solid State Electronics*, **21**, 1391.

Knotek and Feibelman (1978). *Phys. Rev. Lett.* **40**, 964.

Kuwano, H., Yoshida, K., Yamazakj, S. (1980). *Jap. J. Appl. Phys.* **19** 1619.

Lang, D. V., and Kimerling, L. C. (1974). *Phys. Lett.* **33**, 489.

Lanzerotti, L. J., Brown, W. L., Augustyniak, W. M., Johnson, R. E., and Armstrong, T. P. (1982). *Astrophys. J.* **259**, 920.

Lekofsky, J. S. (1975). *Icarus* **25**, 205.

Lekofsky, L. A. (1977). *Nature* **269**, 785.

Mayer, J. W., Eriksson, L., and Davies, J. A. (1970). "Ion Implantation in Semiconductors." Academic Press, New York.

Moran, J. M., and Maydan, D. (1979). *J. Vac. Sci. Technol.* **16**, 1620.

Ollerhead, R., Böttiger, J., Davis, J. A., L'Ecuyer, J., Hangen, H. J., and Matsunami, M. (1980). *Rad. Effects* **49**, 203.

Parish, M. (1978). *J. Vac. Sci. Technol.* **15**, 931.

Pilcher, C. B., Ridgeway, S. T., and McCord, T. B. (1974). *Science* **178**, 309.

Pirronello, V., Brown, W. L., Lanzerotti, L. J., Marcantonio, K. E., and Simmons, E. (1982). *Astrophys, J.* **262**, 636.

Rensch, D. P., Seliger, R. L., Csonsky, G., Olney, R. D., and Stover, H. L. (1979). *J. Vac. Sci. Technol.* **16**, 1897.

Ritchie, R. H., and Claussen, C. (1982). *Nucl. Instrum. Methods* **198**, 133.

Seiberling, L. E., Griffith, J. E., and Tombrello, T. A. (1980). *Rad. Effects* **52**, 201.

Seiberling, L. E., Meins, C. K., Cooper, B. H., Griffith, J. E., Mendenhall, M. H., and Tombrello, T. A. (1982). *Nucl. Instrum. and Methods* (to be published).

Seliger, R. L., Ward, J. M., Wnag, W., and Kubena, R. L. (1979). *Appl. Phys. Lett.* **34**, 310.

Sigmund, P. (1969). *Phys. Rev.* **184**, 383.

Siscoe, G. L. (1979). *In* "Solar System Plasma Physics" (C. F. Kennel, L. J. Lanzerotti and C. N. Parker, eds.) Vol. 2, p. 319. North Holland, New York.

Smith, B. A. *et al.* (1981). *Science* **212**, 163.

Stengl, G., Kaitna, R., Loschner, H., Wolf, P., and Sacher, R. (1979). *J. Vac. Sci. Technol.* **16**, 1883.

Stiegler, J. O., and Noggle, T. S. (1962). *J. Appl. Phys.* **33**, 1894.

Swanson, L. W., Schwind, G. A., Bell, A. E., and Brady, J. E. (1979). *J. Vac. Sci. Technol.* **16**, 1864.

Tai, K. L., Sinclair, W. R., Vadimsky, R. G., Moran, J. M., and Rand, M. J. (1979). *J. Vac. Sci. Technol.* **16**, 1977.

Taylor, G. (1964). *Proc. Roy. Soc. A.* **280**, 383.

Venkatesan, T. (1981). *J. Vac. Sci. Technol.* **19**, 1368.

Venkatesan, T., Taylor, G. N., Wagner, A., Wilkens, B., and Barr, D. (1981). *J. Vac. Sci. Technol.* **19**, 1379.

Vineyard, G. H. (1976). *Rad. Effects.* **29**, 245.

Wagner, A., and Hall, T. M. (1979). *J. Vac. Sci. Technol.* **16**, 1871.

Wagner, A., Barr, D., Venkatesan, T., Crane, W. S., Lamberti, V. E., Tai, K. L., and Vadimsky, R. G. (1981). *J. Vac. Sci. Technol.* **19**, 1363.

Whipple, F. L. (1950). *Astrophys. J.* **11**, 375.

Whipple, F. L. (1977). *In* "Comets Asteroids and Meteorites". (P. H. Delsemme, ed.) p. 25. Univ. of Toledo Press.

Yamazaki, T., Suzuki, Y., and Nakata, H. (1980) *J. Vac. Sci. Technol.* **17**, 1348.

Yoffa, E. J. (1980). *In* "Laser and Electron Beam Processing of Materials" (C. W. White and P. S. Peercy, eds.) p. 59. Academic Press, New York.

Yoshikawa, A., Ochi, O., Nagai, H. and Mizushima, Y. (1976). *Appl. Phys. Lett.* **29**, 677.

Zacharias, A. (1981). *Solid State Technology* **24**, 57.

CHAPTER 6

Ion-Bombardment-Induced Composition Changes in Alloys and Compounds

HANS HENRIK ANDERSEN

Physical Laboratory II, H. C. Orsted Institute
University of Copenhagen, Denmark

ION IMPLANTATION
AND BEAM PROCESSING
ISBN 0 12 756980 4

I. INTRODUCTION

The aim of any ion-implantation experiment is to produce a material containing at least two components. For very low implantation fluences, the depth distribution of the implanted species is given simply by the range distribution in the implantation target. For somewhat larger doses, surface erosion by sputtering must be taken into account. As the implantation proceeds, some of the implanted material is eroded away, together with the substrate, and sputtering will hence limit the obtainable concentrations. This fact was realized more than twenty years ago (Almén and Bruce, 1961a; Carter *et al.*, 1962), and it was stated that the available concentration should be inversely proportional to the sputtering yield for the implanted ion bombarding the unmodified target.

Measurements of sputtering yields as a function of dose, however, made it clear that the sputtering yield changed as implantation proceeded, and hence it was presumably a function of implant concentration (Almén and Bruce, 1961b). In fact, such changes of yield were found to start at very low implantation fluences (Andersen and Bay, 1972) and could continue until a layer up to an order of magnitude thicker than the range of the implanted ion had been sputtered away (Andersen, 1973). Thus, the depth distribution of the implanted species could not be obtained as a simple addition of range profiles measured from a surface retracting with constant speed. A two-component (or several-component) system was sputtered during the implantation. This fact was pointed out in an early review (Andersen, 1974).

For a long time it has been known that continued ion bombardment could redistribute the already implanted species (Davies *et al.*, 1960), although the detailed redistribution mechanisms were not very clear at the time. High-fluence implantation of noble gases into silicon and, in particular, the influence of diffusion on the resulting profiles have been studied in detail (Blank *et al.*, 1976; Wittmaack *et al.*, 1978). The influence of outdiffusion has also been treated in more general terms (Anttila and Hautala, 1979). The recent review by Liau and Mayer (1980) covered a number of the above complications; in particular the influence of preferential sputtering. It is the aim of this chapter to give a somewhat more detailed discussion of alloy sputtering as such, in order to provide a broad background for an understanding of high-fluence implantation profiles. For this discussion, a short review of the sputtering of single-component systems will be necessary. Together with alloy sputtering, a number of redistribution mechanisms will be discussed; for example, recoil implantation, cascade mixing, thermal diffusion, radiation-enhanced diffusion, surface segregation, and radiation-induced segregation.

To a large extent, this chapter is based on two lectures given at the 10th

Yugoslavian Summer School on the Physics of Ionized Gases (Andersen, 1980), although the basic interest there was not high-fluence implantation profiles.

II. SPUTTERING OF ELEMENTAL TARGETS

The study of the erosion of solids during particle bombardment has been going on for a very long time (Grove, 1852), but not until the appearance of Sigmund's (1969) comprehensive theoretical paper could the subject be said to have reached maturity. This paper spurred a considerable amount of experimental activity aimed at testing its predictions, and in recent theoretical (Sigmund, 1981) and experimental (Andersen and Bay, 1981) reviews, it was concluded that we have now reached a fair understanding of most aspects of the sputtering of one-component materials.

The quantity of particular interest is the sputtering yield, which is defined as the average number of target atoms being sputtered per impinging projectile atom. This definition is sufficient for sputtering at low fluence, but as soon as a considerable concentration of implanted atoms builds up at the surface, one is forced to define partial yields for the different target components. Such a definition is also needed for low fluence when multicomponent targets are sputtered. This will be given below. I shall also discuss differential yields in order to describe the distribution of sputtered atoms in angle and energy.

The yield will generally depend on the atomic number of the projectile (Z_1) and its mass (M_1), energy (E), and angle of incidence (θ) with respect to the target normal, as well as on the target atomic number (Z_2) and mass (M_2). Also, the target structure (amorphous, random-polycrystalline, textured-polycrystalline, single-crystal) is important, particularly for the variation of yield with angle of incidence and for the angular distribution of the sputtered material.

Depending on the combination of parameters mentioned above, it is usually possible to characterize sputtering events as belonging to one of the following types:

1. Single-collision and double-collision events (few-collision region).
2. Linear-collision cascades.
3. Nonlinear cascades (spikes).

The *few-collision region* is particularly important close to the sputtering threshold, where sufficient energy for the creation of a regular collision cascade is not available. However, for very light projectiles, the few-collision

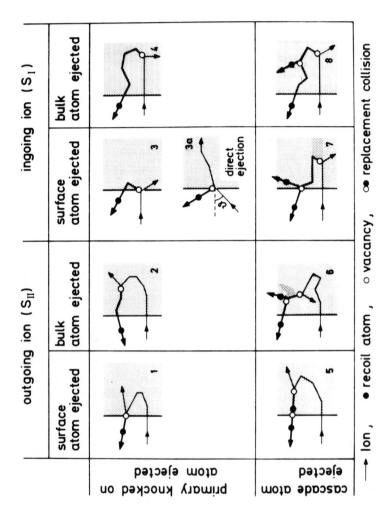

Fig. 1. Schematic presentation of a number of different processes leading to the ejection of target atoms through bombardment by ions near threshold energies. From Behrisch *et al.* (1979); see also Winters and Sigmund (1974).

events may dominate at all energies. A number of different processes leading to the ejection of target atoms is shown in Fig. 1, which is based on ideas originally introduced by Winters and Sigmund (1974) when discussing sputtering of adsorbed gases. Note in particular that owing to momentum conservation, direct ejection (process 3) will never be possible at perpendicular incidence. If target components have widely different masses, and if the projectile is light, preferential ejection of the lighter components of a two-component target will be heavily favoured by the direct ejection process. Sputtering by light projectiles has recently been reviewed by Roth (1980).

Owing to the large number of independent variables in sputtering experiments, it is always useful to find similarity relations for the sputtering yield. It has often been claimed that the energy-transfer factor,

$$\gamma = 4M_1M_2/(M_1 + M_2)^2 \tag{1}$$

should be important for few-collision events. In fact, Bohdansky et al. (1980) recently showed that yields of a number of target materials for incident hydrogen, deuterium, ^{3}He and ^{4}He in the range 0.1–10 keV could be scaled together if the energy axis was chosen as E/E_b, where E_b was the surface-binding energy. The yield-scaling factors were entirely empirical but rather simple functions of Z and M. Littmark and Fedder (1981) showed that only processes 1 and 2 of Fig. 1 contributed appreciably to the yield. Using previously calculated backscattering energy spectra, they obtained absolute agreement with experimental results (Fig. 2).

The *linear-collision cascade region* is the one treated in most detail theoretically (Sigmund, 1969). In this region, the projectile makes a number of collisions with target atoms, and transfers sufficient energy to several recoils to allow them to remove further target atoms from their sites. A collision cascade results. Such collision cascades are best treated by transport equations (as discussed in Chapter 3), from which a number of averages over many cascades with identical macroscopic starting parameters may be calculated. The calculation will, in principle, yield the double-differential distribution in angle and energy through the target surface, but the yield may be obtained through a double integration. In order to establish the relevant Boltzmann equation, projectile-target and target-target atomic collisions are assumed to be binary between point-like objects. However, it is very difficult to solve the resulting equation if the discontinuity at the surface is introduced as a boundary condition. Hence, the target is treated as an infinite medium with an imaginary surface plane embedded. To solve the Boltzmann equation, it is first linearized. This amounts to assuming that every collision will take place between a moving and a stationary atom. If the cascade is so dense that most atoms within it move, the linearity assumption breaks down. To

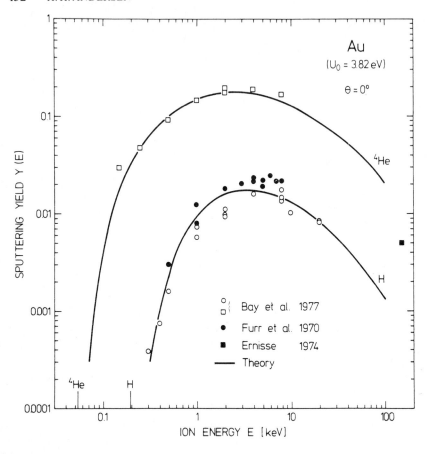

Fig. 2. Light-ion sputtering yields of Au. The theoretical results are from Littmark and Fedder (1982); the data collection of Andersen and Bay (1981) has been used to obtain experimental data.

obtain analytical solutions, it is further assumed that inelastic energy losses (ionization and excitation) may be neglected. This assumption may be by-passed by use of numerical methods. Finally, in a mathematical expansion of the solutions, it is shown that a term which describes the motion within the cascade as isotropic dominates (asymptomatically) at high energy (the expansion parameter is $(E_b/E)^{1/2}$). Dropping all terms beyond the isotropic one, for perpendicular incidence the backsputtering yield as a function of energy becomes

$$Y(E) = 0.042E_b^{-1} \, \alpha(M_2/M_1)S_n(E,Z_1,Z_2) \qquad (2)$$

Here, α is a function of the mass ratio between projectile and target atoms

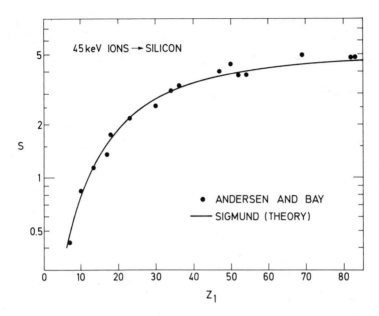

Fig. 3. Si sputtering yields for a number of different projectile atoms at 45 keV. Solid line represents the theoretical prediction of Sigmund (1969) with no fitting parameters. From Andersen and Bay (1975a).

only, and S_n is the specific energy loss in atom–atom collisions (the nuclear-stopping cross-section). As S_n may be written as a universal function of the reduced Thomas–Fermi energy (ε), eqn. (2) involves a very high amount of scaling. Within the region of applicability of eqn. (2), only two functions, $\alpha\,(M_2/M_1)$ and $S_n(\varepsilon)$, need to be known in order to calculate the yield for all projectile energies and projectile-target combinations. The inverse pro-portionality of the yield to the surface-binding energy is a rough approxi-mation only. A more detailed treatment will show Y to vary somewhat more slowly than E_b^{-1}, but not slower than $E_b^{-0.6}$, as discussed below in connection with eqn. (19).

The degree of agreement which may be obtained between the results of theory and experiment is illustrated by the next few figures. Fig. 3 shows the sputtering yield of Si at 45 keV as a function of Z_1 (Andersen and Bay, 1975a). The agreement is probably better than warranted by the accuracy of the experiment and the approximations of the theory. Fig. 4 shows the α function deduced from measurements at 45 keV on Si, Cu, Ag, and Au (Andersen and Bay, 1975b). A universal α function is found to apply with good accuracy. However, for large mass ratios, the value of the function is

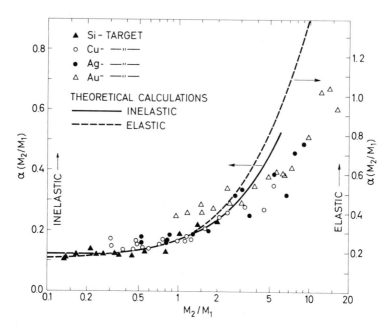

Fig. 4.   Experimental values of the function $\alpha(M_1/M_2)$ from eqn. (2). From Andersen and Bay (1975b).

considerably smaller than predicted theoretically. It is assumed that the multiple crossings of the imaginary surface, which are possible in the theoretical model, will lead to an overestimate of the energy deposition close to the surface; this is the case particularly for light projectiles (i.e. high mass ratios).

The isotropy of the collision cascade implies that the sputtered material should be cosine-distributed. Deviations from such a distribution will thus signal deviations from isotropy of the cascade. Such deviations are clearly seen at low energies, where the angular distributions are under-cosine or even heart-shaped (Wehner and Rosenberg, 1960; Hofer, 1982), as would result from process 3 of Fig. 1. At somewhat higher energies (∼5 keV Ar), the distributions become cosine-like, but at still higher energies, they become over-cosine (Perović and Čobić, 1962). This was earlier believed to be the result of surface-topography changes which are caused by large irradiation fluences but has recently been shown to occur also for rather low doses (Andersen et al., 1982). This result is thought to reflect another anisotropy; viz., that caused by the presence of the target surface.

The randomization of directions within the cascade may be tested more satisfactorily for oblique incidence of the bombarding ions. Whether the

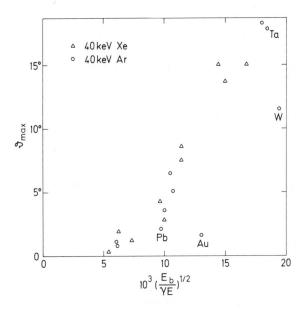

Fig. 5. The angle of preferred emission for Fe, Ni, Cu, Mo, Cd, W, Au, and Pb bombarded by 40 keV Ar and Xe incident 60° away from the normal. Data from Betz *et al.* (1970).

presence of the surface gives rise to some anisotropy in the cascade or not, a properly randomized cascade should yield an angular distribution which is symmetrical around the surface normal. In practice, some preferred emission in the forward direction is found. Fig. 5 shows the angle of maximum intensity as a funtion of $(E_b/\gamma E)^{1/2}$ for 40 keV Ar and Xe incident on Fe, Ni, Cu, Zn, Mo, Cd, Ta, W, Au, and Pb at 60° away from the normal. Only the Ar data for Au and W deviate from the clear correlation indicated by the remaining data points. These heavy targets have a low and a high binding energy, respectively. However, for Pb and Ta targets, which may be characterized by the same statements, the Ar data agree nicely with the rest. It is concluded that the degree of anisotropy is clearly correlated with the parameter $(E_b/\gamma E)^{1/2}$ and hence indicates one limit to the applicability of eqn. (3).

The recoil density within the cascade (i.e., the energy distribution of the recoils when set into motion) is found, from cascade theory, to be proportional to T^{-2} where T is the recoil energy. This spectrum diverges, and hence, when considering sufficiently low energies, all atoms within the cascade will be in motion and the linearity assumption breaks down. The energy spectrum of the flux through a plane in the target is modified by the slowing down of the recoils, but it is still approximately inversely proportional to the

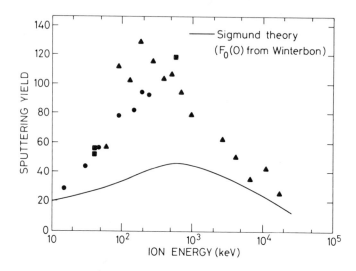

Fig. 6. Energy dependence of self-sputtering of Au. Data from Bay *et al.* (1976) (▲), Almén and Bruce (1961a), Merkle and Pronko (1974), and Andersen and Bay (1975b) (■). Finally, sputtering data for Au are from Johar and Thompson (1979) (●).

square of the energy. Modified by the passage through a planar surface-binding potential (E_b), the energy spectrum of the sputtered atoms will again approximately be given as (Thompson, 1959, 1981):

$$N(E')dE' = E'dE'/(E' + E_b) \qquad (3)$$

As mentioned above, conditions for the existence of a linear cascade must break down at some low energy. If the break down occurs at energies relevant for sputtering, i.e. at energies not much smaller than E_b, we pass into the *nonlinear cascade region*. This region predominates if the energy density within the cascade is high. This will naturally occur at energies around the maximum in the nuclear stopping power, and also in heavy targets where recoil ranges are short. Finally, targets with low binding energies are more liable to exhibit nonlinear effects than targets with high binding energies. If a nonlinear cascade is created, it will live longer than a linear cascade in the same material. Hence, more atoms will have a greater chance of surmounting the surface binding, and sputtering yields will be enhanced. (For a clear and non-technical discussion, see Sigmund, 1977 and 1981.) This effect is illustrated by the energy dependence of the self-sputtering of gold (Fig. 6).

Experimental nonlinear effects may clearly be seen when yields from atomic-ion and molecular-ion bombardments of heavy targets are compared (as was first shown by Andersen and Bay, 1974). Recently, for the first time, measurements with 1-50 keV Xe and Xe_2 ions on gold showed that the nonlinear effects also disappear at low energies (Oliva-Florio et al., 1979). The nonlinear, dense cascades are the subject of Chapter 4. They have also been reviewed recently, in great detail, by Thompson (1980, 1981).

It may be asked whether a temperature may be defined for the nonlinear cascade (also called the spike). If a thermal equilibrium exists and if the spike is hot enough to be treated as a gas, the temperature must be given by

$$kT_{spike} = \tfrac{2}{3}E/N\Omega \tag{4}$$

where N is the target atomic density and Ω is the cascade volume. The question whether a thermal equilibrium does indeed exist may seem academic but is of particular importance for preferential sputtering under spike conditions. This has most recently been discussed by Sigmund and Claussen (1980, 1981). A thermal equilibrium does not imply that the electron system within the spike is necessarily equilibrium, as assumed by Kelly (1979), who used temperatures of the order of 3000K, deduced from electronic excitations of the sputtered particles, to show that spike effects were of no importance. As these temperatures are of the order of 0.1 E_b, this conclusion is hardly surprising, but it remains doubtful whether the electron temperature used is of relevance for the spike.

The different sputter-mechanism regions are sketched in Fig. 7 by two planar cuts through the three-dimensional (E,Z_1,Z_2) space. The figure is designed particularly to show the region of applicability of eqn. (2); i.e., of the linear, analytical cascade theory.

III. SPUTTERING OF TWO-COMPONENT SYSTEMS

A. Qualitative Discussion of Preferential Sputtering

In this section, I shall present a general overview of preferential sputtering. In doing so, I will concentrate on the data presented in the literature. Then I shall attempt to indicate how these data may yield evidence of other mechanisms for subsurface modification of the composition of the bombarded targets. A very large number of papers pertinent to the subject have appeared during the past decade. Apart from an early summary (Andersen, 1974), reviews have not appeared until recently (Andersen, 1979; Coburn, 1979; Betz, 1980; Kelly, 1980; Sigmund, 1980). The main aim of these reviews has been to assess the validity of different theoretical predictions of non-stoichiometric sputtering. Andersen (1979) and Kelly (1980) also discussed a number of other experimental effects which may give rise to concentration-profile

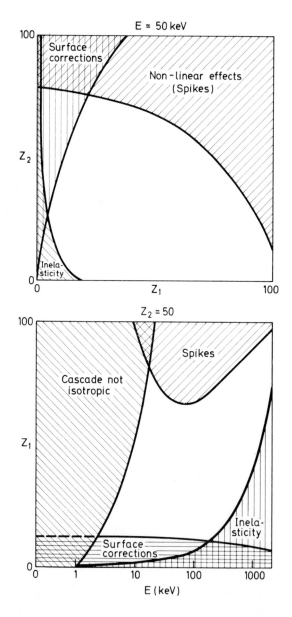

Fig. 7. The region of applicability of the linear, analytic sputtering theory, illustrated by two planar cuts through the (E, Z_1, Z_2) space. The upper figure shows the (Z_1, Z_2) plane for $E = 50$ keV, and the lower figure shows the (E, Z_1) plane for $Z_2 = 50$. Boundaries are approximate only. From Andersen and Bay (1981).

modifications, which, in turn, may be interpreted as being caused by preferential sputtering. In ion implantation, these effects may be of equal or greater importance than preferential sputtering itself. They have been considered elsewhere (Andersen, 1980). Special attention should also be directed to the recent, very detailed review by Betz and Wehner (1983).

The discussion of sputtering of multi-component targets will be limited to systems that, at least in principle, may be treated within the models outlined in section II. This means that I shall not treat systems in which excitation and ionization play a decisive role in the bombardment-induced erosion of the target. Most notably, I shall exclude alkali halides (the electron sputtering of which has recently been reviewed by Townsend, 1980), oxides (see Coburn, 1979; Kelly, 1980; and Betz and Wehner, 1983) and frozen noble gases (see Chapters 4 and 5). Examples in this chapter will mainly be taken from investigations of metal alloys and semiconductors. In dealing with the latter, one needs to be aware that stoichiometric molecular solids can have a much smaller surface-binding energy than the individual atoms. For example, when studying energy spectra of sputtered GaAs, Szymoński and Bhattacharya (1979) found that eqn. (3) could be fitted to the measured spectra with binding energies of 4.0 and 5.0 eV for Ga and As, respectively, but the binding energy found for GaAs molecules was as low as 1.6 eV. This difference must strongly suppress the occurrence of preferential sputtering.

The quantity of principal interest in the sputtering of multi-component targets is the partial yield Y_i, which is the number of emitted i atoms per incoming atom. A total yield may be defined as $Y = \Sigma Y_i$ and is usually obtained experimentally from the sum of the partial yields. Only if all species imbedded in the target have identical atomic volumes may the total yield be obtained directly through a determination of thickness changes (Andersen and Bay, 1981). The use of partial yields will also avoid the difficulties of defining a true sputtering yield during high-dose implantation. We need to employ sputtering yields Y_M and Y_I (for matrix and implant). They will usually both be functions of implant dose. The use of partial yields has been discussed by Sigmund et al. (1981) and Betz and Wehner (1983).

For many purposes, a knowledge of the ratio of the partial yields of a binary target may be sufficient, especially if one intends to focus on preferential or non-stoichiometric sputtering. Over the years, the term "preferential sputtering" has been used in somewhat different contexts. I prefer the following definition (Andersen, 1979a):

Preferential sputtering will be said to occur whenever the composition of the flux of sputtered particles (averaged over all emittance directions) differs from that of the outermost layers of the target.

The use of the term "outermost layers" is purposely somewhat vague. If no strong concentration gradients exist within the first few atomic layers which contribute to the sputtered flux, the definition is sufficiently rigorous. We shall see, however, that this condition is often not fulfilled. Therefore I would suggest a more rigorous definition, which for a two-component alloy (with obvious generalizations to multi-component systems) runs as follows:

Preferential sputtering will be said to occur whenever $Y_A/Y_B \neq \bar{C}_A^s/\bar{C}_B^s$.

Here, $\bar{C}_A^s$ and $\bar{C}_B^s$ are properly weighted averages over the surface composition. Let $y_A(x)dx$ be the contribution to Y_A from a layer dx at depth x, and let $c_A(x)$ be the depth-dependent concentration of species A; then

$$\bar{C}_A^s = (1/Y_A) \int_0^\infty c_A(x)y_A(x)dx. \tag{5}$$

is one choice for $\bar{C}_A$, but other possibilities exist. An analogous expression may be used for $\bar{C}_B$. Usually, neither $c_A(x)$ nor $y_A(x)$ are well known, and, as will be discussed below, it is rather difficult to determine whether preferential sputtering actually occurs according to the rigorous definition, even for systems which have been extensively studied experimentally. In the spirit of the somewhat naïve approach adopted in this section, I shall for the moment neglect the difference between $\bar{C}^s$ and the "surface concentration". I shall simply use $\bar{C}^s$ and quantify the degree of preferential sputtering through an enhancement factor,

$$f_{AB} = (Y_A/Y_B) [(\bar{C}_A^s/C_B^s)^{-1}]. \tag{6}$$

Here, Y_A and Y_B are the partial yields and C_A and C_B are the concentrations. The target components are indexed by A and B, and superscript s stands for surface.

Coburn (1979) defined preferential sputtering with regard to the bulk composition of the target. From an applied-physics viewpoint, Coburn's definition may be convenient, but as large doses always lead to a flux composition identical to that of the bulk, his definition makes the enhancement factor fluence-dependent and equal to *one* for all targets at high fluence. With some qualifications (given below) our definition allows a given projectile-target combination to be characterized by an enhancement factor.

An example of determination of an enhancement factor from a flux-composition measurement is shown in Fig. 8 as a function of irradiation fluence. The Ag–Au target was sputtered by 100 keV Ar, and the sputtered material was collected for later composition analysis. The actual enhancement factor for this run was 1.84, but an average over several runs gave 1.66.

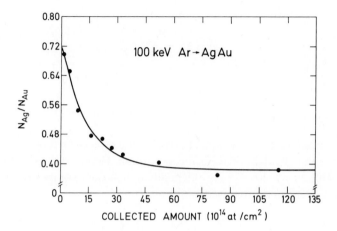

Fig. 8.   Transients in the composition of the flux sputtered by 100 keV Ar from a Ag–Au target. The abscissa may be converted into thickness of removed layer by multiplication by approximately 70. The enhancement factor (eqn. 6) is found to be 1.84. From Andersen *et al.* (1980).

Measurements such as those of Andersen *et al.* (1980; 1982a,b) demonstrate that the steady-state flux has a composition equal to that of the bulk.

Provided that the target was homogeneous right out to the surface before irradiation started (which is in no way certain), such enhancement factors indicate preferential sputtering. For the Cu–Ni system, Saeki and Shimizu (1978a) also found that Y_A / Y_B corresponded to the bulk composition for large doses.

I have already alluded to the steady-state situation. As mass is conserved, sputtering of a thick alloy target must result in a steady state, in which the composition of the sputtered flux is the same as that of the bulk. On the other hand, transients such as those illustrated in Fig. 8 do not remove preferential sputtering. To keep the enhancement factor approximately constant, the surface concentration of the preferentially sputtered component is necessarily lowered to preserve the balance.

If we assume the target to be homogeneous when the irradiation begins

$$C_A^s / C_B^s = C_A^b / C_B^b \tag{7}$$

which, combined with eqn. (6), yields

$$Y_A^0 / Y_B^0 = f_{AB}(C_A^b / C_B^b) \tag{8}$$

Here, index b refers to the bulk, and index 0 refers to the starting situation. In the steady state, mass conservation yields

$$Y_A^\infty / Y_B^\infty = C_A^b / C_B^b \tag{9}$$

or

$$C_A^{s,\infty} / C_B^{s,\infty} = f_{AB}^I (C_A^b / C_B^b) = Y_B^0 / Y_A^0 (C_A^b / C_B^b)^2 \tag{10}$$

The enhancement factor of eqn. (10) is only the same as that of eqn. (8), provided it is independent of surface composition. Hence, the second equality of eqn. (10) only holds if f_{AB} is independent of surface composition.

If the often very dubious assumption

$$Y_A^0 / Y_B^0 = Y(A) / Y(B) \, [C_A^b / C_B^b] \tag{11}$$

is introduced where $Y(A)$ and $Y(B)$ are the pure-element yields, then

$$C_A^{s,\infty} / C_A^{b,\infty} = Y(B) / Y(A) \, [C_A^b / C_B^b] \tag{12}$$

or, as $C_A + C_B = 1$,

$$C_A^{s,\infty} / C_A^{b,\infty} = Y(B) / \{ Y(A) - C_A^b[Y(A) - Y(B)] \} \tag{13}$$

This approximates to

$$C_A^{s,\infty} / C_B^{s,\infty} = Y(B) / Y(A) \tag{14}$$

provided $C_A^b \ll 1$.

Most of these formulae have been given previously in the literature and may seem rather trivial. However, often the different assumptions are not mentioned. For example, eqn. (12) may be quoted as a direct consequence of mass conservation, without any further assumptions being involved. (Incidentally, eqn. (12) was first given in the literature by Patterson and Shirn, 1967). Lam et al. (1980), in a detailed and very careful paper, give eqn. (11) in the alternate form $Y_A^0 = Y(A)C_A$ and $Y_B^0 = Y(B)C_B$, which may also be used to calculate absolute yields. As mentioned in Section IV,B this restrictive assumption is also used in most calculations involving diffusion (see, for example, Webb et al., 1978). Usually eqn. (11) will not hold, but for the Cu–Ni system, it appears that f_{AB} is independent of composition, and eqn.

(11) is valid for all compositions (Shimizu *et al.*, 1973; Shimizu, 1977; Brongersma *et al.*, 1978; all results obtained at low energies). However, absolute yields are smaller than those calculated by Lam *et al.* (1980).

Bear in mind that sputtering yields are roughly inversely proportional to surface-binding energies, as outlined above. In the linear-cascade region, eqn. (11) is thus roughly equilavent to

$$E_A/E_B = E(A)/E(B) \tag{15}$$

where E_A and E_B are the surface-binding energies of components A and B in the alloy, and $E(A)$ and $E(B)$ are the binding energies of the pure materials.

The pair-binding model (e.g. Williams and Nason, 1974; Brongersma *et al.*, 1978), now allows us to get some indication of whether eqn. (11) is realistic. In this model, the surface-binding energy is assumed to be a sum of pair-binding energies (E_{AA}, E_{AB}, E_{BB}), and for a random alloy

$$\begin{aligned} E_A &= n(C_A E_{AA} + C_B E_{AB}) \\ E_B &= n(C_A E_{AB} + C_B E_{BB}) \end{aligned} \tag{16}$$

or

$$E_A/E_B = \frac{C_A E_{AA} + (1 - C_A)E_{AB}}{C_A E_{AB} + (1 - C_A)E_{BB}} \tag{17}$$

where n is the coordination number. This is seen to be dependent on C_A, except for the trivial case $E_{AA} = E_{AB} = E_{BB}$. Hence, within the framework of such a model, f_{AB} must be considered concentration-dependent and eqn. (11) will not hold.

Fig. 9 illustrates eqn. (17) for a number of assumed values of E_{AB}. In all the numerical examples shown, $E_{BB} = 2E_{AA}$. The examples $E_{AB} = \frac{1}{2}(E_{AA} + E_{BB})$ (which perhaps might be expected to result in eqn. 15), $E_{AB} = E_{BB}$, $E_{AB} = E_{AA}$, and, finally, $E_{AB} = 3E_{BB}$ (which will result in a strongly exothermic-mixing reaction and may be characteristic for alloys such as Pd–Zr) are illustrated. None of the examples reproduces eqn. (15), and we may thus expect eqn. (11) to be relevant only for low-energy experiments in which mass ratios dominate surface-binding energy ratios. Note, however, that only for the strongly exothermic reaction may the weaker-bound element exchange with the stronger-bound one. For alloys with this latter property, the more abundant component will always be the weaker-bound one, and sputtering will tend to produce a surface-concentration ratio close to one.

For the Cu–Ni system, eqn. (15) yields 0.79 as the ratio, whereas eqn. (17) with $E_{AB} = \frac{1}{2}(E_{AA} + E_{BB})$ yields 0.88, virtually independent of composition. Hence, the experimental result that the f_{AB} for the Cu–Ni system is

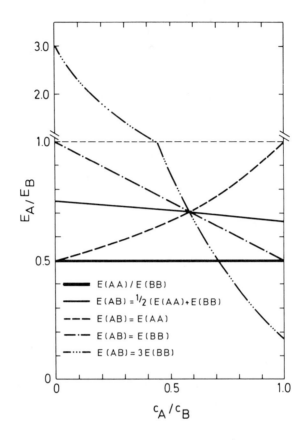

Fig. 9. Surface-binding energy ratios for the pair-binding model with different assumptions for the mixed-pair binding energy. In all examples, $E_{BB} = 2E_{AA}$. From Andersen (1980).

independent of concentration does not contradict this argument. It is not clear whether the precision of the experimental data is sufficient to decide whether f_{AB} is 0.79 or slightly closer to one.

Equation (10) shows that enhancement factors may also be measured in steady state by determining the absolute surface concentration. This is the method most often used. An example, where the surface composition is followed as a function of the sputtered layer, is shown in Fig. 10; the surface composition of an Au–Ni alloy bombarded by 2 keV Ar is followed by means of AES (Auger Electron Spectroscopy) (Tompkins, 1979). If f_{AB} depends on the surface composition, different values must be found by the flux-composition method. Together with a number of other interpretational diffi-

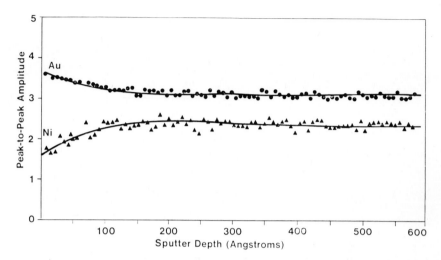

Fig. 10. Changes in peak-to-peak amplitude AES signal from a Au–Ni alloy bombarded by 2 keV Ar as a function of the sputtered-layer thickness. From Tompkins (1979).

culties discussed below, this possibility has, until now, been widely neglected in the literature.

At this stage, one more experimental complication needs to be mentioned. In order to reach steady state (and hence determine f_{AB} from composition measurements), the target must be thicker than the layer which must be removed to reach steady state. For Cu–Ni, investigations of Goto et al. (1978) indicate that a target film must be at least five times thicker than the transient width. If this is not the case, the entire target is gradually depleted of the preferentially sputtered component.

B. Experimental Methods of Investigating Preferential Sputtering

In the previous subsection, the two principal methods for investigating preferential sputtering have been illustrated. To aid a discussion of the merits of the two methods, and to show how they may be carried out in practice, the experimental situation is sketched in Fig. 11.

Flux-composition measurements (left-hand side of Fig. 11) may be carried out either by collection techniques or by direct measurements of the sputtered flux. They may be performed as a function of dose (Andersen et al., 1980) or emission angle (Andersen et al., 1981, 1982). Collection measurements are complicated only when sticking coefficients are different from unity. If very light collector materials (Be or C) are chosen, this will usually

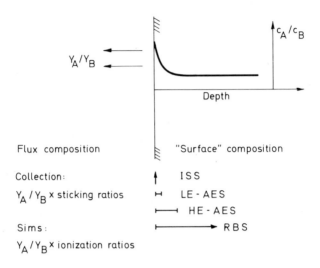

Fig. 11.   The experimental situation in preferential-sputtering measurements. The left-hand side shows possibilities for flux-composition measurements, and the right-hand side illustrates the composition-depth profile and the depth resolution of different analytical techniques. Flux-composition measurements may be performed both as a function of dose and of emission angle. From Andersen (1980).

not constitute a serious complication. If the collected material is analysed by RBS (Rutherford Backscattering Spectroscopy), *absolute* composition ratios are immediately obtained. If the target composition is known, it is not necessary to reach steady state to determine f_{AB}. Secondary Ion Mass Spectrometry (SIMS) may also be used, but here the flux composition is modified by the ionization probabilities. These probabilities will normally depend on surface composition, and absolute measurements are virtually impossible, particularly in the very beginning of a sputtering run. Sputtered Neutral-Mass Spectrometry (SNMS) (Oechsner and Stumpe, 1977; Oechsner *et al.*, 1979), where the neutral (and usually dominating) part of the sputtered flux is ionized and mass-analysed, may offer a solution, but here also absolute measurements are difficult.

For the collection method, it may be concluded that experimental complications are insignificant and that full advantage can be taken of the possibilities of the flux-composition measurements. *The essential information can be obtained at very small fluence from a homogeneous target which is not yet loaded with projectile atoms.*

The right-hand side of Fig. 11 illustrates the different methods which have been used for surface-composition analysis in preferential-sputtering studies. The preferential emission of one species from the target induces a concentration gradient beneath the surface. The sputtered atoms themselves, however, originate mainly from the first two or three layers (Sigmund, 1969). The composition of these layers is therefore what should, ideally, be determined. If the concentration gradient is very steep, ISS (Ion Surface Scattering) may overestimate the enhancement factor f_{AB}. Whether $c_A(0)$ actually differs from $\bar{C}_A^s$ (eqn. 5) may be tested directly by a different collection method. Sigmund et al. (1981) pointed out that if a significant concentration gradient exists within the layer from which the sputtered atoms originate, then the angular distribution of the two components will differ. The component of which the surface is depleted will have a more outward-pointed angular distribution than that with which the surface is enriched. The differences in angular distribution may be understood in terms of a simple shadowing effect by the outermost surface layer. Angular distributions of both components of sputtered binary alloys have been measured (Andersen et al., 1981, 1982a,b).

Provided no difference is found in the angular distribution, concentration gradients may be concluded to be small, and reliable values of f_{AB} may be obtained from both collection and surface-analysis measurements.

Auger Electron Spectroscopy (AES) may be used for surface-composition analysis either in a High-Energy (HE) or Low-Energy (LE) version. The mean-free path of the electrons from high-energy lines (500–1500 eV) is of the order of 15–30 Å, while that of low-energy lines (50–100 eV) is 4–5 Å (Tarng and Wehner, 1972). Thus, even the low-energy lines will carry information about the composition of the uppermost 10 Å (i.e., approximately twice the layer contributing to sputtering), but some information on concentration gradients may be obtained from simultaneous measurements with LE and HE AES, as shown by Quinto et al., (1971) for the Cu–Ni system. If the two components have widely different atomic numbers, backscattering of the electrons from deeper layers, and hence the information depth, may depend on a concentraion gradient (Tarng and Wehner, 1972, Holloway, 1977, Gugliemacci and Gilet, 1980, Tokutaka et al., 1981). These papers all discuss the difficulties that will be encountered if AES is attempted to be used for absolute concentration measurements in sputtering experiments. In this connection, it may be worthwhile to attempt using the total secondary-electron spectrum (Sigmund and Tougaard, 1981).

Rutherford Backscattering Spectroscopy (RBS), even in its glancing-incidence, high-resolution mode, cannot be called a surface-analytical technique when used for studies of polycrystalline or amorphous targets. Nevertheless, the technique may be useful where concentration gradients extend to larger depths, as is the case in Pt and Ni silicides, for example (Liau et al., 1977, 1978a). By using RBS, some of the problems that may occur when the target is loaded with projectile atoms have been illustrated (Liau and Sheng, 1978).

It may be concluded that measurements on the sputtered target are complicated by the lack of a method which combines adequate surface sensitivity with a simple prescription for obtaining absolute concentrations. Furthermore, interpretation of measured f_{AB}'s is hampered by complications introduced by target loading and concentration gradients.

As will be seen in section IV, a number of non-sputtering phenomena introduce further complications. These indicate that unique interpretations may be obtained only if the flux, the absolute surface compositions, and possible concentration gradients are measured simultaneously.

C. Theoretical and Experimental Results

For the *few-collision* region, it is rather easy to state qualitative expectations for preferential sputtering. If the threshold energies for sputtering of the two components of a binary target are different, very strong preferential sputtering of the component with the lower threshold will be observed when the ion energy is reduced close to the higher of the two thresholds. If the target masses are nearly equal, the relative threshold energies are determined by the relative binding energies. If target masses are very different, the relative thresholds are also strongly influenced by the target mass which is nearer to the projectile mass.

These expectations are borne out experimentally. Tarng and Wehner (1971a, 1971b) found that when the energy was lowered to close to the Ni threshold, Cu was sputtered much more preferentially from Cu–Ni, than it was at higher energies. More recent work of Taglauer and Heiland (1980) is illustrated in Fig. 12, which shows surface-concentration ratios of TaC sputtered by He and Ar. Carbon has the lower binding energy and is hence preferentially sputtered by Ar and He. The figure also illustrates that the induced surface-concentration changes are reversible and that lowering of the He energy to 500 eV raises the Ta concentration considerably over its level at 1 keV. The energy-transfer factor from He to C is much higher than that to Ta. The difference is not nearly as large for Ar projectiles. At constant energy, He gives rise to a greater enhancement in Ta-surface concentration than Ar does. Taglauer and Heiland (1978) and Taglauer et al. (1979) found very similar results for Ta_2O_5 targets, but oxides often appear to be dominated by effects not discussed in this chapter (Kelly, 1978, 1980).

Fig. 13 illustrates that for WC, as well as for TaC, the steady-state surface concentration closely follows eqn. (12). As discussed previously in connection

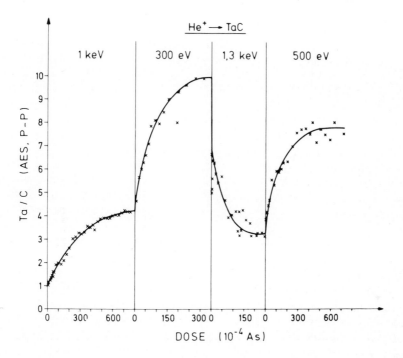

Fig. 12. Peak-to-Peak ratios of Ta to C as measured by AES on TaC bombarded by He and Ar. From Taglauer and Heiland (1980).

with this formula, a number of assumptions have to be fulfilled in order to give such agreement. This is the case under the experimental conditions depicted in Fig. 13.

Angular distributions of the sputtered material have also been measured in the few-collision regime, for example, by Olson and Wehner (1977) and Olson *et al.* (1979). In these experiments Fe–Ni, Ag–Au, and Cu–Ni were irradiated with 300 eV Ar and Hg ions. In addition, isotope effects were studied in Cu, Mo, W, and U. All the results are consistent with sputtering resulting from double collisions, after consideration of the energy-transfer factor, eqn. (1).

The basic theoretical work on the *linear collision-cascade range* was performed by N. Andersen and Sigmund (1974). This work was based on the use of power cross-sections as approximations to the screened Coulomb interaction between slow, heavy ions; viz.,

$$d\sigma(E,T) = C_m E^{-m} T^{-1-m} dT \qquad 0 \le T \le T_{max} \tag{18}$$

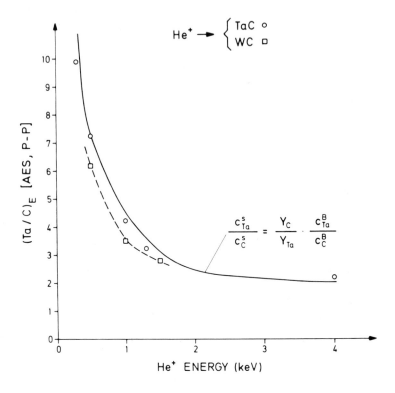

Fig. 13. Ta-to-C and W-to-C surface concentrations as a function of He ion energy. Solid and dashed curves represent eqn. (12). From Taglauer and Heiland (1980).

Here C_m is a constant and m varies, depending on the energy range in question. E is the projectile energy and T is the recoil energy of the struck atom. At high energies $m = 1$, and eqn. (18) reflects the Rutherford cross-section. Decreasing energies mean lower, although always positive, values of m.

N. Andersen and Sigmund then proceeded to solve the Boltzmann equation for the two-component system and found that the recoil energy is concentrated preferentially in the lighter component, causing this component to be sputtered preferentially with an enhancement factor

$$f_{AB} = (M_B/M_A)^{2m}(E_{b,B}/E_{b,A})^{1-2m} \qquad (19)$$

provided the same value of m is used for both components, which is by no means obvious. Relevant values of m should lie in the range $0 \leq m \leq 0.2$ (see also the discussion of eqn. (5) above). Actually, internal flux ratios were derived but the authors stopped short of directly quoting the result (eqn. 18), because of the difficulties of defining relevant values of $E_{b,A}$ and $E_{b,B}$ to insert in the equation. A further elementary step is needed to arrive at an actual yield formula, as Sigmund (1981) recently demonstrated. Nevertheless, the fact that Andersen and Sigmund did not state a yield ratio has caused many authors (e.g. Haff, 1977; Kelly, 1978; Liau et al., 1978; Watson and Haff, 1980) to claim that no preferential sputtering was predicted.

Haff et al. (1981) calculated mass effects from another viewpoint. They assumed that the layers contributing to the sputtered flux were not part of the collision cascade. If this is the case, the energy-transfer factor, eqn. (1), will be of critical importance for the energy transfer from the bulk to the surface layers. Matrix effects will need to be predicted (i.e., from a dilute solution of two isotopes), the heavier isotope will be sputtered preferentially if the solvent is heavy, and the light isotope will be sputtered preferentially if the solvent is light. No experimental test of these predictions has been published as yet.

From eqn. (19) it can be seen that a weak dependence of f_{AB} on mass ratios and a strong dependence on binding-energy ratios are predicted. Nevertheless, even though isotope effects are predicted to be very small and most experimental results are only qualitative, it should be somewhat easier to interpret them. Measurements are mostly performed either on the sputtered target or, if on collected material, after rather large doses. Fluit et al. (1961) were the first to measure preferential sputtering of a light isotope; viz., ^{6}Li over ^{7}Li. Preferential sputtering by the solar wind has been held responsible for the enrichment of ^{18}O over ^{16}O and ^{30}Si over ^{28}Si in lunar materials (Taylor and Epstein, 1973). Arai et al. (1976) evaporated Mg onto Re wires in UHV and sputtered with H. They found the remaining material to be enriched in ^{26}Mg over ^{25}Mg and ^{24}Mg. Finally, Russell et al. (1980) collected Ca from several minerals sputtered by 100 keV N^+ and measured the isotopic composition as a function of dose. Enrichments of ^{40}Ca over ^{44}Ca by slightly less than 2% indicate a value of m of 0.2. All of these investigations give the expected qualitative mass dependence according to eqn. (19); namely, preferential sputtering of the light isotope. In addition, the results of Russell et al. even yield the quantitatively expected result. However, none of the quoted results contradict the predictions of Haff et al. (1981). Note, in particular, with respect to the Mg experiment, that H backscattered from the Re substrate will sputter the light isotope preferentially. Hence the interpretation is more in line with a few-collision experiment. Attention is once again drawn to the theory of light-projectile sputtering (Littmark and Fedder, 1981).

Russell et al. (1980) also performed crude measurements of angular distributions. In accordance with the prediction of Sigmund et al. (1981), they found that the preferentially sputtered ^{40}Ca was emitted preferentially in the forward direction.

Very few of the investigations listed in Table I at the end of this section were obtained in the linear-cascade region, but just a few examples may indicate the interpretational difficulties. For the Ag–Au system, it has been found (Andersen et al., 1980) that $f_{AB} = 1.58$, but eqn. (19) yields 1.46 if the maximum value for m (viz. 0.2) is used. In this case, the pure-element binding energies have been inserted, but the discussion in connection with Fig. 9 showed that this is most probably an over-estimate of the binding-energy ratio.

Many authors (e.g. Färber et al., 1976; Betz et al., 1977; and Tompkins, 1979) found no preferential sputtering from Cu–Au. However, these data were obtained at low energies, whereas Liau et al. (1977) found preferential sputtering of Cu in the higher-energy cascade region. This latter result is comforting, because $f_{CuAu} = 1$ implies a negative m, which is not physically realistic. Note, however, that Gillam (1959), Asada and Quasabarth (1929) and Ogilvie (1959) found Au enrichment of the surface; i.e., preferential sputtering of Cu. Ogar et al. (1969) found the collected material to be enriched in Au, but these results were obtained after such large doses that they are hardly reliable.

As the Ag–Au target is a rather heavy one, the large value of f_{Ag-Au} may be due to *spike effects*. Sigmund (1981) gives the formula

$$f_{AB} = (M_B/M_A)^{1/2}(E_{b,A}/E_{b,B})^2 \exp(\Delta E_b/kT). \qquad (20)$$

This formula is expected to hold only if the spike mechanism is the dominating one; i.e., if $E_b/kT \simeq 1$ for at least the looser-bound element. Hence, the formula does not hold for the case of a very small spike contribution in a dilute cascade (small kT), where a very large f_{AB} would be expected. As soon as spike effects contribute significantly, eqn. (20) will predict a larger f_{AB} than eqn. (19).

Finally, it should be mentioned that the surface-binding energies to be used in eqn. (20) are even more uncertain than those relevant for eqn. (9). Unfortunately, no preferential sputtering yield measurements have been performed under clear and dominant spike conditions.

It has been shown that sputtered *energy spectra* look different for the two components in the linear cascade regime, with that of the heavy component dropping off considerably more steeply at high energies than that of the light one (Andersen and Sigmund, 1974). (This result corresponds to the use of different exponents for the interaction potential of the two components in the alloy; cf. eqns. 18 and 19.) Adylov et al. (1972) studied the W–Mo system but measured the spectra of the charged component only, while Szymoński et al. (1978) irradiated Ag–Au with 6 keV Xe. A clear spike contribution was observed in their spectra, which, for both components, is proportional to E^{-2} at high energies. Szymoński (1980) has also measured spectra from other alloys without observing differences in the spectra of the two components. He points out (Szymoński, 1981) that measurements of energy spectra demand large doses and are hence performed under steady-state conditions. If the lighter component is sputtered preferentially, this component will be depleted from the surface. Generally, the lighter ions will thus originate from slightly deeper within the target and will lose more energy than the heavy ones on the way out. This effect counteracts the cascade-induced differences in energy distributions. Once again, the preferential effects for the sputtered particles are seen only at small doses (see also Sigmund et al., 1982).

I shall conclude this section by listing (in Table I) all the experiments which were known at the time of writing and which have relevance for preferential sputtering of alloys. The compilation of this table has been greatly facilitated by the existence of similar tables in Coburn (1979) and Betz and Wehner (1983). As most measurements are performed on the target, I have chosen, as Coburn did, to characterize preferential sputtering by the element exhibiting enhanced surface concentration. For the few compounds for which measurements have been performed on the sputtered material, surface enhancement has been assumed to occur according to eqn. (10). More detailed information, together with a listing of sputtered oxides, will be found in Betz and Wehner (1983).

Apart from the observed enhancements, the element with the lower elemental yield, larger mass, and larger pure-element surface-binding energy has been listed for qualitative comparison with theoretical predictions. In contrast to Kelly (1980), I have not limited myself to a listing of systems in which the elements are completely miscible. I do not deny that the existence of solubility gaps in the phase diagrams may be of importance, but a recent result of Tsaur et al. (1980) showed that a continuous composition series of one-phase Ag–Cu alloys could be found under the non-equilibrium conditions of ion bombardment. If this result can be generalized, the sputtering situation itself may convert a number of two-phase systems into homogeneous, solid solutions.

It has occasionally been claimed in the literature that preferential sputtering consistently takes place in the element with either the lower binding energy or the lower mass. Inspection of Table I discloses that no single rule applies. However, it appears significant that mass ratios dominate over binding energies only for systems containing Al (with Au, Cu, or Pd) and Si (with Ni, Pd, Pt, and Ti). Systems for which binding-energy ratios dominate are considerably more diversified. In this connection, it might be important that, for strongly exothermic systems only, the rato between binding energies may change signs from that of the elemental constituents, as shown in Fig. 9.

Table I does, perhaps, contain one anomaly. From the Gd containing systems (with Co, Co plus Cu, and with Fe), Gd sputters preferentially in spite of the fact that it has a lower elemental yield and a larger mass than that of the constituents. However, as the sign of the preferential sputtering effect

TABLE I
Bibliography of alloy sputtering

System	Enhanced surface concentration	Lower elemental yield	Larger mass	Larger E_b	References
Ag–Au	Au	Au	Au	Au	Liau et al. (1977), Färber et al. (1976), Färber & Braun (1974), Overbury & Somorjai (1976), Ho et al. (1977), Betz et al. (1977), Yabumoto et al. (1978, 1979), Andersen et al. (1980), Szymoński et al. (1978), Betz (1980).
Ag–Au–Cu	None	Au	Au	Au	Nelson (1976), Yabumoto et al. (1979), Swartzfager et al. (1981).
	Au, Cu	Au, Cu	Au	Au	Betz et al. (1980).
Ag–Au–Pd	Au, Pd	Au, Pd	Au	Au	Betz et al. (1981).
Ag–Co	Co	Co	Ag	Co	Dahlgren & McClanahan (1972).
Ag–Cu	Cu	Cu	Ag	Cu	Färber et al. (1976), Betz et al. (1977), Anderson (1969), Braun & Färber (1975).
Ag–Ni	Ni	Ni	Ag	Ni	Dahlgren & McClanahan (1972).
Ag–Pd	Pd	Pd	Similar	Pd	Gillam (1959), West (1976), Mathieu & Landolt (1975), Betz (1980a, b), Slusser & Winograd (1979), Garvassi & Parravano (1978).
Al–Au	Au	Al	Au	Au	Liau et al. (1977), Opitz et al. (1980b).
Al–Cr	Cr	Similar	Cr	Cr	Opitz et al. (1980b).
Al–Cu	Cu	Al	Cu	Cu	Howard et al. (1975), Chu et al. (1976).
Al–Fe	Fe	Similar	Fe	Fe	Opitz et al. (1980b).
Al–Ga–As	None	Al	Similar	Al	Arthur & LePore (1977).
Al–Mg	Al	Al	Similar	Al	Kelly (1979), Betz & Wehner (1982).
Al–Ni	Ni	Al	Ni	Ni	Opitz et al. (1980b), Yu & Reuter (1981).
Al–Pd	Pd	Al	Pd	Pd	Lewis & Ho (1979), Ho et al. (1979), Yu & Reuter (1981).
Al–Si	Si	Si	Similar	Si	Lewis & Ho (1979), Ho et al. (1979).
As–Ga	Ga, none	?	Similar	Ga	van Oostroom (1976), Jacobi & Ranke (1976), Singer et al. (1978, 1981a, b).
	Both	?	Similar	Ga	McGuire (1978).
As–Ge–Te	AsGe	Ge	Te	Ge	Farren & Scaife (1968), Bolker (1977).
Au–Cr	Cr	Cr	Au	Cr	Holloway (1977).

System					References
Au–Cu	Au, none	Au[a]	Au	Au	Liau et al. (1977), Gillam (1959), Färber et al. (1976), Betz et al. (1977), Asada & Quasebarth (1929), Tompkins (1979), Ogilvie (1959), Andersen et al. (1980), Betz (1980a).
	Cu	Cu[b]	Au	Au	Ogar et al. (1969).
		Au[a]			
		Cu[b]			
Au–In	In	In	Au	Au	Thomas (1974).
Au–MgO	MgO	MgO	Au	–	Henrich & Fan (1974).
Au–Ni	Ni	Ni	Au	Ni	Tompkins (1979).
Au–Pd	None	Pd	Au	Similar	Maire et al. (1976), Swartzfager et al. (1981).
	Pd	Pd	Au	Similar	Betz et al. (1980), Betz (1980a, b), Jablonski et al. (1977).
Au–Sn	Au	?	Au	?	Overbury & Somorjai (1977).
Be–Cu	Cu	Be	Cu	Cu	Koshikawa & Shimizu (1973).
Bi–Pb	Pb	?	Similar	Similar	Dumoulin et al. (1981).
C–Si	None, C	C	Si	–	Mohri et al. (1978), Sone et al. (1981).
C–Ta	Ta	Ta	Ta	Ta	Taglauer & Heiland (1980), Roth et al. (1980).
C–Ti	None	C	Ti	C	Wehner (1974).
C–W	W	W	W	W	Taglauer & Heiland (1980), Taglauer et al. (1979), Gambino & Cuomo (1978), Roth et al. (1980), Tonson et al. (1978), Ross & Stonehart (1975).
Cd–Hg–Te	Cd, Te	?	Hg	?	Nitz et al. (1981), Solzbach & Richter (1980).
Co–Gd	Co	Gd?	Gd	Co	Cuomo et al. (1974), Funakoshi & Manabe (1975), Hirano et al. (1977), Heiman et al. (1978), Nishihara et al. (1978).
Co–Cu–Gd	Co	Gd?	Gd	Co	Heiman et al. (1978).
Co–Ni	Co	Co	Ni	Co	Goretzki et al. (1977).
Cr–Fe	None	Similar	Similar	Similar	Frankenthal & Malm (1976), Frankenthal & Thompson (1979).
Cr–Fe–Mo	Mo	Mo	Mo	Mo	Mathieu & Landolt (1979).
Cr–Fe–Ni	FeCr	Fe, Cr	Similar	Cr	McIntyre & Stancell (1979), Dahlgren & Graybeal (1970), Roth et al. (1977), Opitz et al. (1980a).
Cr–Ni	Cr	Cr	Similar	Ni	Patterson & Shirn (1967).
		Cr	Similar	Ni	Yu & Reuter (1981).
Cr–Pd	None	Cr	Pd	Cr	West (1976).
Cu–Ga	None	Ga	Similar	Cu	Dove et al. (1977).
Cu–In	Cu	Cu	In	Cu	Rivaud et al. (1981).

TABLE I—*continued*

System	Enhanced surface concentration	Lower elemental yield	Larger mass	Larger E_b	References
Cu–Mo	Mo	Mo	Mo	Mo	Tarng & Wehner (1972).
Cu–Ni	Ni	Ni	Ni	Ni	Tarng & Wehner (1971). Quinto et al. (1971). Nakayma et al. (1972). Ono et al. (1972, 1975). Shimizu et al. (1973, 1975). Brongersma & Buck (1975). Helms & Yu (1975). Yamashina et al. (1975). Narasuwa et al. (1976). Ho et al. (1976). Watanabe et al. (1976, 1977a, 1977b). Shimizu & Saeki (1977). Koshikawa et al. (1977, 1979). Goto et al. (1977, 1978a, 1978b). Goretzki et al. (1977). Saeki & Shimizu (1978a, 1978b). Brongersma et al. (1978). Shimizu (1977). Rehn et al. (1979). Yabumoto et al. (1979). Rodriquez-Murcia & Beske (1976). Satake et al. (1976). Vasilbev et al. (1973). Toyokawa et al. (1981). Shikaya & Shimizu (1980). Yu & Reuter (1981).
Cu–Pd	None	Ni	Ni	Ni	Okutani et al. (1980). Swartzfager et al. (1981).
Cu–Pt	Pd	Pd	Pd	Pd	West (1976). Betz (1980b).
Cu–Sn	Pt	Pt	Pt	Pt	Betz (1980a). Brongersma et al. (1978). Andersen et al. (1984).
Cu–Zn	None, Cu	Similar	Sn	Cu	Taga & Nakajima (1977).
Fe–Gd	Cu	Cu	Similar	Cu	Abbati et al. (1978). Szymönski (1980).
Fe–Ni	Fe	Gd?	Gd	Fe	Heiman et al. (1978). Nishihara et al. (1978).
	Fe, none	Fe	Similar	Ni	Lee (1979). Kay (1965). McIntyre & Stancell (1979). Opitz et al. (1980a).
	Ni	Fe	Similar	Ni	Yu & Reuter (1981).
Fe–Pd	Fe	Fe	Pd	Fe	Lee (1979). Lee et al. (1978).
Fe–Si–W	Fe, W	W	W	W	Wittmaack & Blank (1980).
Ga–P	Ga, none	?	Ga	P	Liau et al. (1977). Jacobi & Ranke (1976).
Ge–Nb	None	Similar	Nb	Nb	Tongson et al. (1976). Buitrago et al. (1979).
Ge–Si	None	Si	Ge	Si	Liau et al. (1977).
Ge–Te	Ge	Ge	Ge	Ge	Fagen et al. (1974).
Hg–Te	Te	?	Hg	Te	Solzbach & Richter (1980).

System					Reference
In-P	None	?	In	In	Liau et al. (1977).
In-Pb	In	In	Pb	In	Berglund & Somorjai (1973), Frankenthal & Siconolfi (1981b).
In-Sb	Both	Similar	Similar	Sb	McGuire (1978).
Mn-Pd	None	Mn	Pd	Pd	West (1976).
Mo-Ni	Mo	Mo	Mo	Mo	Rehn et al. (1978).
Mo-W	W	W	W	W	Dawson & Petrone (1981).
Nb-U	Nb	Nb	U	Nb	West (1976).
Ni-Pd	Ni	Ni	Pd	Ni	Mathieu & Landolt (1975).
Ni-Pd	Pd	Ni	Pd	Ni	Yu and Reuter (1981).
Ni-Pt	Pt	Similar	Pt	Pt	Betz (1980a).
Ni-Si	Ni	Si	Ni	Si	Rehn et al. (1978), Liau et al. (1977), Poate et al. (1976).
Ni-Ti	Ti	Ti	Ni	Ti	Rehn et al. (1978).
Ni-W	W	W	W	W	Oechsner & Bartella (1980).
Pb-Sn	Sn	Sn	Pb	Sn	Frankenthal & Siconolfi (1980, 1981a), Dumoulin et al. (1981).
Pd-Pt	Pt	Pt	Pt	Pt	Kuijers et al. (1978).
Pd-Si	Pd	Si	Pd	Si	Lewis & Ho (1979), Ho et al. (1979).
Pt-Si	Pt	Si	Pt	Pt	Liau et al. (1977, 1978a, 1978b), Poate et al. (1976).
Pt-Sn	Pt	Pt	Pt	Pt	Bouvman et al. (1973), Thomas (1977).
Si-Ti	Ti	Similar	Ti	Ti	Narasuwa et al. (1976).

[a] low energy
[b] high energy

is in agreement with the binding energies, I remain somewhat in doubt about the assignment of elemental yields within these systems. Further, all the end results were obtained under so-called bias-sputtering conditions where a film is sputter deposited and slightly sputter eroded simultaneously. Here, the usual mass-conservation rule does not apply and surface segregation (Section IV, D) may cause a preferential emission of the segregating element. This preferential emission need not be preferential sputtering in the sense discussed here. In fact, a basic uncertainty when using Table I is that we cannot be sure that the listed effects reflect preferential-sputtering behaviour. (Alternatively, the result may be directly in error, as discussed above for the Cu–Au system.) A number of related effects, which are often misinterpreted as preferential sputtering, will be discussed in the following section.

IV. PARTICLE FLUXES AT THE SURFACE

A. General Remarks

Up to this point, I have considered only the composition of the flux leaving the surface in the outward direction. According to the definition of preferential sputtering, the very existence of this effect implies that sputtering of two-component systems is usually not a simple peeling-off of surface layers. The preferentially sputtered component must be replenished from the bulk, and as the surface composition differs from that of the bulk, this process could be driven, for example, by chemical diffusion down the concentration gradient.

This picture, however, may be too simple. Other mechanisms can contribute to a non-stoichiometric flux below the surface. Some of these are shown in Fig. 14. A further complication is that some of these effects may cause both the flux composition and the surface composition to deviate, at least temporarily, from that of the bulk.

All of the effects depicted in Fig. 14 were previously related to preferential sputtering (Andersen, 1979a), although the relevance of some of them (in particular diffusion) was noted earlier (Ho et al., 1976; Pickering, 1976; Collins, 1978). Other effects such as recoil implantation (Sigmund, 1979; Sigmund et al., 1982), surface segregation (Yabumoto et al., 1978, 1979), and radiation-enhanced segregation (Marwick and Piller, 1978; Rehn et al., 1979; Lam et al., 1979, 1980) have been discussed in detail in connection with surface-composition problems and sputtering. To a large extent, the discussion below will be based on results from these and other recent publications.

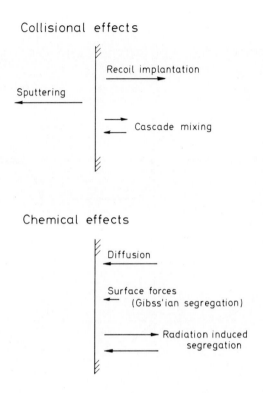

Fig. 14. Components of particle flux above and below the surface. From Andersen (1980).

B. Diffusion

At an early stage, it was realized that preferential sputtering must be accompanied by a transport of preferentially sputtered components to the surface. In the first attempts to model this situation, only the topmost layers were incorporated in the analysis as they were sequentially uncovered by the sputtering process (Patterson and Shirn, 1967; Shimizu et al., 1973). Although this approach described the surface composition of the Cu–Ni system satisfactorily, Ho (1978) pointed out that the time constants involved in establishing steady state were much shorter than those found experimentally. Basically, a strong composition gradient is created close to the surface, and this gradient must be assumed to act as a driving force for diffusion.

Qualitatively, the situation is illustrated in Fig. 15. Ordinarily, diffusion constants depend only on temperature and not on the irradiation conditions.

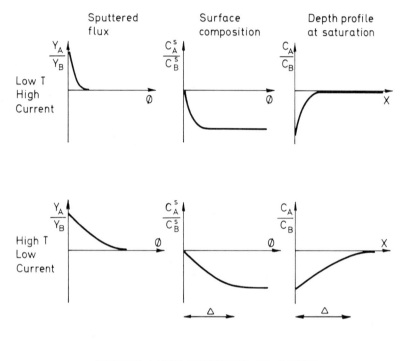

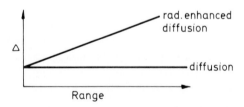

Fig. 15. Schematic diagram illustrating how the composition of the sputtered flux and the surface change as a function of fluence. Diffusion is assumed to constitute the only feeding mechanism for the preferentially sputtered element. From Andersen (1980).

Thus, it will be a characteristic of ordinary diffusion-feeding mechanisms that the higher the projectile current density (flux) and sputtering yield, the steeper the gradient, and hence the thinner the altered layer. As is customary, the term "altered layer" will be used when diffusion and preferential sputtering are discussed. However, the term is not well defined when recoil implantation and segregation play a role. Some examples of concentration profiles, which have up to three extrema before they settle to the bulk value, are discussed below. On the other hand, a higher temperature means a higher diffusion coefficient and thus a thicker altered layer. Andersen et al. (1980) made an attempt to look for the flux dependence but it was only possible to vary the flux by less than a factor of two, because of the limitation that the flux should be homogeneous over the irradiated area. No significant changes in the length of the transient within this limited range of variation were found. Systematic variations of the temperature have been rarely studied, and these may lead to the disclosure of strong segregation effects (Rehn et al., 1979).

Mathematically, assumptions must be made about absolute yields, because time is involved in the diffusion equations, and the absolute erosion rate must therefore be known. Usually, the alternate version of eqn. (11) (Lam et al., 1980), which involves absolute yields, is included in calculations, in spite of its uncertainties. If the diffusion equation is set up in length units and not in atomic layers, the atomic density of the material must also be used in the definition of sputtering yields (Ho et al., 1976; Ho, 1978; Webb et al., 1978). Lam et al. (1979, 1980) and Lam and Wiedersich (1981a,b) have shown that it is possible to formulate the relevant equations, using only lattice sites and atomic concentrations. In any case, particle conservations such as those expressed in eqns. (12) or (13) must result. All the publications quoted above except that by Webb et al. (1978), which will be discussed below, and the recent work of Ishitani and Tamura (1979), are consistent with particle conservation.

For the Cu–Ni system, Ho et al. (1976) and Ho (1978) found the diffusion coefficient to increase from 1.1 to 8.0 $\times$ 10^{-16} cm^{-2} sec^{-1} when the argon-ion energy increased from 0.5 to 2 keV and concluded that the diffusion, in some way, was enhanced by the irradiation. The numerical values deduced for the diffusion coefficients were also much higher than those based on ordinary diffusion. As pointed out by Ho, this discrepancy could be accounted for by radiation-enhanced diffusion. Usually, this term implies a mechanism in which radiation enhances the concentration of mobile vacancies (which are a necessary part of most diffusion mechanisms) considerably over the thermodynamic equilibrium value. (For a review, see Sizmann, 1978; Marwick and Piller, 1977.) Thus, the concept implies that the diffusion coefficient is enhanced over a depth slightly larger than the range of the projectiles and that the enhancement is proportional to the flux. Although the term "radiation-enhanced diffusion" is used, the concept of flux proportionality is lacking both in Ho (1978), who also uses a position-independent diffusion coefficient, D, and in Webb et al. (1978). In this latter paper, D is only enhanced over the range of the projectile. It appears that, except for infinite range, R, the analytical solutions do not fulfil the particle-conservation requirement. These authors have recently rectified this situation (Carter et al., 1979a,b), and have also dealt with the flux-proportional situation for D. Pickering (1976) was probably the first to use the concept in connection with preferential sputtering, but to obtain analytical solutions to his equations, he assumed the concentration of the preferentially sputtered component to be zero on the surface, an assumption that would be compatible only with an infinite yield ratio.

A very clear piece of evidence for radiation-enhanced diffusion during sputtering has been given by Eltoukhy and Greene (1980) and Rivaud et al. (1981, 1982), who studied Cu–In alloys bombarded by 3 keV argon. They found diffusion coefficients' orders of magnitude larger than thermal values.

For a comparison with experiment, the salient features of a radiation-enhanced feeding mechanism may be briefly summarized as follows. The width of the altered layer will be roughly proportional to the particle range (see also Fig. 15). For a given particle energy, the width will be independent of particle flux and temperature.

As discussed above, little reliable information about the dependence on flux and temperature is available. Many experiments have suggested an altered layer with a thickness comparable to the ion range, but nearly all these experiments have been performed at low energy and over a very limited energy interval. Two experiments are particularly relevant to this discussion. Liau et al. (1978a) irradiated Pt–Si with 10–80 keV argon. Their result is shown in Fig. 16. A six-fold increase in the width of the altered layer is seen when going from the lowest to the highest energies. If the altered layer is interpreted as being caused by preferential sputtering, then this constitutes one more piece of evidence for radiation-enhanced diffusion. (An alternative explanation is quoted below in connection with recoil implantation.)

A contrasting piece of evidence is given in Andersen et al. (1980). The composition of the sputtered flux was measured from Ag–Au bombarded with 15–200 keV argon. Transients were fitted with an exponential (solid curve, Fig. 8) and the amount of material that had to be sputtered off before the transients decayed to half their initial value were determined. No systematic variation in the transients with energy was found, and it was concluded that the feeding mechanism was ordinary diffusion. Recent data for 10–320 KeV argon sputtering of Cu–Pt also show the altered layer to be independent of projectile range (Andersen et al., in press). These data (which were obtained at 77 K) as well as the older Ag–Au data can be interpreted as being caused by radiation–enhanced diffusion but with a trapping distance for the

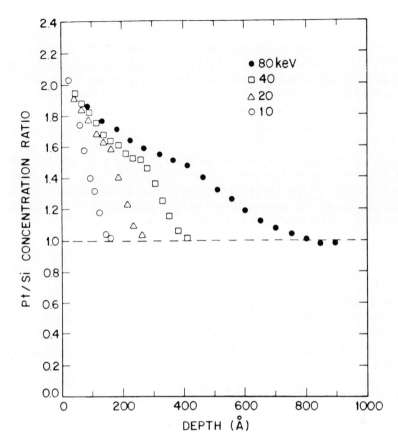

Fig. 16. Composition-versus-depth profile as measured by RBS on Pt-Si samples bombarded at different Ar energies. From Liau *et al.* (1978a).

mobile defects which is longer than the longest range involved. However, it should be borne in mind that two different materials, silicides and metal alloys, were used in these investigations, and feeding mechanisms may well be different for the two systems. There is a clear need for data on more materials.

C. Recoil Implantation

When a two-component target is bombarded with energetic ions, sputtering will not be the only effect of momentum transfer in the target. Some ions will receive an appreciable momentum in the inward direction, and these ions will be recoil-implanted. If the two components are recoil-implanted at different rates, transient changes in the surface composition will take place. It has been pointed out (Andersen, 1979, Sigmund, 1979; Sigmund et al., 1982) that in order to distinguish these changes from those caused by preferential sputtering, some care must be exercised. The theory of the phenomenon has been worked out in detail by Sigmund (1979) and Winterbon (1980). The main conclusion is that the lighter component will be implanted more efficiently, and thus the surface will initially be depleted of that species (Fig. 17). If the compositions of the sputtered flux is measured on an absolute scale, the difference from the situation depicted in Fig. 15 will be evident. If this is not done, or if the surface concentration only is measured (relatively or absolutely), a layer larger than the range must be removed to make sure that the composition does not revert to its original value. If no preferential sputtering occurs, both flux and surface composition will of course return to the bulk values in steady state.

If the near-surface gradient of the composition profile is very steep and the depth resolution is not high enough to resolve the return to bulk composition at the surface, the results presented in Fig. 16 may, in reality, be modelled by the profile in the upper right of Fig. 17.

Fig. 17 also illustrates the complications that may result when recoil implantation and preferential sputtering occur simultaneously. Other combinations of the relative influences of the two phenomena may give somewhat different curves, but this is simply one attempt to illustrate some of the characteristic features. The complexity of the combined phenomena is also amply illustrated in the recent paper by Sigmund et al. (1982).

D. Cascade Mixing

Apart from the influence of recoil implantation, the random movement of higher-order recoils within the collision cascades will cause a general mixing (Andersen, 1979; Hofer and Littmark, 1979; Carter et al., 1979c; Littmark and Hofer, 1980a,b; Armour et al., 1980; Sigmund and Gras-Marti, 1980, 1981; Gras-Marti et al., 1982). Such effects could be considered effective feeding mechanisms for a preferentially sputtered component, but a general argument indicates that this is not the case. For example, we know that the sputtered particles originate mainly from a few upper layers. Let us assume that the energy is sufficiently high so that the recoil flux at the surface and a few layers below it is the same. In this case, a particle flux across a plane three layers below the surface will be the same as that at the surface. To remove an atom from the surface, the threshold energy will be E_b. To move an atom permanently across a plane within the solid, it must have received

RECOIL IMPLANTATION

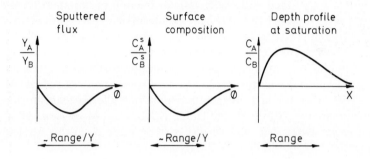

PLUS PREFERENTIAL SPUTTERING OF LIGHT MASS

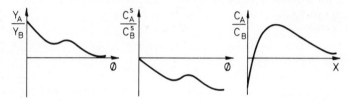

PLUS PREFERENTIAL SPUTTERING OF HEAVY MASS

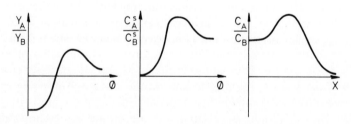

Fig. 17. Flux and surface composition as a function of fluence, and the steady-state composition profile, for recoil implantation alone and recoil implantation combined with preferential sputtering of the light and the heavy component. From Andersen (1980).

an energy larger than the displacement energy E_d. Both fluxes are roughly inversely proportional to their threshold energies, and their ratio is thus E_b/E_d, which is approximately 0.1. Hence, while the layer contributing to sputtering is sputtered away, only a small fraction of the atoms contained within it is fed in from below through cascade mixing, which cannot therefore be an important feeding mechanism.

The above argument does not imply that cascade mixing is unimportant in determining the depth resolution of sputter profiling. In fact, this was the context in which the term cascade mixing was originally discussed (Andersen, 1979). Also, for high-fluence implantations, the mechanism must be taken into account (Littmark and Hofer, 1980b; Gras-Marti et al., 1982; Sigmund et al., 1982). This will be discussed in more detail by Appleton in chapter 7.

What has here been termed cascade-mixing is only the collisional part of the movements within the cascade. Diffusion and subsequent trapping of point defects within individual damaged zones may well lead to a substantially larger amount of relocation (Sigmund, 1983) and hence may be of importance for the development of the near-surface profile.

E. Surface Segregation

In all the arguments I have used thus far, the non-irradiated target has been assumed to have the homogeneous bulk composition at the surface. This is not entirely true, since on most alloys the first one or two atomic layers have a composition different from that of the bulk. This is quite natural if one recalls the discussion of the pair-bond model in Sect. III A. According to that model, if an element has a lower surface-binding energy than the other component, then energy will also be gained if a strongly bound atom species from the surface exchanges its position with a weakly bound element from the interior. As thermodynamic equilibrium requires an optimization of free energy (or Gibbsian free energy) rather than enthalpy, an entropy term must also enter the picture, in order to prevent the surface from being entirely composed of the weaker-bound components. In one of the most-studied alloys, Cu–Ni, Cu is found to precipitate to the surface if the temperature is high enough to ensure the necessary mobility (e.g., Brongersma et al., 1978; Ng et al., 1979a,b, 1980; Okutani et al., 1980; Swartzfager et al., 1981). Many other alloys have been studied, and the results of a few shall be mentioned below. In Pt–Au, Au segregates, but the segregated layer is 3–4 atomic layers thick (Biloen et al., 1979, Ng et al., 1979b, Tsong et al., 1980), in contrast to most other alloys, for which the Ni–Cu (5%) results illustrated in Fig. 18 are typical. Cu–Pt has also been studied and shows Cu segregation (e.g. Brongersma et al., 1978). It is of particular interest here that segregation is much

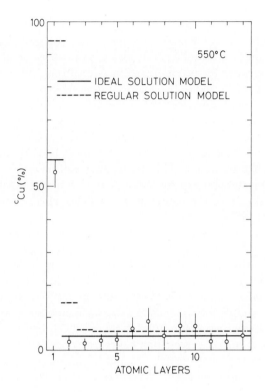

Fig. 18.   Depth profile of a Ni-Cu(5%) alloy annealed at 550°C as measured in the atom-probe field-ion microscope. From Ng *et al.* (1979).

stronger to the (110) surface than to the (111) surface (Shek *et al.*, 1981). A similar result has been found for Cu–Ni, where the segregation is to the (100) surface (Wandelt and Brundle, 1981). The surface specificity is important. It may lead to lateral surface inhomogeneities on ion-implanted and sputtered polycrystalline samples. Extensive tabulations of studied systems have been given by Miedema (1978), Hamilton (1979), Sachtler and van Santen (1979), Swartsfager and Kelley (1980), Sachtler (1980), Abraham (1981), and Abraham and Brundle (1981) in connection with discussions of the systematics of surface segregation.

All the above results are related to systems in which differences in surface-binding energies constitute the driving force. However, differences in size may also trigger surface segregation (Sachtler, 1980, Abraham and Brundle, 1981). According to linear-elasticity theory, we should always expect the minority component of a dilute alloy to segregate, but if non-linear terms are accounted for, it is found that the driving force is substantially larger on the larger components. Although no theory exists for concentrated alloys, we should expect the larger component of a concentrated alloy to segregate. Abraham and Brundle (1981) give a particularly good discussion of the interplay between the two segregation mechanisms. An example of size-misfit segregation is found in the Au–Ni system (Kelley et al., 1980).

The general trends discussed above may be reversed by impurities on the surface. In particular, if O is supplied from the background gas or ion bombardment, the component with the stronger O bond will segregate (Sachtler, 1980; Gupta and Peraillon, 1981). Yu and Reuter (1981) claim the opposite effect from O bombardment. This discrepancy will be resolved below. The influence of O is discussed in Andersen et al. (1980) on Cu_3Au and in Berry et al. (1980) on Ni–1%Th. Sulphur has similar effects on Cu–Ni (e.g., Ichimura et al., 1981).

The mathematics involved in a thermodynamic description of surface segregation may be found in Brongersma et al. (1978), Kelly (1980), Brailsford (1980) or Abraham and Brundle (1981). Owing to low mobility, the thermodynamic equilibrium is reached only at high temperatures. An example of segregation in a Ni–5% Cu alloy at 550°C is shown in Fig. 18. The annealed sample was quenched to room temperature and profiled in the atom-probe field-ion microprobe (Ng et al., 1979, 1980).

The theory of surface segregation has recently been studied very actively. Atomic theories are found in Balseiro and Morán-Lopez (1980), Brailsford (1980), Lee and Aaronson (1980), Molinari et al., (1979), Morán-Lopez and Wise (1980) and Morán-Lopez and Falicov (1978), while Hamilton (1979), Miedema (1978), and Swartzfager and Kelley (1980) relate surface segregation to different macroscopic data. If the table of systems in Hamilton (1979) or Abraham and Brundle (1981) is compared with Table I of preferential sputtering, striking similarities will be noted. Such similarities are hardly surprising, since all elements which are preferentially sputtered as a result of low binding energies will segregate to the surface, unless segregation is prevented by lattice-strain energy differences of the opposite sign.

In Fig. 19, the now well-known diagrams of sputtered flux, surface composition, and depth profiles at saturation under different conditions are represented. The diagrams are drawn under the assumption that radiation-enhanced diffusion is negligible (i.e., surface segregation occurs at a rate determined only by temperature). If a comparison is made with Fig. 15, it appears that neither relative nor absolute measurements of flux composition can be used to discern between preferential sputtering and continuous surface segregation. If the surface composition is measured with ISS and found to be equal to that of the bulk, it may be concluded that profiles like that in Fig. 19 have been established (e.g. Yabumoto et al., 1978, 1979, for AgAu;

SURFACE SEGREGATION

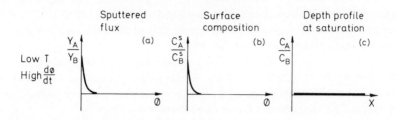

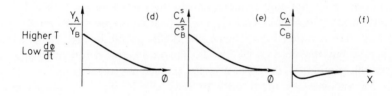

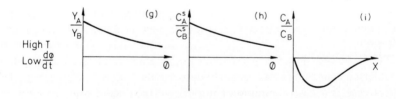

Fig. 19.   The flux and surface composition as a function of fluence, and the steady-state depth profile. Curves are shown for different temperatures and fluxes for an alloy displaying surface segregation but no preferential sputtering. From Andersen (1980).

Okutani et al., 1980, for CuNi; Swartzfager et al., 1981 for CuNi, AgAu, and AuPd). If sputtering occurs only from the topmost layer, such data would show that preferential sputtering does not occur in any of the above systems. However, sputtering has contributions from more than the top layer, and eqns. (5) and (6) show that preferential sputtering does indeed occur if the surface composition, in saturation, equals that of the bulk, and a concentration gradient exists simultaneously. Profiles such as those of Fig. 19 have recently been proposed also by Williams and Baker (1981) while discussing sputtering-depth profiling. If the segregation is essentially to a single monolayer, AES measurements, even at low energies, will substantially overestimate the enhancement factor of preferential sputtering.

Direct proof of the existence of concentration gradients at the surface has only recently been obtained from measurements of angular distributions of sputtered material (Andersen et al., 1982a). As discussed in section III, a surface-segregated component will have a broader angular distribution than the component of which the surface is depleted. The data shown in Fig. 20, therefore, show that copper segregates to the surface of an Ar-bombarded Cu–Pt surface, even though the target is kept at liquid nitrogen temperatures, and the flux is rather high. Hence, the depth profile in Fig. 19c would be expected but that in Fig 19i results. Therefore, the segregation must be radiation-stimulated, in contrast to the underlying assumptions of Fig. 19. At very low energies, the trend is reversed (Andersen et al., 1982b), and a concentration gradient determined only by preferential sputtering is obtained (as shown in Fig. 15). It can be concluded that at 20 keV, where a very weak concentration gradient is seen, but where preferential sputtering of copper presumably takes place, ISS and AES should consistently show a Cu concentration lower than that of the bulk. If angular-distribution measurements show an absence of a concentration profile under given irradiation conditions, surface-concentration measurements will be easier to interpret.

For a Ni–Pd alloy, Pd segregated to the surface when irradiated with Ar (Andersen et al., 1982b) whereas O bombardment gave Ni segregation. This latter case is a clear example of impurity-driven segregation. As Yu and Reuter (1981) found the O-bombarded surface to be depleted of Ni when measured with AES, it can be concluded that the segregated layer is thin, and that the layers beneath the surface are depleted of Ni in order to maintain the concentration gradient. According to the definition, this does not imply preferential sputtering of Ni.

Thus surface segregation and preferential sputtering are intimately connected. They are partly attributable to the same differences in surface-binding energies, and ion bombardment in a sputtering experiment may even trigger the segregation.

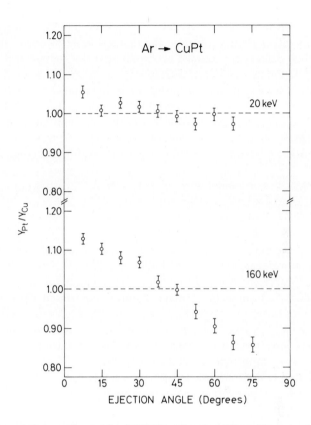

Fig. 20.   The ratio between the angular distribution of sputtered Cu and Pt during Ar bombardment of Cu–Pt at 20 and 160 keV. The high-energy bombardment shows clear evidence of Cu segregation to the surface. From Andersen *et al.* (1982a).

F. Radiation-Induced Segregation

I have already mentioned that the sputtering of a solid is always accompanied by defect production within the solid. This gives rise to an enhanced concentration of vacancies, which may assist diffusion. If one of the components of an alloy has strong binding energies either to vacancies or interstitials, this component may be trapped to the defects which are diffusing out of the damage zone. It should be mentioned that the binding of a particular component to defects is favoured when this component is oversize or undersize with respect to the other components. Lattice-strain energy is minimized by such binding to defects. Smaller atoms will thus migrate as interstitials and larger atoms against the vacancy flux. The trapped component may either be dragged into the damage zone or out to the region where mobile defects are trapped or annihilated; i.e., either to the surface or to grain boundaries or defect clusters within the solid. Depending on the relative size of the component the result is a segregation of the involved component either within the damage zone or around the defect traps. This segregation will build up until balanced by back diffusion. This therefore provides a mechanism by which a component of an alloy may be transported *against* a concentration gradient, and in this respect, it is similar to Gibbsian segregation.

This effect was originally introduced to account for segregation on voids in neutron-irradiated alloys (Okamoto *et al.*, 1973; Lam *et al.*, 1978a; Marwick *et al.*, 1978) and it has been described in several reviews (Johnson and Lam, 1978; Okamoto and Rehn, 1979; Cahn, 1979). The temperature dependence of the effect is a complicated interplay of several mechanisms. At low temperatures, vacancies move slowly and a large vacancy concentration builds up. Freshly created and highly mobile interstitials annihilate locally, and the defect flux out of the damage region is suppressed. (This effect will also suppress radiation-enhanced diffusion.) At high temperatures, the higher, thermally generated vacancy concentration results in enhanced annihilation of interstitials and a small vacancy-concentration gradient. Back diffusion is more important and defect-solute binding energies are less dominant compared to thermal energies, kT. As a result, radiation-induced segregation will be important only at intermediate temperatures such as approximately $\frac{3}{4}(T_m)$.

The effects of segregation may extend to much larger depths than the range of the particles, as shown in Fig. 21 (Piller and Marwick, 1978, 1979; Lam *et al.*, 1978b; Bartels *et al.*, 1979; Marwick *et al.*, 1979; Marwick and Piller, 1980). Particularly striking cases may be met in the first wall of proposed fusion reactors. Neutrons create damage homogeneously throughout the wall and low-energy neutrals erode its surface. If the segregated component is removed stoichiometrically, or even preferentially, the entire wall may be depleted of one component.

A schematic plot illustrating radiation-induced segregation is shown in Fig. 22. As shown radiation-induced segregation is apparently the only effect which causes flux-*vs*-concentration curves to start out with a horizontal tangent. This feature, if resolved, makes the effect easy to identify, even when using relative concentration measurements. In the absence of preferential sputtering, concentration ratios return to the bulk value, as they do for recoil implantation, but not until a layer considerably thicker than the range has been sputtered off.

The curves of Fig. 22 are partly based on experimental (Marwick and

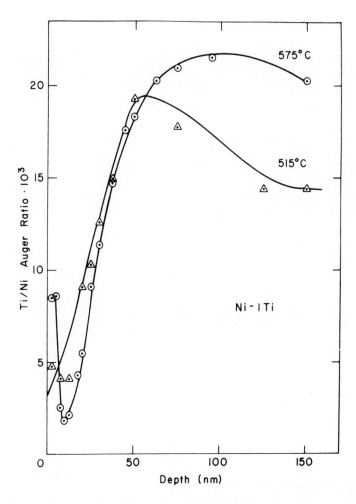

Fig. 21. Depth profile of Ti concentration in a Ni–Ti(1%) alloy irradiated with 3.5 MeV Ni to a total dose of five displacements per atom at 515°C and 575°C. From Rehn *et al.* (1978).

Piller, 1978; Rehn *et al.,* 1979) and theoretical (Lam *et al.,* 1979, 1980) studies of the interplay between radiation-induced segregation and preferential sputtering. An example of theoretical studies is shown in Fig. 23. In this example, a set of coupled equations describing particle and defect flows were set up. Sputtering yields were assumed to be elemental yields multiplied by surface concentration (alternate version of Eqn. 11), and the entire set of equations was solved numerically. Indeed the steady-state surface concentrations were found to be in agreement with Eqn. (13). The pronounced temperature dependence can be noted. However, it is ascertained here, with some

RADIATION - INDUCED SEGREGATION

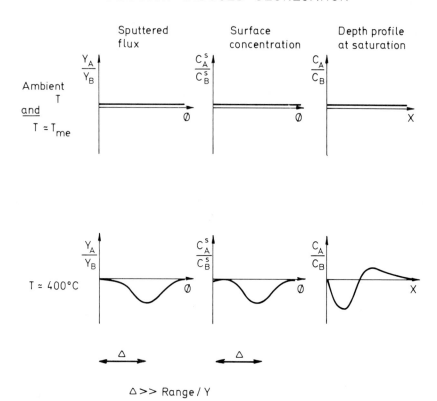

Fig. 22.   Flux and surface concentrations as a function of fluence and depth-concentration profile at steady state for an alloy showing radiation-induced segregation but no preferential sputtering. From Andersen (1980).

relief, that no systems appear to show radiation-induced segregation at room temperature.

In the latest calculations from the Argonne group (Lam and Wiedersich, 1982a), Gibbsian segregation has also been included. For the case of 5 keV argon incident on Cu_3Ni_2, these authors have mathematically modelled all the flux contributions shown in Fig. 14. The results for the steady-state profiles at different temperatures are shown in Fig. 24. Once again, the alternate version of eqn. (11) was used to obtain absolute yields. The strong temperature dependence of the Gibbsian segregation is apparent because the irradiation stimulation of the surface segregation illustrated in Fig. 19 is

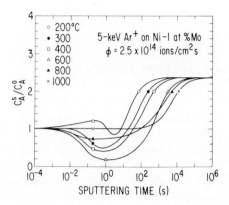

Fig. 23. Calculated surface concentration of Mo as a function of fluence for a Ni-Mo(1%) alloy bombarded with 5 keV Ar at different temperatures. Steady state is not reached until aprox. 100 projectile ranges have been removed. From Lam *et al.* (1980).

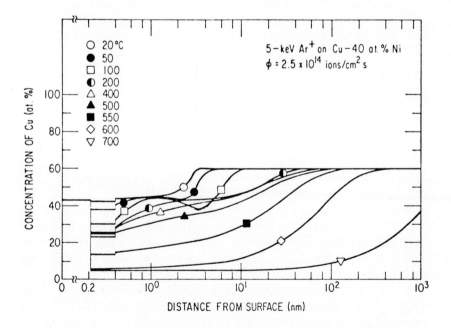

Fig. 24. Steady-state concentration profiles of Cu in a Cu–Ni alloy sputtered at various temperatures. All the different flux components of Fig. 14 have been taken into account, but surface segregation has been assumed not to be radiation-stimulated. From Lam and Wiedersich (1982a).

neglected. It is not known whether this is realistic or not for the Cu–Ni system at the relatively low projectile energy chosen.

V. HIGH FLUENCE ION IMPLANTATION

In the previous section, a number of complicating effects were discussed in relation to the interpretation of preferential-sputtering effects. All of these effects may also influence high-fluence ion-implantation profiles. As this influence, in many cases, will be similar to that noted in the previous section, the discussion in this section is less detailed.

In a zeroth-order (low-fluence) approximation, implantation profiles may be regarded as range profiles (an aspect I shall not discuss here). However, *sputtering* is unavoidable during high-fluence implantation, and in the first-order approximation, the saturation profiles may be regarded as a superposition of range profiles with a continuously displaced origin. The implants may also modify the range distributions. It was realized rather early that sputtering would limit the obtainable implant concentrations, as well as the total amount of implanted material (Almén and Bruce, 1961a; Carter *et al.*, 1962). If the implant is indexed with I and the target matrix with M,

$$Y_I / Y_M = C_I / C_M \tag{21}$$

where C_I and C_M are atomic concentrations; i.e., $C_I + C_M = 1$.
At steady state $Y_I = 1$ and

$$C_I = (Y_M + 1)^{-1} \tag{22}$$

within the range R of the implant. With the low-fluence profile shown in Fig. 25a, the high-fluence profile will be as shown in Fig. 25b, and the total amount collected per unit area will be approximately $C_I \times R_I$. It is important to realize that Y_M should be the partial matrix yield at the implanted saturation concentration. This yield will usually differ from the pure-element yield. I shall not discuss the "deposition" case, where both Y_I and Y_M are smaller than one.

If the first-order approximation is extended to incorporate any of the complications of the previous section, at least one more parameter of interest is introduced. As discussed extensively in sections III and IV, virtually all the complications necessitate a distinction between surface and bulk concentrations. In the implantation situation, a well-defined bulk concentration may not be attained. This situation is discussed below. For diverse applications, a number of different properties may be of interest. For example, the surface concentration will determine catalytic activity and, to some extent, corrosion resistance. The maximum concentration, which may also be influenced by the detailed shape of the entire profile, is of importance for corrosion and wear-resistance and also for electrical activity in semiconductors. The total collected amount was the main parameter of interest in the original studies of Almén and Bruce (1961a), where the aim was to produce sources for nuclear-spectroscopy studies. The total amount may also be of importance for modern attempts to improve chemical and mechanical properties of materials.

In the steady state ($Y_I = 1$) under *preferential-sputtering* conditions, the surface concentrations will, from eqn. (6), be found as

$$1/Y_M = f_{I,M} \times (C_I^s/C_M^s) \tag{23}$$

which, with $C_I^s + C_M^s = 1$, yields

$$C_i^s = (1 + f_{I,M} Y_M)^{-1} \tag{24}$$

This is identical to the result of Liau and Mayer (1980) which was given in a rather different notation ($S = Y_M + Y_I = Y_M + 1$) and obtained without normalization of the concentrations. Such normalization would correspond to setting $C_M = 1$ and allowing the density to increase proportionally to $1 + C_I$. (This is further discussed by Beanland in Chapter 8.) Note that if diffusion and segregation effects may be neglected, the level of the concentration profile (Fig. 25c and d) will still be given by eqn. (22).

The main effect of *cascade mixing* and *recoil implantation* (Fig. 25e) is an increase in the total collected amount (Blank and Wittmaack, 1979; Littmark and Hofer, 1980b; Collins, 1981). For example, Fig. 26 shows calculated collected amounts with and without mixing. In their calculation of the build-up of the implanted concentration under preferential-sputtering conditions, Liau and Mayer (1980) assumed the mixing to be sufficiently effective to ensure the implant concentration was constant over the implant range. It should be recalled here that in Section IV,D evidence that cascade mixing does not constitute an effective feeding mechanism under preferential-sputtering conditions was given. If other strong diffusive mechanisms are neglected, the results of Liau and Mayer (1980) will probably not hold. However, such other mechanisms may often be present.

Particularly for the case of noble gas implants into semiconductors, stress-driven *diffusion* of the implanted species can occur and transport the implant away from the depth of high concentration. As noble gases are simultaneously strongly preferentially sputtered ($f_{I,M} \gg 1$), profiles such as that shown in Fig. 25f will result. The implantation of Xe and Ar into silicon has

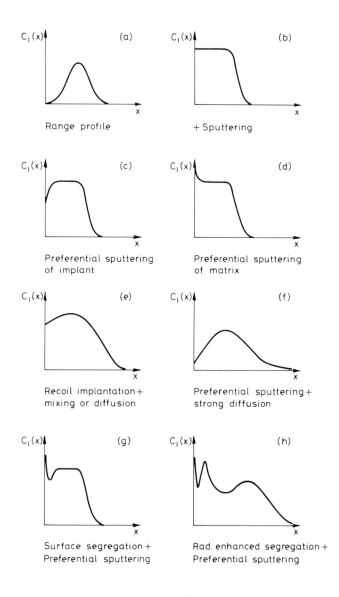

Fig. 25. High-fluence implantation profiles for ions with the range distribution shown in (a). The influence of sputtering, preferential sputtering, recoil implantation, cascade mixing, diffusion, surface segregation, and radiation-enhanced segregation is shown.

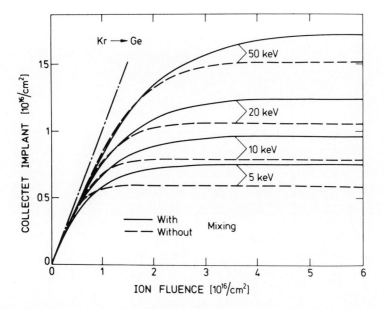

Fig. 26. Collected amount as a function of dose, with and without recoil implantation and cascade mixing. From Littmark and Hofer (1980b).

been studied in detail by Blank *et al.* (1976) and Wittmaack *et al.* (1978). Figure 27 shows the saturation profile obtained for 500 keV Xe-implanted Si. Usually, such behaviour will result in the collected amount being lower than the amount calculated, if diffusion and preferential sputtering is neglected.

The role of *surface segregation,* in connection with ion implantation, has never been considered seriously, although it might be practically important, particularly for applications involving catalysis. In view of the anomalous sputtering behaviour of the Bi-implanted Cu system (Andersen, 1973), the angular distribution of Bi-sputtered Cu and Bi were measured from a target irradiated to saturation (Andersen *et al.,* 1980b). A weak Cu segregation was found. There is clearly a need for studies of systems of more practical interest.

Hobbs and Marwick (1981) investigated *radiation-enhanced segregation* while implanting 20 keV Mg into Ni. They found the Mg to diffuse against the defect flux. Hence, the saturation distribution exhibited a pronounced peak at a depth where the damage production was maximum. Not all redistribution processes lead to a broadening of the distribution. Fig. 25h shows the opposite situation, in which the implant and defect fluxes are assumed to be in the same direction. A hole appears in the distribution at the depth of maximum defect production. To illustrate how complicated distributions

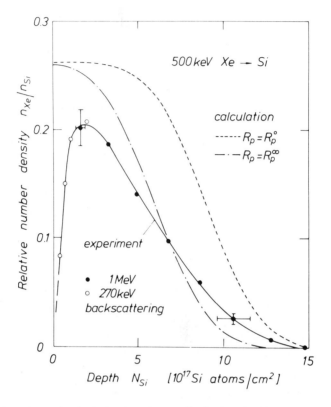

Fig. 27.   Experimental and calculated steady-state distribution of 500 keV Xe in Si. From Wittmaack *et al.* (1978).

may result, preferential sputtering has also been assumed. By suitable involvement of extra transport mechanisms, more extrema may be introduced into the distributions, even though only one species is implanted at one energy.

VI. CONCLUSIONS

In spite of the vast amount of literature on preferential sputtering, it is difficult to establish experimental proof of the mere existence of preferential sputtering, let alone to confirm the various proposed mechanisms. This confusion is caused by a large number of effects, some aspects of which may readily be attributed to preferential sputtering.

The ideal experiment has not yet been performed on any system. It will consist of a simultaneous, absolute measurement of flux-concentration and surface-concentration ratios as a function of sputtering fluence, all performed in UHV. Also, it should be possible to measure the concentration-depth profile in steady state. The uncertainties are even larger for high-fluence implantation distributions. Many of the complicating mechanisms have hardly been studied in this context. Hopefully, this review might serve as a guide when complicated profiles are encountered.

REFERENCES

Abbati, I., Braicowich, L., and de Michelis, B. (1978). *Phys. Lett.* **67A**, 413.
Abraham, F. F. (1981). *Phys. Rev. Lett.* **46**, 546.
Abraham, F. F., and Brundle, C. R. (1981). *J. Vac. Technol. Sci.* **18**, 506.
Adylov, A. A., Veksler, V. I., Reznik, A. M., and Furer, S. A. (1972). *Fix. Tverd. Tela.* **14**, 477 [Eng. transl. *Sov. Phys. Solid State* **14**, 396 (1972)]
Almén, O., and Bruce, G. (1961a). *Nucl. Instrum. Methods* **11**, 257.
Almén, O., and Bruce, G. (1961b). *Nucl. Instrum. Methods* **11**, 279.
Andersen, H. H. (1973). *Rad. Effects* **19**, 257.
Andersen, H. H. (1974). *In* "Symposium on the Physics of Ionized Gases 1974" (V. Vujnović, ed.), p. 361. Inst. of Phys., Ljubljana.
Andersen, H. H. (1979a). *J. Vac. Sci. Technol.* **16**, 770.
Andersen, H. H. (1979b). *Appl. Phys.* **18**, 131.
Andersen, H. H. (1980). *In* "Symposium on the Physics of Ionized Gases 1980" (M. Matic, ed.) p. 421. Boris Kidric Inst. of Nucl. Sci. Beo grad.
Andersen, H. H., and Bay, H. L. (1972). *Rad. Effects* **13**, 67.
Andersen, H. H., and Bay, H. L. (1974). *J. Appl. Phys.* **45**, 953.
Andersen, H. H., and Bay, H. L. (1975a). *J. Appl. Phys.* **46**, 1919.
Andersen, H. H., and Bay, H. L. (1975b). *J. Appl. Phys.* **46**, 2416.
Andersen, H. H., and Bay, H. L. (1981). *In* "Sputtering by Particle Bombardment I" (R. Behrisch, ed.), p. 145. Springer, Berlin.
Andersen, H. H., Besenbacher, F., and Goddiksen, P. (1980). *In* "Symposium on Sputtering" (P. Varga, G. Betz and F. P. Viehböck, eds.) p. 446. Inst. Allgem. Physik, Vienna.
Andersen, H. H., Chevallier, J., and Chernysh, V. (1981). *Nucl. Instrum. Methods* **191**, 241.
Andersen, H. H., Chernysh, V., Stenum, B., Sørensen, T., and Whitlow, H. J. (1982). *Surf. Sci.* **123**, 39.
Andersen, H. H., Stenum, B., Sørensen, T., and Whitlow, H. J. (1983) *Nucl. Instrum. Methods,* **209/10**, 487.
Andersen, H. H., Stenum, B., Sørensen, T., and Whitelow, H. J. (1984). *Nucl. Instrum. Methods* (in press).
Andersen, N., and Sigmund, P. (1974). *K. Dan. Vidensk. Selsk. Mat. Fys. Medd.* **39** No. 3.
Anderson, G. S. (1969). *J. Appl. Phys.* **40**, 2884.
Anttila, A., and Hautala, M. (1979). *Appl. Phys.* **19**, 199.
Armour, D. G., Carter, G., Webb, R. P., Ingram, D. C., and Newcombe, R. (1980). *Rad. Effects. Lett.* **50**, 45.
Arai, O., Kobayashi, K., Shimamura, T., and Tazawa, Y. (1976). *Jap. J. Appl. Phys.* **15**, 407.
Arthur, J. R., and Le Pore, J. L. (1977). *J. Vac. Sci. Technol.* **14**, 979.
Asada, T., and Quasebarth, K. (1929). *Z. Phys. Chem. A.* **143**, 435.
Balseiro, C. A., and Moran-Lopez, J. L. (1980). *Phys. Rev. B.* **21**, 349.

Bartels, A., Dworschak, F., Meurer, H. P., Abroweit, C., and Wollenberger, H. (1979). *J. Nucl. Mater.* **83**, 24.

Bastasz, R., and Bohdansky, J. (1980). *In* "Symposium on Sputtering" (P. Varga, G. Betz, and F. P. Vieböck, eds.), p. 430. Inst. Allgem, Physik, Vienna.

Bay, H. L., Andersen, H. H., Hofer, W. O., and Nielsen, O. (1976). *Nucl. Instrum. Methods* **132**, 301.

Behrisch, R., Maderlecher, G., Scherzer, B. M. U., and Robinson, M. T. (1979). *Appl. Phys.* **18**, 391.

Berglund, S., and Somorjai, G. A. (1973). *J. Chem. Phys.* **59**, 5337.

Berry, C., Majunder, D., and Chung, Y. W. (1980). *Surf. Sci.* **94**, 293.

Betz, G. (1980a). *Surf. Sci.* **92**, 283.

Betz, G. (1980b). *Microchim. Acta* **115**, 191.

Betz, G., and Wehner, G. K. (1983). *In* "Sputtering by Particle Bombardment II" (R. Behrisch, ed.). Springer, Berlin.

Betz, G., Dobrozemsky, R., and Viehböck, F. P. (1970). *Nederlands Tijdschrift voor Vacuumtechniek* **8**, 203.

Betz, G., Braun, P., and Farber, W. (1977). *J. Appl. Phys.* **48**, 1404.

Betz, G., Marton, P., and Braun, P. (1980a). *Nucl. Instrum. Methods* **168**, 541.

Betz, G., Arias, M., and Braun, P. (1980b). *Nucl. Instrum. Methods* **170**, 347.

Betz, G., Dudonis, J., and Braun, P. (1981). *Surf. Sci.* **104**, L185.

Biben, P., Bouwman, R., van Santen, R. A., and Brongersma, H. H. (1979). *Appl. Surf. Sci.* **2**, 532.

Blank, P., and Wittmaack, K. (1976). *Nucl. Instrum. Methods* **132**, 387.

Blank, P., and Wittmaack, K. (1979). *Rad. Effects. Lett.* **43**, 105.

Bohdansky, J., Roth, J., and Bay, H. L. (1980). *J. Appl. Phys.* **51**, 2861.

Bolker, B. F. T. (1977). *J. Vac. Sci. Technol.* **14**, 254.

Bouwman, R., Toneman, L. H., and Holscher, A. A. (1973). *Surf. Sci.* **35**, 8.

Brailsford, A. D. (1980). *Surf. Sci.* **94**, 387.

Braun, P., and Färber, W. (1975). *Surf. Sci.* **47**, 57; **51**, 342.

Brongersma, H. H., Spaarnaay, M. K., and Buck, T. M. (1978). *Surf. Sci.* **71**, 657.

Brown, W. L., Augustyniak, W. M., Brody, E., Cooper, B., Lanzerotti, L. J., Ramirez, A., Evath, R., and Johnson, R. E. (1980). *Nucl. Instrum. Methods* **170**, 321.

Cahn, R. W. (1979). *Nature* **278**, 125.

Carter, G., Colligon, J. S., and Leck, J. H. (1962). *Proc. Phys. Soc.* **72**, 299.

Carter, G., Webb, R., and Collins, R. (1979a). *Rad. Effects. Lett.* **43**, 125.

Carter, G., Webb, W., Collins, R., and Thompson, D. A. (1979b). *Rad. Effects.* **40**, 119.

Carter, G., Armour, D. G., Ingram, D. C., Webb, R., and Newcombe, R. (1979c). *Rad. Effects. Lett.* **43**, 233.

Chu, W. K., Howard, J. K., and Lever, R. F. (1976). *J. Appl. Phys.* **47**, 4500.

Coburn, J. W. (1979). *Thin Solid Films* **64**, 371.

Collins, R. (1978). *Rad. Effects.* **37**, 13.

Collins, R. (1979). *Rad. Effects. Lett.* **43**, 111.

Collins, R. (1981). *Rad. Effects. Lett.* **58**, 133.

Cuomo, J. J., Chaudhari, P., and Gambino, R. J. (1974). *Electron, J. Mater.* **3**, 517.

Dahlgren, S. D., and Greybeal, A. G. (1970). *J. Appl. Phys.* **41**, 3181.

Dahlgren, S. D., and McClanahan, E. D. (1972). *J. Appl. Phys.* **43**, 1514.

Davies, J. A., McIntyre, J. D., Cushing, R. L., and Lounsbury, M. (1960). *Can. J. Phys.* **38**, 1535.

Dawson, P. T., and Petrone, S. A. (1981). *J. Vac. Sci. Technol.* **18**, 529.

Dove, D. B., Pantano, C. G., and Andrews, J. B. (1977). *J. Appl. Phys.* **48**, 2776.

Dumoulin, Ph., Caillerie, J. L., and Guttmann, M. (1981). *Surf. Sci.* **104**, 559.

Eltoukhy, A. U., and Greene, J. E. (1980). *J. Appl. Phys.* **51**, 4444.

Fagen, E. A., Nowicki, R. S., and Seguin, R. W. (1974). *J. Appl. Phys.* **45**, 50.

Färber, W., and Braun, P. (1974). *Vakuum Technik* **23**, 239.

Färber, W., Betz, G., and Braun, P. (1976). *Nucl. Instrum. Methods* **132**, 351.

Farren, J., and Scaife, W. J. (1968). Harwell Report AERE-R-5717.

Fluit, J. M., Friedman, L., Boerbom, A. J. M., and Kistemaker, J. (1961). *J. Chem. Phys.* **35**, 1143.

Frankenthal, P., and Malm, D. L. (1976). *J. Electrochem. Soc.* **123**, 186.

Frankenthal, R. P., and Siconolfi, D. J. (1980). *J. Vac. Sci. Technol.* **17**, 3515.

Frankenthal, R. P., and Siconolfi, D. J. (1981a). *Surf. Sci.* **104**, 205.

Frankenthal, R. P., and Siconolfi, D. J. (1981b). *Surf. Sci.* **111**, 317.

Frankenthal, R. P., and Thompson, D. E. (1979). *J. Vac. Sci. Technol.* **16**, 6.

Funakoshi, N., and Manabe, T. (1975). *Jap. J. Appl. Phys.* **14**, 1623.

Gambino, R. J., and Cuomo, J. J. (1978). *J. Vac. Sci. Technol.* **15**, 295.

Garvassi, F., and Parravano, G. (1978). *Surf. Sci.* **71**, 42.

Gillam, E. (1959). *J. Phys. Chem. Sol.* **11**, 55.

Goretzki, H., Mühlratzer, A., and Nickl, J. (1977). In "Proc. 7th Int. Vacuum Congress and 3rd Int. Conf. on Solid Surfaces" (R. Dobrozemsky, F. Rüdenauer, F. P. Viehböck, and A. Breth, eds.), p. 2387. Vienna.

Goto, K., Koshikawa, T., Ishikawa, K., and Shimizu, R. (1977). In "Proc. 7th Int. Congress and 3rd Int. Conf. on Solid Surfaces" (R. Dobrozemski *et al.* eds.), p. 1493. Vienna.

Goto, K., Koshikawa, T., Ishikawa, K., and Shimizu, R. (1978a). *J. Vac. Sci. Technol.* **15**, 1695.

Goto, G., Koshikawa, T., Ishikawa, K., and Shimizu, R. (1978b). *Surf. Sci.* **75**, L373.

Gras-Marti, A. and Sigmund, P. (1981). *Nucl. Instrum. Methods* **180**, 211.

Gras-Marti, A., Jimenez-Rodriguez, J., Peon-Fernandez, J., and Rodriguez-Vidal, M. (1982), *Phil. Mag.* **45**, 191.

Grove, W. R. (1852). *Phil. Trans. Roy. Soc.*, p. 87.

Guglielmacci, J. M., and Gillet, M. (1980). *Surf. Sci.* **94**, 424.

Gupta, R. P., and Peraillon, B. (1981). *Surf. Sci.* **103**, 397.

Haff, R. K. (1977). *Appl. Phys. Lett.* **31**, 259.

Haff, P. K., Watson, C. C., and Tombrello, T. A. (1981). Kellogg Rad. Lab. Preprint LiAp-41.

Hamilton, J. C. (1979). *Phys. Rev. Lett,* **42**, 989.

Helms, C. R., and Yu, K. Y. (1975). *J. Vac. Sci. Technol.* **12**, 276.

Henrich, V. E., and Fan, J. C. C. (1977). *Surf. Sci.* **42**, 139.

Hirano, M., Katayama, T., Koizumi, Y., Kawakami, M., and Tsusimu, T. (1977). *J. Phys. Soc. Jap.* **42**, 347.

Ho, P. S. (1978). *Surf. Sci.* **72**, 253.

Ho, P. S., Lewis. J. E., Wildman, H. J., and Howard, J. K. (1976). *Surf. Sci.* **57**, 393.

Ho, P. S., Lewis, J. E., and Howard, J. K. (1977). *J. Vac. Soc. Technol.* **14**, 322.

Ho, P. S., Lewis, J. E., and Chu, W. K. (1979). *Surf. Sci.* **85**, 19.

Hobbs, J. E., and Marwick, A. D. (1981). *Rad. Effects. Lett.* **58**, 83.

Hofer, W. O. (1983). In "Sputtering by Particle Bombardment III" (R. Behrisch, ed.), Springer, Berlin (in press).

Hofer, W. O., and Littmark, U. (1979). *Phys. Lett.* **71A**, 457.

Holloway, P. H. (1977). *Surf. Sci.* **66**, 479.

Howard, J. K., Chu, W. K., and Lever, R. F. (1976). In "Ion Beam Surface Layer Analysis" (O. Meyer, G. Linker and F. Käppeler, eds.), p. 125. Plenum, New York.

Ichimura, S., Shikata, M., and Shimizu, R. (1981). *Surf. Sci.* **108**, L393.

Ishitani, T., and Tamura, H. (1979). *Rad. Effects. Lett.* **43**, 149.

Jablonsky, A., Overbury, S. H., and Somorjai, G. A. (1977). *Surf Sci.* **65**, 578.

Jacobi, K., and Ranke, W. (1976). *J. Electr. Spectr. Relat. Phen.* **8**, 225.

Johar, S. S., and Thompson, D. A. (1979). *Surf. Sci.* **90**, 219.

Johnson, R. A., and Lam, N. Q. (1978). *J. Nucl. Mater.* **69**, 424.

Kay, E. (1965). *J. Electrochem. Soc.* **112**, 590.

Keiman, N., Kazama, N., Kyser, D. F., and Minkewicz, V. J. (1978). *J. Appl. Phys.* **49**, 366.

Kelley, M. J., Gilmour, P. W., and Swartzfager, D. S. (1980). *J. Vac. Sci. Technol.* **17**, 634.

Kelly, R. (1978). *Nucl. Instrum. Methods.* **149**, 553.

Kelly, R. (1979). *Surf. Sci.* **90**, 280.

Kelly, R. (1980). *In* "Symposium on Sputtering" (P. Varga, G. Betz and F. P. Viehböck, eds.), p. 390. Inst. Allgem, Physik, Vienna.

Koshikawa, T., Goto, K. Saeki, N., and Shimizu, R. (1977). *In* "Proc. 7th Int. Vacuum Congress and 3rd Int. Conf. on Solid Surfaces" (L. Dobrozemsky, F. Rüdenauer, F. P. Viehböck and A. Breth, eds.), p. 1489. Vienna.

Koshikawa, T., Goto, K., Saeki, N., and Shimizu, R. (1979). *Surf. Sci.* **79.** 461.

Koshikawa, T., and Shimizu, R. (1973). *Phys. Lett.* **A44**, 112.

Kuijers, F. J., Tieman, B. M., and Ponec, V. (1978). *Surf. Sci.* **75**, 657.

Lam, N. Q., and Wiedersich, H. (1982a). *Rad. Effects. Lett.* **67**, 107.

Lam, N. Q., and Wiedersich, H. (1982b). *In* "Metastable Materials Formation by Ion Implantation" (S. T. Picraux and W. M. Choyke, eds.) p. 35. North Holland, New York.

Lam, N. Q., Okamoto, P. R., and Wiedersich, H. (1978a). *J. Nucl. Mater.* **74**, 101.

Lam, N. Q., Okamatoto, P. R., Johnson, R. A. (1978b). *J. Nucl. Mater,* **78**, 408.

Lam, N. Q., Leaf, G. L. and Wiedersich, H. (1979). *J. Nucl. Mater* **85/86**, 1085.

Lam, N. Q., Leaf, K. G., and Wiedersich, H. (1980). *J. Nucl. Mater.* **88**, 289.

Lee, W.-Y. (1979). *J. Vac. Sci. Technol.* **16**, 774.

Lee, W. Y., and Aaronson, H. I. (1980). *Surf. Sci.* **95**, 227.

Lewis, J. E., and Ho, P. S. (1979). *J. Vac. Sci. Technol.* **16**, 772.

Liau, Z. L., and Mayer, J. W. (1980). *In* "Ion Implantation" (J. K. Hirvonen, ed.), p. 17. Academic Press, New York.

Liau, Z. L., and Sheng, T. T. (1978). *Appl. Phys. Lett.* **32**, 716.

Liau, Z. L., Brown, W. L., Homer, R., and Poate, J. M. (1977). *Appl. Phys. Lett.* **30**, 626.

Liau, Z. L., Mayer, J. W., Brown, W. L., and Poate, J. M. (1978a). *J. Appl. Phys.* **49**, 5295.

Liau, Z. L., Doherty, C. J., Melliar-Smith, C. M., and Poate, J. M. (1978b). *Thin Solid Films* **55**, 83.

Littmark, U., and Fedder, S. (1982). *Nucl. Instrum. Methods* **194**, 611.

Littmark, U., and Hofer, W. O. (1980a). *Nucl. Instrum. Methods* **168**, 329.

Littmark, U., and Hofer, W. O. (1980b). *Nucl. Instrum. Methods* **170**, 177.

Maire, G., Hillaire, L., Legere, P., Gault, F. G., and O'Cinneide, A. (1976). *J. Catalysis,* **44**, 293.

Marwick, A. D., and Piller, R. C. (1977). *Rad. Effects.* **33**, 245.

Marwick, A. D., and Piller, R. C. (1978). Harwell Report AERE-R-9175.

Marwick, A. D., and Piller, R. C. (1980). *Rad. Effects.* **47**, 195.

Marwick, A. D., Kennedy, W. A. D., Mazey, D. J., and Hudson, J. A. (1978). *Scripta Metallurgica* **12**, 1015.

Marwick, A. D., Piller, R. C., and Sivell, P. W. (1979). *J. Nucl. Mater.* **83**, 35.

Mathieu, H. J., and Landolt, D. (1975). *Surf. Sci.* **53**, 228.

Mathieu, H. J., and Landolt, D. (1979). *Appl. Surf. Sci.* **3**, 348.

McGuire, G. E. (1978). *Surf. Sci.* **76**, 130.

McIntyre, N. S., and Stancell, F. W. (1979). *J. Vac. Sci. Technol.* **16**, 798.

Merkle, K. L., and Pronko, P. P. (1974). *J. Nucl. Mater.* **53**, 231.

Miedema, A. R. (1978). *Z. Metallkunde.* **69**, 455.

Mohri, M., Watanabe, K., and Yamashina, T. (1978). *J. Nucl. Mater.* **75**, 7.

Molinari, C., Joud, J. C., and Desire, P. (1979). *Surf. Sci.* **84**, 141.

Morán-Lopez, J. L., and Falicov, L. M. (1978). *Phys. Rev. B.* **18**, 2542; **18**, 2549.

Morán-Lopez, J. L., and Wise, H. (1980). *Appl. Surf. Sci.* **4**, 93.
Nakayama, K., Ono, M., and Shimizu, H. (1972). *J. Vac. Sci. Technol.* **9**, 749.
Narusawa, T., Sataka, T., and Komiya, S. (1976). *J. Vac. Sci. Technol.* **13**, 514.
Nelson, G. C. (1976). *Surf. Sci.* **13**, 974.
Ng, Y. S., Tsong, T. T., and McLane, S. B., Jr. (1979a). *Phys. Rev. Lett.* **42**, 588.
Ng, Y. S., Tsong, T. T., and McLane, S. B., Jr. (1979b). *Surf. Sci.* **84**, 31.
Ng, Y. S., McLane, S. B., and Tsong, T. T. (1980). *J. Vac. Sci. Technol.* **17**, 154.
Nishihara, Y., Katayama, K., Yamaguchi, Y., Ogawa, S., and Tsuchima, T. (1978). *Jap. J. Appl. Phys.* **17**, 1083.
Nitz, H. M., Ganschow, O., Kaiser, U., Wiedman, L., and Benninghoven, A. (1981). *Surf. Sci.* **104**, 365.
Oechsner, H., and Bartella, J. (1980). *In* "Proc. 7th Int. Conf. Atomic Collisions in Solids" (Yu. V. Bulgakov and A. F. Tulinov, eds.), Vol. 2, p. 55. Moscow University Press, Moscow.
Oechsner, H., and Stumpe, E. (1977). *Appl. Phys.* **14**, 43.
Oechsner, H., Rühe, W., and Stumpe, E. (1979). *Surf. Sci.* **85**, 289.
Ogar, W. T., Olson, N. T., and Smith, H. P. (1969). *J. Appl. Phys.* **40**, 4997.
Ogilvie, G. J. (1959). *Aust. J. Phys.* **13**, 402.
Okamoto, P. R., Harkness, S. D., and Laidler, J. J. (1973). *Am. Nucl. Soc. Trans.* **16**, 70.
Okamoto, P. R., and Rehn, L. E. (1979). *J. Nucl. Mater.* **83**, 2.
Okutani, T., Shikata, M., and Shimizu, R. (1980). *Surf. Sci.* **99**, L410.
Oliva-Florio, A. R., Alonso, E. V., Baragiola, R. A., Ferron, J., and Jakas, M. M. (1979). *Rad. Effects. Lett.* **50**, 3.
Olson, R. R., and Wehner, G. K. (1977). *J. Vac. Sci. Technol.* **14**, 319
Olson, R. R., King, M. E., and Wehner, G. K. (1979). *J. Appl. Phys.* **50**, 3677.
Ono, M., Takasu, Y., Nakayama, K., and Yamashina, T. (1971). *Surf. Sci.* **26**, 313.
Ono, M., Shimizu, H., and Nakayama, K. (1975). *Surf. Sci.* **52**, 681.
Opitz, M., Betz, G., and Braun, P. (1980a). *In* "Proc. 8th Int. Conf. on Solid Surfaces and 3rd Europ. Conf. on Surface Science" p. 1225. Cannes.
Opitz, M., Betz, G., and Braun, P. (1980b). *Acta Phys. Acad. Sci. Hung.* **49**, 119.
Overbury, S. H., and Somorjai, G. A. (1977). *J. Chem. Phys.* **66**, 3181.
Patterson, W. L., and Shirn, G. A. (1967). *J. Vac. Sci. Technol.* **4**, 343.
Perović, B., and Čobic, B. (1961). *In* "Proc. 5th Int. Conf. on Ion Phenomena in Gases" (M. Maecker, ed.) p. 1165. North Holland, Amsterdam.
Pickering, H. V. (1976). *J. Vac. Sci. Technol.* **13**, 618.
Piller, R. C., and Marwick, A. D. (1978). *J. Nucl. Mater.* **71**, 309.
Piller, R. C., and Marwick, A. D. (1979). *J. Nucl. Mater.* **83**, 42.
Poate, J. M., Brown, W. L., Homer, R., Augustyniak, W. M., Mayer, J. W., Tu, K. N., and van der Weg, W. F. (1976). *Nucl. Instrum. Methods* **132**, 345.
Quinto, D. T., Sundaram, V. S., and Robertson, W. D. (1971). *Surf. Sci.* **28**, 504.
Rehn, L. E., Okamoto, P. R., Potter, D. I., and Wiedersich, H. (1978). *J. Nucl. Mater.* **74**, 242.
Rehn, L. E., Danyluk, S., and Wiedersich, H. (1979). *Phys. Rev. Lett.* **43**, 1764.
Rivaud, L., Ward, I. D., Eltoukhy, A. H., and Greene, J. E. (1981). *Surf. Sci.* **102**, 610.
Rivaud, L., Eltoukhy, A. H., and Greene, J.E. (1982). *Rad. Effects* **61**, 83.
Rodriguez-Murcia, H., and Beske, H. E. (1976). KFA Julich Report Jul-1292.
Ross, P. N., Jr., and Stonehart, P. (1975). *J. Catalysis* **39**, 298.
Roth, J. (1980). *In* "Symposium on Sputtering" (P. Varga, G. Betz and F. P. Viehböck, eds.), p. 773. Inst. Allgem, Physik, Vienna.
Roth, J., Bohdansky, J., Hofer, W. O., and Kirschner, J. (1977). *In* "Plasma Wall Interaction" p. 309. Pergamon, London.
Roth, J., Bohdansky, J., and Martinelli, A. P. (1980). *Rad. Effects.* **48**, 213.
Russell, W. A., Papanastassiou, D. A., and Tombrello, T. A. (1980). *Rad. Effects.* **52**, 41.

Sachtler, W. M. H., and von Santen, R. A. (1979). *Appl. Surf. Sci.* **3**, 121.

Saeki, N., and Shimizu, R. (1978a). *Surf. Sci.* **71**, 479.

Saeki, N., and Shimizu, R. (1978b). *Jap. J. Appl. Phys.* **17**, 59.

Satake, T., Narasuwa, N., Tsukakoshi, O., and Komiya, S. (1976). *Jap. J. Appl. Phys.* **15**, 1359.

Shek, M. L., Stefan, P. M., Weissman-Wenocur, D. L., Pate, B. B., Lindau, I., and Spicer, W. E. (1981). *J. Vac. Sci. Technol.* **18**, 533.

Shikata, M., and Shimizu, R. (1980). *Surf. Sci.* **97**, L363.

Shimizu, H., Ono, M., and Nakayama, K. (1973). *Surf. Sci.* **36**, 817.

Shimizu, H., Ono, M., and Katayama, K. (1975). *J. Appl. Phys.* **46**, 460.

Shimizu, R. (1977). *Surf. Sci.* **62**, 251.

Sigmund, P. (1969). *Phys. Rev.* **184**, 383.

Sigmund, P. (1977). *In* "Inelastic Ion-Surface Collisions" (N. H. Tolk, J. C. Tully and W. Heiland, eds.), p. 121. Academic Press, New York.

Sigmund, P. (1979). *J. Appl. Phys.* **50**, 7261.

Sigmund, P. (1980). *J. Vac. Sci. Technol.* **17**, 396.

Sigmund, P. (1981). *In* "Sputtering by Particle Bombardment I" (R. Behrisch, ed.), p. 9. Springer, Berlin.

Sigmund, P. (1983). *Appl. Phys.* 430, 43.

Sigmund, P., and Claussen, C. (1980). *In* "Symposium on Sputtering" (P. Varga, G. Betz and F. P. Viehböck, eds.), p. 113. Inst. Allgem. Physik, Vienna.

Sigmund, P., and Claussen, P. (1981). *J. Appl. Phys.* **52**, 990.

Sigmund, P., and Gras-Marti, A. (1980). *Nucl. Instrum. Methods* **168**, 389.

Sigmund, P., and Gras-Marti, A. (1981). *Nucl. Instrum. Methods* **182/183**, 25.

Sigmund, P., and Tougaard, S. (1981). *In* "Inelastic Particle–Surface Collisions" (E. Taglauer and W. Heiland, eds.), p. 2. Springer, Berlin.

Sigmund, P., Oliva, A., and Falcone, G. (1982). *Nucl. Instrum. Methods* **194**, 541.

Singer, I. L., Murday, J. S., and Cooper, L. R. (1978). *J. Vac. Sci. Technol.* **15**, 725.

Singer, I. L., Murday, J. S., and Cooper, L. R. (1981a). *Surf. Sci.* **108**, 7.

Singer, I. L., Murday, J. S., and Comas, L. (1981b). *J. Vac. Sci. Technol.* **18**, 161.

Sizmann, R. (1978). *J. Nucl. Mater.* **69-70**, 386.

Slusser, G. J., and Winograd, N. (1979). *Surf. Sci.* **84**, 211.

Solzbach, U., and Richter, H. J. (1980). *Surf. Sci.* **97**, 191.

Sone, K., Saidoh, S., Nakumara, K., Yamada, R., Murakami, Y., Shikama, T., Fukumoti, M., Kitajami, M., and Okada, M. (1981). *J. Nucl. Mater.* **98**, 270.

Swartzfager, D. G., and Kelley, M. J. (1980). *Phys. Lett.* **76A**, 86.

Swartzfager, D. G., Ziemecki, S. B., and Kelley, M. J. (1981). *J. Vac. Sci. Technol.* **19**, 185.

Szymoński, M. (1980). *Appl. Phys.* **23**, 89.

Szymoński, M. (1982). *Nucl. Instrum. Methods* **194**, 523.

Szymoński, M., and Bhattacharya, R. S. (1979). *Appl. Phys.* **20**, 207.

Szymoński, M., Bhattacharya, R. S., Overeijnder, H., and de Vries, A. E. (1978). *J. Phys. D: Appl. Phys.* **11**, 751.

Taga, Y., and Nakajiama, K. (1977). *Trans. Jap. Inst. Met.* **18**, 535.

Taglauer, E., and Heiland, W. (1978). *Appl. Phys. Lett.* **33**, 950.

Taglauer, E., and Heiland, W. (1980). *In* "Symposium on Sputtering" (P. Varga, G. Betz and F. P. Viehböck, eds.), p. 423. Inst. Allgem. Physik, Vienna.

Taglauer, E., Heiland, W., and MacDonald, R. J. (1979). *Surf. Sci.* **90**, 50.

Tarng, M. L., and Wehner, G. K. (1971a). *J. Vac. Sci. Technol.* **8**, 23.

Tarng, M. L., and Wehner, G. K. (1971b). *J. Appl. Phys.* **42**, 2449.

Tarng, M. L., and Wehner, G. K. (1972). *J. Appl. Phys.* **44**, 1534.
Taylor, H. P., Jr., and Epstein, S. (1973). *Geochim. Cosmochim. Acta Suppl.* **4**, 1657.
Thomas, S. (1976). *Surf. Sci.* **55**, 764.
Thomas, S. (1979). *Appl. Phys. Lett.* **24**, 1.
Thompson, D. A. (1980). *In* "Symposium on Sputtering" (P. Varga, G. Betz and F. P. Viehböck, eds.), p. 62. Inst. Allgem. Physik, Vienna.
Thompson, D. A. (1981). *Rad. Effects.* **56**, 104.
Thompson. M. W. (1959). *Phil. Mag.* **4**, 3.
Thompson, M. W. (1981). *Phys. Rep.* **69**, 335.
Tokutaka, H., Nishimoni, K., Tanaka, K., Takashima, K., Hérícy, J. L., and Langerson, J. P. (1981). *J. App. Phys.* **52**, 6109.
Tompkins, H. H. (1979). *J. Vac. Sci. Technol.* **16**, 778.
Tongson, L. L., Rogowski, D. A., and Knox, B. E. (1976). *J. Appl. Phys.* **47**, 5059.
Tongson, L. L., Biggers, J. V., Dayton, G. O., Bird, J. M., and Knox, B. E. (1978). *J. Vac. Sci. Technol.* **15**, 1133.
Townsend, P. D. (1980). *In* "Symposium on Sputtering" (P. Varga, G. Betz and F. P. Viehböck, eds.), p. 757. Inst. Allgem. Physik, Vienna.
Toyokawa, F., Furuya, K., and Kikuchi, T. (1981). *Surf. Sci.* **110**, 329.
Tsaur, B. Y., Lau, S. S., and Mayer, J. W. (1980). *Appl. Phys. Lett.* **36**, 823.
Tsong, T. T., Ng, Y. S., and McLane, S. B., Jr. (1980). *J. Chem. Phys.* **73**, 1464.
Vasilbev, M. A.. Ivaschenko, Y. I., and Charepin, V. T. (1973). *Met. Fizoka* **45**, 91.
Wandelt, K., and Brundle, C. R. (1981). *Phys. Rev. Lett.* **46**, 1529.
Watanabe, K., Hashiba, M., Fukuda, Y., and Yamashina, T. (1977a). *Bull. Fac. Eng. Hokkaido Univ.* **83**, 139.
Watanabe, K., Hashiba, M., and Yamashina, T. (1977b). *Surf. Sci.* **69**, 721.
Watson, C. C., and Haff, P. K. (1980). *J. Appl. Phys.* **51**, 691.
Webb, R., Carter, G., and Collins, R. (1978). *Rad. Effects.* **39**, 129.
Wehner, G. K. (1974). *Jap. J. Appl. Phys. Suppl.* **2**, 495.
Wehner, G. K. (1977a) *Appl. Phys. Lett.* **30**, 185.
Wehner, G. K. (1977b). *J. Vac. Sci. Technol.* **14**, 479.
Wehner, G. K., and Rosenberg, D. (1960). *J. Appl. Phys.* **31**, 177.
West, L. A. (1976). *J. Vac. Sci. Technol.* **13**, 198.
Wiedersich, H., Okamoto, P. R., and Lam, N. Q. (1979). *J. Nucl. Mater.* **83**, 98.
Williams, F. L., and Nason, D. (1975). *Surf. Sci.* **45**, 377.
Williams, F. L., and Nelson, G. C. (1979). *Appl. Surf. Sci.* **3**, 409.
Williams, P., and Baker, J. E. (1981). *Nucl. Instrum. Methods* **182–83**, 15.
Winterbon, K. B. (1980). *Rad. Effects.* **48**, 97.
Winters, H. F., and Sigmund, P. (1974). *J. Appl. Phys.* **45**, 4760.
Wittmaack, K., and Blank, P. (1980). *Nucl. Instrum. Methods* **170**, 331.
Wittmaack, K., Blank, P., and Wach, W. (1978). *Rad. Effects.* **39**, 81.
Wolsky, S. P., Zdanuk, E. J., and Shooter, D. (1964). *Surf. Sci.* **1**, 110.
Yabumoto, M., Watanabe, K., and Yamashina, T. (1978). *Surf. Sci.* **77**, 615.
Yabumoto, M., Kakibayashi, H., Mohri, M., Watanabe, K., and Yamashina, T. (1979). *Thin Solid Films* **63**, 263.
Yu, M. L., and Reuter, W. (1981). *Appl. Phys. Lett.* **38**, 525.

CHAPTER 7

Ion Beam and Laser Mixing: Fundamentals and Applications

B. R. APPLETON

Solid State Division, Oak Ridge National Laboratory
Oak Ridge, Tennessee, USA

I. INTRODUCTION

Significant advances in materials science are usually preceded by the development or application of new processing techniques. Ion implantation doping is a valid example of this, as the contents of this book attest. In recent years the use of both ion beams and lasers for processing materials has received new emphasis. One aspect of this has been the application of energetic heavy ion bombardment and pulsed or scanned (cw) lasers to induce

ION IMPLANTATION
AND BEAM PROCESSING
ISBN   0 12 756980 4

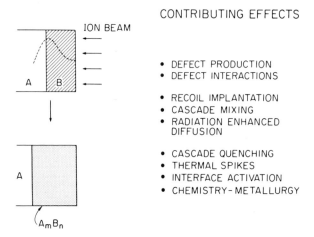

Fig. 1.   Schematic representation of ion beam mixing process.

materials interactions in thin-film composite samples or ion-implanted solids. These processing techniques, which have come to be called ion beam and laser mixing, have led to a variety of materials alterations that cannot be achieved with normal equilibrium processing techniques. In some cases the materials properties are simply extensions of what can be produced with non-equilibrium techniques such as splat quenching, but in many instances new metastable structures result.

There are several excellent reviews of ion beam mixing which cover the evolution of the field (Mayer *et al.*, 1980, 1981; Tsaur *et al.*, 1980c, 1981). The literature on ion implantation is well represented in the other chapters of this book. There is a close relationship between many high-dose ion-implantation effects and ion beam mixing (Mayer *et al.*, 1980; Liau and Mayer, 1980; Myers, 1980a,b; Poate and Cullis, 1980) some of which are covered here, and some in Chapters 2, 4, 6 and 8. Ion beam mixing effects are also prevalent in sputtering and the use of sputtering for depth profiling (Williams and Baker, 1981), as discussed in Chapter 6. Laser processing of materials is a relatively new area with tremendous potential. The scope of this field can be assessed from an early review (White *et al.*, 1979a), and from the proceedings of the four symposia that have been held to evaluate laser and electron beam interactions with solids and their use as materials process-ing techniques (Ferris *et al.*, 1979; White and Peercy, 1980; Gibbons *et al.*, 1981; Appleton and Celler, 1982).

The ion beam and pulsed laser mixing concepts are illustrated in Figs. 1 and 2. If a thin film of element *B* is deposited on a solid *A* and bombarded

CONTRIBUTING EFFECTS

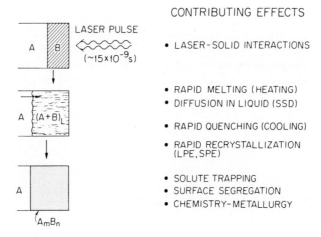

* LASER-SOLID INTERACTIONS

* RAPID MELTING (HEATING)
* DIFFUSION IN LIQUID (SSD)

* RAPID QUENCHING (COOLING)

* RAPID RECRYSTALLIZATION
  (LPE,SPE)

* SOLUTE TRAPPING
* SURFACE SEGREGATION
* CHEMISTRY-METALLURGY

Fig. 2.   Schematic representation of pulsed laser mixing process.

with an energetic ion beam as depicted in Fig. 1, a variety of complex, interacting effects are initiated. Each ion slows down through a series of collisions with the target atoms along its path. Some of the ion's energy is deposited in inelastic ionizing collisions and the remainder in elastic displacement collisions. In most ion-mixing experiments the ion beam parameters are chosen so that the energy deposited in displacement damage has a depth dependence like the dashed profile in Fig. 1. This deposits the maximum energy at the interface. The damage cascades initiated along the ion trajectory result in the displacement of many atoms of both A and B and the creation of many mobile defects. In many situations, the damage energy deposited into each cascade is dissipated to the surrounding lattice atoms in times $\sim 10^{-13}$s; thus each cascade volume undergoes a kind of rapid quenching. The various contributing effects in Fig. 1 mix the atoms and combine with the rapid quenching aspects of the cascade to induce a materials interaction, referred to in the figure as $A_m B_n$. The degree of mixing, the final material formed, etc., depend on the relative importance of the contributing mechanisms. Section II of this chapter reviews these fundamental mechanisms and attempts to establish their contribution to the ion beam mixing process. Section III is devoted to applications.

Most of the laser processing discussed in this chapter is limited to cases which utilize pulsed lasers. A typical pulsed laser mixing experiment is outlined in Fig. 2. A thin-film target of B deposited on A is irradiated with an intense laser. An example would be a Q-switched ruby laser with a pulse duration ~ 15 ns. Depending on the properties of B and the laser, the energy is absorbed into the electronic system of B and is rapidly converted to heat. At sufficient laser energy densities, the near surface of the materials can melt, A and B can mix by liquid diffusion, and as the heat is conducted away to the solid substrate, the mixture undergoes rapid solidification. At laser energy densities below the melting threshold, the near surface undergoes rapid heating and cooling in the solid state. The quenching rate of this resolidification process depends on a number of materials and laser properties, but it can be as fast as 10^8 to 10^{13} K s^{-1}. Thus, analogous to ion beam mixing, pulsed laser mixing provides a mechanism for non-equilibrium materials processing.

II. FUNDAMENTAL MECHANISMS

A. Ion-Solid Interactions

1. Mixing Mechanisms

Ion beam mixing is an all inclusive term which embraces some of the most complex phenomena in ion-solid interactions and, as such, it can be anticipated that materials alterations induced by ions will be very difficult to attribute to a single mechanism.

In a typical experiment, a composite target of a thin film of one material deposited on another will be bombarded with energetic heavy ions. These ions produce defects as they slow down and ultimately come to rest and form an implanted impurity. The depth distribution of the implanted defects is largely responsible for the mixing process. Defect production mechanisms comprise a vast field studied since the early 1950s (Billington and Crawford, 1961; Robinson and Young, 1975; Peterson and Harkness, 1975; Corbett, 1966; Peterson and Siegel, 1978; Albany, 1979), and most of these studies have been in pure metals, simply because alloys were too complicated. The complexity begins in the defect production process. Once created, the defects migrate, annihilate, diffuse, cluster, and generally interact in a complex manner. Again, it is only in pure materials that defect interactions are well understood; thus the composite target and implanted impurity are a great source of uncertainty in extrapolating these understandings. Even in pure materials, defect-production is most studied at low doses and low temperatures, but in ion beam mixing we deal with high doses, high dose rates, and usually high temperatures. The whole mixing process is fraught with synergism. For example, normal atom mobilities are drastically altered by the presence of huge defect flux gradients in the solid, and normal segregation/precipitation processes can be altered. The relationships among these various processes are presented concisely in Peterson and Harkness (1975).

Even the materials interactions which would be predictable under normal equilibrium mixing are very different in the presence of displacement cascades. First, the atoms are mixed, and materials interactions occur on a microscopic scale, the dimensions of which are the order of an individual ion-induced cascade volume (i.e. a few thousand atoms). Second, these interactions experience vast energetic (temperature) and temporal perturbations, because the energy in an individual cascade is dissipated to the surrounding lattice in times 10^{-10} to 10^{-12} s. The micrometallurgy or microthermodynamics in combination with such rapid quenching effects present a formidable problem.

It is clear from this discussion that an understanding of the mixing process is too much to expect, but we can identify some of the fundamental mechanisms involved. A review of what is known about these mechanisms may be helpful in isolating and identifying the most important mechanism in a particular situation.

2. Defect Production

The elements of defect production that are important for an understanding of mixing are the processes which produce defects in the solid, those which govern the initial depth distribution of the defects, and those which determine the final distribution of the primary ions. The starting point for introducing these various pertinent phenomena is the *collision cascade*. A schematic representation of an energetic ion entering a crystalline solid and initiating a collision cascade is shown in Fig. 3. As discussed in detail in Chapters 2, 3, and 4, an energetic ion loses energy along its trajectory in the solid as a result of elastic collisions with the shielded atomic nuclei and electronic excitations of the atomic electrons. These combined processes determine the ultimate implantation profile of the incident ions and the defect production. In metals, semiconductors and some insulators, the electronic excitations serve mainly as a energy-loss mechanism for slowing the ion but do little in the way of damage. In these systems it is the elastic collisions or nuclear stopping which leads to the atomic displacements that contribute to mixing. It is clear from the results presented in Chapter 5, however, that the energy deposited into electronic processes can lead to significant structural damage in certain insulating materials. Consequently, this can be an important "mixing mechanism" in these materials. Electronic energy deposition can

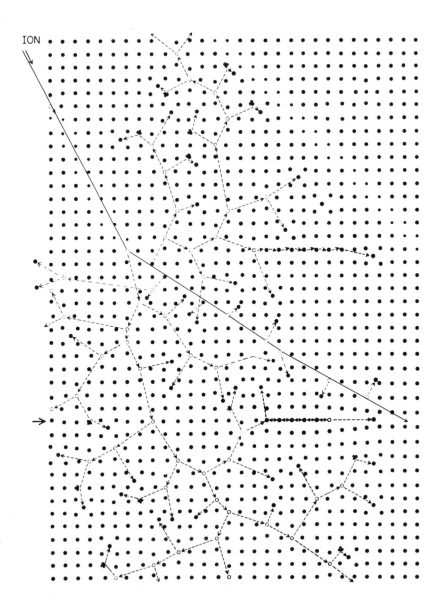

Fig. 3. Schematic representation of a possible collision cascade initiated by an energetic ion in a crystalline solid.

also affect *defect interactions* in insulators and semiconductors, since these defect and impurity centers are charge-state dependent (Corbett, 1966; Corbett *et al.*, 1981; Narayan and Tan, 1981).

The complexity of the collision cascade can be imagined from the interactions arranged for the ion in Fig. 3, which is a representation of a heavy ion entering a metal or semiconductor. Immediately upon entering the solid it begins losing energy by inelastic collisions. In each collision between the ion and a target atom (called a primary collision), the ion of mass M_1 and energy E_1 transfers momentum to a stationary target atom of mass M_2; and when the transferred kinetic energy, T, exceeds the threshold energy for displacement, E_d, the primary lattice atom recoils from its site and survives as a stable defect. The maximum value for T is given by

$$T_m = [(4M_1M_2)/(M_1 + M_2)^2]E_1 \qquad (1)$$

This transferred energy can range from a few eV to tens of keV depending on the collision, and when $T > E_d$, $E_d = $ 10-30 eV, these knock-on atoms recoil through the lattice, creating their own displacements by secondary collisions. The energy and angular distributions of the recoiling atoms depend critically on the scattering cross-section and interatomic potential; and even E_d depends on material and crystallographic direction (Nelson, 1973; Robinson and Young, 1975; Robinson, 1981). As the energy of these recoils decreases, their probability for initiating recoils increases and consequently, as the dotted trajectories in Fig. 3 show, a large number of displaced atoms are produced.

The defects produced can be simple defects such as interstitial atoms (filled circles in Fig. 3) and vacancies (closed circles). A displaced atom can be recaptured by its own vacancy if its energy $T - E_d$ is less than the threshold for capture; or it can traverse many atom distances and initiate other displaced atoms or produce more complicated collisions, such as the focusing and replacement collisons also shown in Fig. 3 (Nelson, 1973; Robinson, 1981; Brice, 1976). Once created, defects often cluster and form more complex defect aggregates. An important distinction in characterizing cascades is how the damage energy is distributed within the cascade (Lindhard *et al.*, 1963; Sigmund, 1974, 1977, 1981; Andersen, 1979). Those cascades in which only a small number of atoms are in motion have been termed "linear cascades". In these the damage energy can be shared among a large number of atoms, and local conditions approaching equilibrium are possible. In dense cascades (called "spikes"), the damage energy is dissipated at a high rate among essentially all the atoms in the cascade volume, and collective atomic interactions occur. These effects are discussed in detail in Chapters

2, 4 and 6 and will not be reassessed here. Nevertheless, many damage cascades initiated in ion beam mixing and high-dose ion implantations fall into the spike category and, in later sections dealing with applications, it will be clear that the mixing and rapid quenching aspects of the dense cascade are often invoked in order to explain many of the observed metastable materials interactions.

It is instructive to consider calculations of the initial depth distributions of defects and to evaluate, if possible, how these agree with measurements. Among the programs most widely used by experimentalists for calculating deposited damage energy versus depth are TRIM (Biersack and Haggmark, 1980), E-DEP-1 (Manning and Mueller, 1974), and the tabulations of Brice (1975) and Winterbon (1975). The damage energy $S_n(x)$ (MeV μm^{-1} versus depth is shown plotted in Fig. 4 for a dose of 1×10^{16} As cm^{-2} at an energy of 100 keV incident in silicon as calculated from E-DEP-1 and Brice's tables. Both programs calculate the energy deposited into the creation of defects and the depth profile of the implanted ions. Both take into account the inelastic energy lost by the primary ion as well as the inelastic losses of the secondary knock-on atoms in the damage cascade. The main conceptual difference is that in the computer code E-DEP-1, the damage energy which goes into the creation of primary knock-on events is assigned to the depth interval where this event occurs, which Brice utilizes a transport equation approach (see Chapter 3, Section II) to calculate the energy deposition distribution. The TRIM code, which is a Monte Carlo computer simulation, gives a damage energy distribution very similar to E-DEP-1. The other important elements that go into the calculations, which are different for each code, are their treatments of the elastic scattering events (potentials, screening parameters, etc.) and the electronic energy loss process. The interestsed reader is referred to the original references. Also shown for reference is the calculated projected mean range of the implanted As distribution, R_p, which is nearly the same for all three codes.

Consideration of the various processes which contribute to the creation of defects shows that the number of displacement per target atom per second (DPA) initiated by an ion flux Φ can be related to the damage energy $S_n(x)$ by the modified Kinchin-Pease relationship

$$DPA = (0.8/2E_d) \, S_n(x) \, (\Phi/N) \tag{2}$$

where $E_d = 13$ eV for Si and N is the atomic density (see Peterson and Harkness, 1975, for example). This conversion is shown on the right abscissa of Fig. 4, calculated for 10^{16} As cm^{-2}. As discussed in Chapters 2, 3, 4, and 8, several implantation parameters determine the critical dose (Φc) of ions required to make silicon amorphous. Based on a simple amorphous model

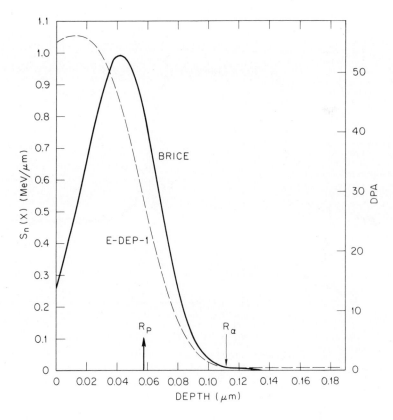

Fig. 4. Damage energy ($S_n(x)$ and *DPA*) versus depth calculated for 100 keV, 1 × 10^{16} As$^+$ cm^{-2} implanted in Si.

(Morehead and Crowder, 1971), this critical dose for 100 keV As at room temperature can be estimated to be $\Phi c \sim 10^{14}$ cm^{-2}. The equivalent *DPA* corresponding to this critical dose for the implant conditions of Fig. 4 is marked by the dashed line in the lower right-hand corner of the figure, and the corresponding depth to which the silicon should be amorphous is marked on the figure as R_α.

Experimental measurements for comparison to these calculations are shown in Fig. 5 and Fig. 6. A Si(100) single crystal was implanted at room temperature with 1.0 × 10^{16} As cm^{-2} at an energy of 100 keV, and incident in a random direction of the crystal. The implanted sample was analyzed by 2.0 MeV ion scattering/channeling (Fig. 5). A random reference spectrum obtained by continuous rotation of the crystal while recording the scattered

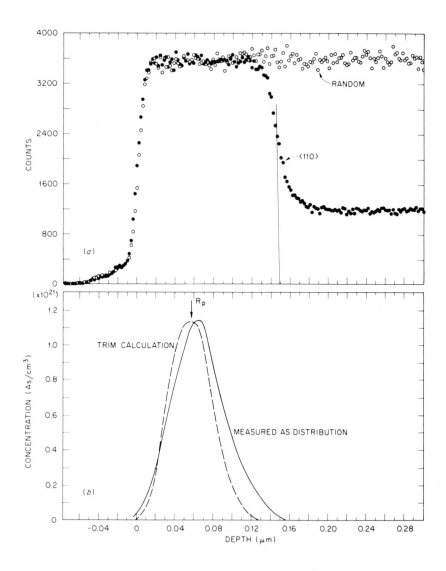

Fig. 5.   (a) 2.0 MeV He$^+$ ion scattering/channeling analysis of a Si(100) single crystal implanted at room temperature with 1×10^{16} As$^+$ cm^{-2} at 100 keV for aligned (<110> ●) and rotating random (○) orientations. (b) Comparison of measured As implantation depth profile to TRIM calculations.

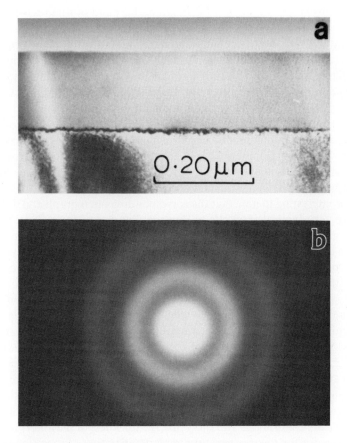

Fig. 6. Cross-section transmission-electron micrographs showing the amorphous surface layer induced in Si(100) (a) by room temperature implanation of 1×10^{16} As$^+$ cm^{-2} at 100 keV. Diffraction patterns from the amorphous regions are shown in (b).

ions is compared to the spectrum taken with the He$^+$ beam aligned along the <110> axial direction of the as-implanted sample in Fig. 5a. The corresponding implanted As distribution is shown in Fig. 5b, together with a calculation using the TRIM code. The mean projected range using E-DEP-1 and Brice's tables fall within the arrow marked R_p and, in general, all three calculations are in good agreement when comparable screening parameters, etc., are used. Conversion of the ion scattering/channeling measurements to depth distributions shows that the As implantation has turned the single crystal amorphous, to a depth of 0.15 μm. A cross-section transmission electron micrograph taken from the same Si(100) sample (Fig. 6) shows an induced amorphous layer to a depth of 0.15 μm and a band of high-density defects 0.02 μm thick between this layer and the single crystal substrate. The diffraction pattern from the amorphous region (Fig. 6b) shows a diffuse ring pattern characteristic of an amorphous structure. These two measurements of the amorphous layer for Si(100) suggest that the depth to which the crystal was turned amorphous as a result of the implantation is considerably greater than the R_α predicted from the considerations discussed in connection with Fig. 4. The source of this discrepancy could either be in the calculations, or in the nature of the fundamental energy deposition and damage processes (discussed further in Chapters 2, 3, 4 and 8). Both possibilities suggest areas where more work is needed so that the fundamental mechanisms involved might be clarified.

It is interesting to note that the corresponding micrograph and diffraction pattern for identical implants to those in Fig. 6, but for a Si(111) sample, although qualitatively the same, show a thicker amorphous layer and features which suggest a difference in the nature of the amorphous layer. These differences can be understood in terms of the constraints on atomic reordering at the (100) and (111) interfaces (Narayan, 1982). As discussed in Chapters 3, 4 and 8 the energy deposition distribution and implantation profiles may be well represented by the calculations, but the final damage may be determined by more complex lattice collapse, spikes, or defect migration processes. With regard to the last of these, it is known, for example, that the interstitial in Si is mobile at even the lowest temperatures (Watkins, 1963), and that defect mobility, which restructures the damage at room temperature or higher, usually reduces rather than increases the amorphous state. Measurements for identical implants in Si(100) at liquid nitrogen and room temperature confirm this and show that the thickness of the amorphous layer is *broader* for the low temperature implants than that at room temperature. This indicates that some annealing has occurred at the high temperature (Appleton and Holland, 1982). It also means that the actual extent of the implantation damage, which is more accurately represented by the liquid nitrogen measurement, is at even greater variance with calculations.

In any given ion beam mixing experiment in which materials interactions are introduced by ion bombardment and it is important to identify the fundamental mechanisms responsible (atomic mixing, enhanced diffusion, defect interactions, etc.), it is necessary to know the initial damage energy distribution and ion depth profile. In many cases these interactions occur over only a few hundred angstroms; so an accurate determination is important. It is clear from the preceding discussion that experimental measurements, which were devised to isolate the contributing mechanisms and discern their importance, are an integral partner to developing accurate calculations. In the next sections some recent experiments directed to this end will be presented.

3. Atomic Mixing

In this section I will discuss those atomic collision processes that are responsible for mixing and, then, in the next section I will emphasize the defect interactions and annealing effects that contribute to or enhance the mixing process. In many of the examples cited, however, a clean division is not possible. Several recent publications and references therein address the atomic mixing process specifically (Andersen, 1979; Andersen and Bay, 1982; Sigmund, 1974; Sigmund and Gras-Marti, 1981; Littmark and Hofer, 1980; Christel et al., 1981; Moline et al., 1973). Because these various reviews are available to the reader, no discussion will be given of the theoretical aspects of the various atomic processes. Instead a few specific measurements and their interpretations will be presented so as to provide a feeling for the relative importance of the processes involved.

When a beam of energetic ions impinges on a solid which has an impurity layer on its surface, an implanted impurity, or a thin-film composite in or on it, the elastic collisions between ions and secondary knock-on atoms and the impurity atoms can cause compositional changes (mixing). The detailed mechanisms associated with the mixing processes within a cascade can often be assessed separately in calculations but can be difficult to separate experimentally. The mixing phenomena can be subdivided into:

1. Primary recoil mixing (ion-impurity knock-ons). This corresponds to impurity atom relocations as a result of direct interactions with the incident ions, and is a well-defined problem which can be treated theoretically. It is sometimes termed "recoil implantation" (cf. Chapter 6, Section IV,C) but, as we shall see, it is not the only contributing phenomenon in most measurements called by that name.
2. Secondary recoil (cascade) mixing. This recognizes that bombarding ions initiate many secondary matrix atom recoils which can then collide with an impurity atom and relocate it.

Subtle distinctions, which depend on the ion/target configuration, and many other factors, exist between (1) and (2). It is often instructive in theoretical treatments to distinguish between high-energy cascades (recoils initiated by elastic collisions at keV or higher energies) and low-energy cascades (recoils in the eV region), and also between isotropic and anisotropic collision cascades.

An example that will help place these mixing mechanisms in perspective is the situation that is often referred to experimentally as "recoil implantation" (Moline et al., 1973; Christel et al., 1981). This technique consists of depositing a thin film (impurity) on a solid and bombarding it with energetic heavy ions as a means of transporting atoms from the thin film into the substrate. Recoil implantation has considerable practical importance for near-surface modification of metals, for doping semiconductor devices, and perhaps most importantly because it is so important in the technology of semiconductor device fabrication (Christel et al., 1981; Moline et al., 1973; Hirvonen, 1980; Grob et al., 1981). Many devices are made by implanting the dopant ions through an insulating film (SiO_2 on Si, Si_3N_4 on GaAs, etc.), and recoil implanted impurities from this film can have serious detrimental effects on device performance. Practical experimental observations of this phenomenon involve transport of the impurity atoms into the substrate by both primary and cascade recoils. The relative importance of these mechanisms can be deduced from calculations. An example of the transport calculations used to determine the expected recoil distributions of O atoms in Si that result from the implantation of 125 keV As through 750 Å of SiO_2 on Si is given in Fig. 7. (Details of the calculations are given in Chapter 3, Section III.) This figure shows that the secondary recoils contribute significantly to the O profile very near the SiO_2-Si interface. A careful dissection of the transport calculations of Christel et al. (1981) showed that the O at the greatest depths came from recoils produced with high energy (low yield) far from the interface; most of the oxygen within a few hundred angstroms came from low-energy (high-yield) secondary recoil collisions; and the central region contained contributions from higher energy recoils produced far from the interface, as well as low energy recoils produced near the interface. Although these calculations showed generally good agreement with experimental results, it was noted that they do not properly account for low-energy recoils. Such recoils could enhance true O concentrations very near the interface by as much as a factor of four (Christel et al., 1981).

A second useful example which considers the relative contributions of these mixing mechanisms on buried markers in a solid can be taken from the results of Tsaur et al., (1979a) and Matteson et al. (1981a,b), and the theoretical calculations of Sigmund and Gras-Marti (1981). The experimental technique used is illustrated in Fig. 8. Various targets with a thin metal layer sandwiched between amorphous Si films sequentially vacuum deposited on Si were prepared. The films served as markers to monitor, at the depth of the film, the mixing induced by heavy ion bombardment. The ion induced spreading of the marker profiles was systematically determined by high-resolution ion scattering and was used to infer mixing mechanisms. The magnitude and dependence of the mixing obeyed a random walk process which was identified as collision-cascade mixing. Sigmund et al. (1981) considered the theoretical aspects of atomic mixing and selected the particular case of a thin (30Å) Pt marker embedded in amorphous Si to illustrate the relative importance of the various atomic collision processes involved. The

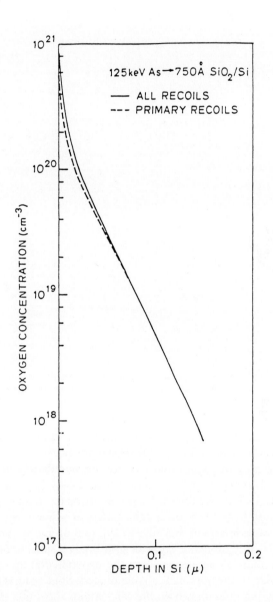

Fig. 7. Calculations showing the effects of secondary recoil generation on the oxygen recoil distribution. From Christel *et al.* (1981).

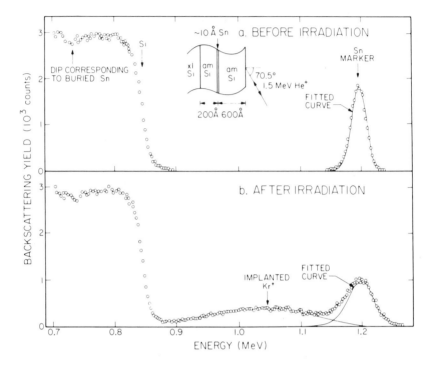

Fig. 8. Ion scattering analysis before (a) and after (b) ion beam mixing with 220 keV, 1 × 10^{16} Kr$^+$ cm^{-2} of a ∼10 Å Sn marker deposited at ∼600 Å in amorphous Si. From Matteson *et al.* (1981a).

calculated broadening and peak shifts that would result from the various mixing mechanisms are shown as a function of fluence in Fig. 9, and are compared with measurements for 300 keV Xe ion bombardment at a fluence 2 × 10^{16} cm^{-2} (Tsaur *et al.*, 1979b). These calculations apply to dilute impurity concentrations such as the thin-film case discussed or an ion-implanted distribution, and to heavy ions on a light matrix in which mixing is initiated in the linear cascade region. Recoil implantation or ion impurity knock-on is seen to have little influence on peak shift but is a substantial contributor to r.m.s. spreading. In agreement with the experimental analyses, cascade mixing is seen to be the dominant mixing process. Sputtering is not included, but the sputtering rates shown on the calculations show that the results are severely affected above fluences of 10^{17} ions cm^{-2}. A more detailed discussion of high-dose effects on materials composition is given by Liau *et al.* (1980). Correlated analysis (Sigmund and Gras-Marti, 1981) showed that up to 10^{16} ion cm^{-2} the impurity profile is determined by single ion impurity knock-on,

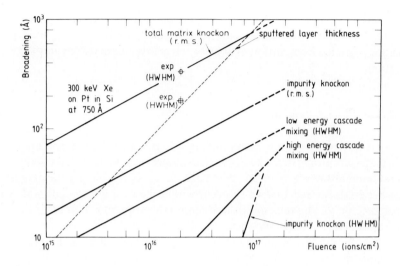

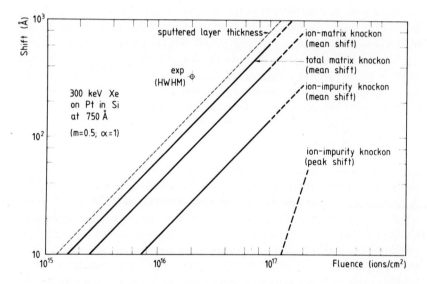

Fig. 9. Theoretical calculations of the broadening and shifting induced by 300 keV Xe⁺ ion bombardment of various fluences on a thin Pt layer at 750 Å in amorphous Si. From Sigmund and Gras-Marti (1981).

but at higher fluences $\sim 10^{17}$ ion cm^{-2} multiple relocation becomes important. Also, while mixing by heavy ions on light targets is determined by matrix relocation, light ion bombardment of heavy targets is dominated by impurity relocation.

4. Collision Cascades and Rapid Quenching Effects

A major attractiveness of ion beam mixing is that it leads to new and meta-stable materials properties. The discussions in previous sections have shown that ion bombardment can be an effective mixing process, but it is the details of the materials interactions which occur within the collision cascade which are responsible for the nonequilibrium materials properties. Part of this results from defect interactions; these are discussed in the following section. Here, contributions from the dynamics of the cascades themselves will be considered.

The energy deposited in collision cascades such as shown in Fig. 3 is dissipated through atomic motion in times $\sim 10^{-13}$ s. Cascades are sometimes referred to as spikes. Brinkman (1954) and Seeger (1958) envisaged the damage region around the track of a primary recoil as consisting of a core of vacancies surrounded by a shell of interstitials. Brinkman (1954) argued that this spike could collapse to form a disordered region which he called a displacement spike. Sigmund (1977) draws the distinction between collision cascades and spikes on the basis of energy dissipation within the cascade volume. The linear cascade concept applies when the number of atoms set in motion is small and the energy dissipation is linear. As discussed in Chapter 4, a spike refers to the situation when most atoms in the cascade volume are in motion and energy dissipation is nonlinear. An excellent distinction between these two situations is demonstrated by the measurements of Andersen and Bay (1974) in comparing atomic and molecular ion sputtering yields. A useful map of where these nonlinear effects are applicable has been given by Andersen in Chapter 6 (Fig. 7). A crude approximation applicable to ion mixing and ion implantation is that spikes are generated by heavy ions in heavy targets at ion energies that are not too high, a situation that is not unusual.

One variety of dense cascade is often referred to as a thermal spike (Seitz and Koehler, 1956; Nelson, 1973; Dienes and Vineyard, 1957). If an energy E is deposited into a cascade volume V in a target of atomic density N, and if it is imagined that the atoms in motion within the cascade can be treated as a hot gas in equilibrium, a spike temperature T_s can be defined as

$$T_s \approx (\tfrac{2}{3})(E/KNV) \tag{3}$$

There is much supposition in this equation. It is not clear whether thermal equilibrium can be attained on these time scales or how the energy couples to the lattice or electronic system. The thermal spike concept is an old one that has been examined by a number of researchers over the years with some useful conclusions for ion mixing. It is usually assumed that the thermal energy is dissipated by lattice thermal conductivity, and typically a cascade volume can be expected to contain $\gtrsim$ 1000 atoms. Nelson (1973, 1965) examined thermal spike behavior in a number of solids and concluded that within $1-5 \times 10^{-12}$ s the temperature of the spike volume was only a few hundred degrees higher than the surrounding lattice. Similarly, Dienes and Vineyard (1957) concluded from calculations that the spike temperature in copper dropped to $\sim 500°C$ in 3×10^{-11} s. The high local "temperature" should cause some homogenization of the vacancy core-interstitial shell suggested by Brinkman, but the ultimate materials interactions induced locally and long range depend very strongly on the particular materials system, as we shall see.

This rapid dissipation of energy from the cascade region may be the most significant aspect of ion beam mixing. Whether this "quenching" effect results from a spike that is gaseous or liquid in nature and that converts to the solid state, or whether the energy is dissipated by atomic collisions is probably secondary to the fact that it occurs so rapidly. Many metastable and amorphous materials have been produced by the more conventional techniques of vapor quenching and splat cooling (liquid quenching), which have quenching rates of $\sim 10^{10}$ K s^{-1} and $\sim 10^6$ K s^{-1} respectively (Guntherodt and Lapka, 1980; Bergmann, 1976). The quenching rate of a spike cascade can be estimated to be $\sim 10^{13}$ K s^{-1}. Thus, a variety of new materials properties can be expected from this extremely rapid quenching. The ultimate observable alteration, however, will depend sensitively on the defect interaction and annealing properties of the solid, as well as on the details of the cascade. For example, the As implanted sample of Fig. 5 became amorphous because: (i) each incident ion created a dense cascade which became amorphous as a result of the rapid quenching, and these cascades eventually overlapped to form an amorphous layer; and (ii) because Si is a solid with strong covalent bonding which can stabilize in an amorphous structure at room temperature. If electrons, which create only simple displacement damage, are used, not even the highest fluences can make Si amorphous (Corbett, 1966). Similarly, because of their annealing behavior, pure metals irradiated with self ions to much higher doses than Si never become amorphous even for the low temperature irradiations (Robinson and Young, 1975; Peterson and Harkness, 1975).

In Section III, numerous recent results which provide insights into the rapid quenching aspects of the spike cascade will be presented. In this section, where we are still concerned with fundamental mechanisms, it is instructive to consider some of the measurements designed to verify the spike concept and dynamics of the collision cascade. Studies in ordered alloys have been used since the early 1950s as tools to investigate the atomic rearrangement initiated by neutrons, electrons and positive ions (e.g. Billington and Crawford, 1961; Piercy, 1963; Blewitt and Coltman, 1952; Aronin, 1954; Kirk et al., 1977; Jenkins et al., 1979). Piercy (1963) was able to deduce the size of a spike cascade by irradiating ordered Pt_3Fe with fission neutrons at 60°C. Since the ordered alloy is non-magnetic, while the disordered alloy is ferromagnetic, by measuring the magnetization curves, he was able to conclude that each fission neutron produced an average of 2–3 spikes with ~ 3300 atoms per spike. Utilizing the order-dependent ferromagnetic properties of Ni_3Mn, Kirk et al. (1977) demonstrated the existence of replacement collision sequences (e.g. Fig. 3), investigated their average length, and separated the damage due to replacement collisions from random disorder. Transmission electron microscopy techniques have been developed by Jenkins et al. (1979) to yield quantitative information on the sizes and shapes of displacement cascades in ordered alloys. These techniques utilize the difference in structure factors for superlattice reflections between the well-ordered matrix and damaged (disordered) regions, thus making it possible to image the individual displacement cascades.

In more recent investigations, Matteson et al. (1981a) utilized the buried metal film technique discussed in connection with Fig. 8 to test for the presence of spike effects in cascade mixing. Results from that study are shown in Fig. 10, which compares the spreading of a 30 Å Pt layer embedded in amorphous silicon after bombardment with As_1^+, As_2^+, and As_3^+ to a constant dose (5×10^{15} As atoms cm^{-2}) and the same energy per atom (120 KeV per atom). By using As_2^+ and As_3^+, the energy density deposited in each collision cascade is respectively two and three times that deposited by As_1^+. The authors attribute the broadening observed in Fig. 10 to spike effects in the molecular ion induced cascades.

5. Defect Interactions and Enhanced Diffusion

As indicated at the beginning of this section on ion-solid interactions, radiation damage and annealing is a field too vast and too complicated to review here. Nevertheless, the numerous reports from studies of induced phase changes, accelerated precipitation, redissolution of precipitates, solute segregation, etc., resulting from neutron and ion irradiation of alloys, make it clear

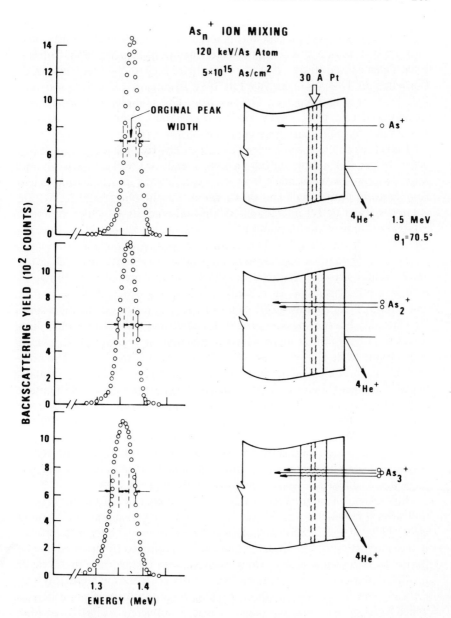

Fig. 10.   Ion scattering analysis of the broadening induced in a 30 Å Pt marker embedded in amorphous Si after irradiation with As_1^+, As_2^+ and As_3^+ ions to a constant dose of 5×10^{15} As atoms cm^{-2} of equivalent energy per ion. From Matteson *et al.* (1981a).

that defect interactions and defect-enhanced diffusion will be major contributors to the mixing process during ion irradiation (Billington and Crawford, 1961; Robinson and Young, 1975; Dienes and Vineyard, 1957; Corbett, 1966; Petersen and Siegel, 1978; Crawford and Slifkin, 1972; Albany, 1979; Corbett et al., 1981; Narayan and Tan, 1981; Brinkman, 1954; Andersen and Bay, 1974; Seitz and Koehler, 1956; Nelson, 1965; Guntherodt and Lapka, 1980; Bergmann, 1976; Piercy, 1963; Blewitt and Coltman, 1953; Aronin, 1954; Kirk et al., 1979, and references therein).

Defect interactions have been studied extensively for more than thirty years. In general, simple defects in pure metals are well understood, and some progress has been made in recent years toward understanding defect aggregates in pure metals and dilute alloys. On the other hand, very little is known about defect interactions in concentrated alloys, which comprise a large fraction of useful materials (Robinson and Young, 1975; Corbett, 1966; Petersen and Siegel, 1978). Our understanding of the defects in ionic solids, oxides and other insulators varies greatly: some materials, such as the alkali halides, are well characterized, while our understanding of radiation defects in other insulators is certainly inadequate (Corbett, 1966; Crawford and Slifkin, 1972; Albany, 1979). Semiconductors are among the most studied materials, but they possess special characteristics, particularly when subjected to radiation, that make defect interactions very complex (Crawford and Slifkin, 1972; Corbett et al., 1981; Narayan and Tan, 1981). The difficulty in interpreting most ion beam mixing experiments is that they contain many of the least understood aspects. The target is usually a combination of dissimilar materials in the form of thin-film composites; mixing is done with high fluence heavy ions at room temperature; and the resultant mixture is subject to rapid quenching, is seldom an equilibrium alloy, is rarely uniform in composition, and is loaded with complex defects. This can result in spectacular materials interactions but makes the extraction of fundamental mechanisms difficult.

Enhanced diffusion effects are intimately related to defect interactions, and several reviews of this subject are available (e.g. Sizmann, 1978; Adda et al., 1975; Myers, 1980b). Ordinary diffusion in metals proceeds through defect interactions. Normal defects which are produced by thermodynamic lattice disorders show such a strong decrease with temperature that little or no diffusion occurs at room temperature. Under energetic ion bombardment, diffusion can be greatly enhanced because huge numbers of point defects which accelerate normal thermally activated diffusion, are produced and, also, new defects which introduce additional diffusion mechanisms are created. These phenomena are called radiation-enhanced or defect-enhanced diffusion. Ion bombardment not only creates huge numbers of defects, which can accelerate substitutional, interstitial or vacancy diffusion mechanisms, but also establishes solute atom and point defect fluxes, which can act as strong driving forces in the mixing process (e.g. Marwick and Piller, 1981). The enhanced diffusion discussed so far results from defects created by elastic ion-atom collisions that cause atomic displacements. In semiconductors and insulators the inelastic ionization losses of the ion beam may also cause enhanced defect mobilities. It is particularly relevant to mention that, in semiconductors, defects can become charged, and thus experience enhanced mobility. Watkins (1963) observed that even at temperatures $\sim$4K the Si interstitial undergoes long-range migration in the lattice and replaces substitutional Al impurities. Similar effects have been observed for many impurities in Si and Ge, and numerous other ionization-assisted effects have been observed at higher temperatures in all the semiconductors (Crawford and Slifkin, 1972; Albany, 1979; Corbett et al., 1981; Narayan and Tan, 1981).

The relevance of enhanced diffusion effects in ion beam mixing is illustrated by the results in Fig. 11 (from Matteson et al., 1979). In this work, 1400 Å films of Nb were vacuum deposited on clean Si (100) single crystals, and the samples were bombarded with 275keV^{28} Si$^+$ to induce mixing. The energy of the Si$^+$ was chosen to produce maximum displacement damage at the Nb-Si interface. The effect of substrate temperature on mixing was studied by bombarding a series of identical samples held at temperatures from 19°C to 380°C with 1.2×10^{17} Si$^+$ cm^{-2}. The quantity of intermixed silicon, Q in units of atoms cm^{-2}, was determined from each sample by high resolution ion scattering analysis, and the logarithm of Q is shown plotted in Fig. 11 versus the inverse of the mixing temperature. The data show that below about 200°C the mixing is independent of temperature, while above 200°C the mixing shows a pronounced temperature dependence. Analysis of these results led Matteson et al. to conclude that the increase in mixing at higher temperatures was due to radiation-enhanced thermal diffusion, while the temperature-independent region was dominated by what they termed "dynamic collision cascade mixing". The observed intermixing below 200°C was an order of magnitude greater than predicted by simple cascade mixing theories, and it is not clear whether some other mechanism (spike cascades and recoil implantation were ruled out) or uncertainties in the theory were responsible (Matteson et al., 1979). The differences in silicide formation in these two mixing regions was equally complex and challenging. Results which show that this same, unexplained, enhanced mixing is prevalent in other metal–semiconductor systems to temperatures as low as 4K will be discussed later. Such results emphasize the need for carefully designed experiments, such as those where target combinations, ion species and target temperature are manipulated so as to isolate and identify the fundamental mechanisms involved in the mixing process.

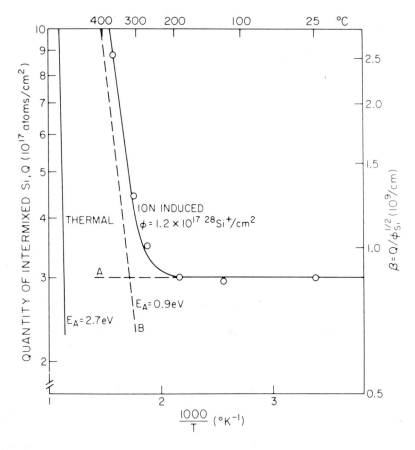

Fig. 11. Temperature dependence of ion induced mixing of Nb–Si by Si$^+$ bombardment at constant fluence. From Matteson *et al.* (1979).

B. Laser-Solid Interactions

1. Mixing Mechanisms

The laser-solid interactions relevant to the pulsed laser mixing process are well understood and documented (Ferris *et al.*, 1979; White and Peercy, 1980; Gibbons *et al.*, 1981; Appleton and Celler, 1982). For several reasons the present brief discussion will emphasize results from pulsed laser annealing of Si and Ge. First, Si is the material on which most fundamental studies of interest have been made. Second, semiconductors are technologically the most relevant materials as far as laser processing is concerned, and consequently most mixing experiments have involved Si and Ge. Finally, fundamental laser-solid interactions have been more controversial in semiconductors and thus are more interesting.

When an energetic pulse from a laser is incident on Si, the photons are absorbed into the electronic system of the solid primarily by the creation of electron hole pairs. Through electron-phonon interactions, the absorbed energy is rapidly transferred from the electronic system to the lattice atoms as heat, in times $\sim 10^{-11}$ s (Bloembergen et al., 1982). Thus, for sufficiently intense laser pulses, the near surface melts. This is a dominant feature of pulsed laser heating for mixing applications. The fact that such large amounts of energy can be absorbed into the near surface of a solid in such a short time leads to both melting, which is the primary source of mixing, and rapid quenching, which initiates non-equilibrium materials interactions.

The dominant mixing mechanism in pulsed laser mixing is diffusion in the liquid phase during the time the surface is molten. This was established from measurements of dopant redistribution in Si, following pulsed laser annealing, and model calculations of the melting process (e.g. White et al., 1979b, 1980; Wang et al., 1978; Baeri et al., 1978; Baeri, 1982). Several techniques have been used to calculate the time, temperature and space dependence of the molten surface layer and the dopant redistribution. The method most commonly used is a numerical solution to the diffusion equations for mass and heat transport expressed in finite differences. This method will be discussed here for illustrative purposes and the treatment follows the recent paper by Wood and Giles (1981). This formulation of the problem allows for inclusion of important target (absorption, reflectivity, conductivity, etc.) and laser (pulse shape, duration, energy density, etc.) parameters, and it can be used to calculate the explicit time and space dependence of the liquid-solid interface (Baeri, 1982; Wood and Giles, 1981). A calculation of the temperature and time variation with distance into a Si sample subjected to a 25 ns pulse from a Q-switched ruby laser at two different laser energy densities is shown in Fig. 12 (Wood and Giles, 1981). Figure 12a shows the temperature profiles at various times up to 200 ns following the absorption of a 1.75 J cm^{-2} pulse, and Fig. 12b the same information for a 1.25 J cm^{-2} pulse. From calculations such as these the position of the melt front as a function of time can be constructed. Fig. 13 shows such a plot for laser pulses of various energy densities. These calculations provide at least a conceptual understanding of the pulsed laser mixing process. Considering the calculations for 1.75 J cm^{-2} in Figs. 12 and 13, it is clear that the absorbed energy from the laser pulse leads to surface melting to a depth of ~ 0.7 μm within ~ 50 ns; and the surface remains melted over a depth ~ 0.1 μm for greater than ~ 200 ns. (More details of the rapid melting and resolidification processes in

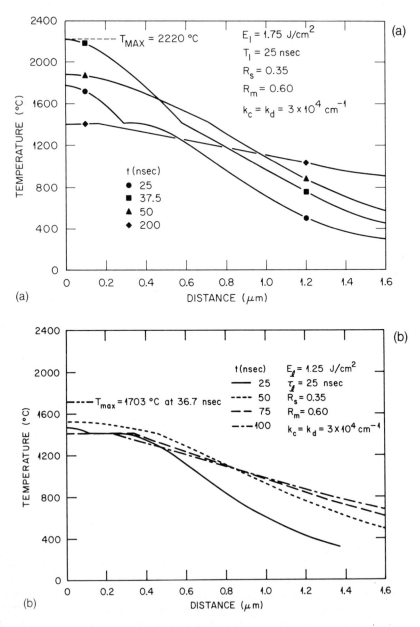

Fig. 12. (a) Calculated temperature versus depth profile from the surface of a silicon sample at several different times during and after a 25 nsec, 1.75 J cm[-2] laser pulse using the absorption coefficients K_d and K_c in the damaged and crystalline regions and the reflectivity coefficients in solid, R_s, and molten, R_m, silicon as shown. From Wood and Giles (1981). (b) Same as Fig. 12a except for a 1.25 J cm[-2] laser pulse.

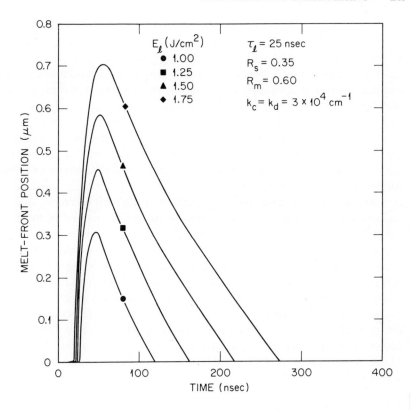

Fig. 13. Melt front position versus time from calculations in Fig. 12. From Wood and Giles (1981).

semiconductors have been given in Chapter 2, Section IV.) A composite metal–semiconductor sample with a ~ 0.1 μm thick Si layer on the surface for absorption could be expected to undergo similar melting behavior, with mixing occurring by liquid-phase diffusion. In general, surface melting is necessary for extensive mixing, since diffusion in the liquid phase is $\sim 10^5$ greater than in the solid phase. Of course, the absorbing material need not be a semiconductor. The various wavelengths, pulse durations, energy densities, etc., which exist for continuous, scanned cw and pulsed lasers, make it possible to process virtually any material. Similarly, electron beams are widely used for materials processing (Ferris *et al.,* 1979; White and Peercy, 1980; Gibbons *et al.,* 1981; Appleton and Celler, 1982). To date, calculations of the type presented in Figs. 12 and 13 have not been extended to composite thin-film structures of dissimilar materials like those usually employed for ion beam mixing. However, the calculations have been modified to include subtle differences such as phase changes, effects of pulse shape, duration and energy density, latent heat, etc. (Baeri, 1982; Wood and Giles, 1981), and in principle they could be adapted to mixing problems.

It would be remiss in any discussion of fundamental mechanisms not to mention the recent controversy surrounding the melting of Si during pulsed laser annealing. The controversy concerned whether the energy absorbed from the laser pulse into the electronic system of Si was transferred rapidly to phonons and thus to simple thermal melting, as presented here, or whether the energy remained in the electronic system in the form of a hot, dense plasma while the lattice remained cool, as proposed by Van Vechten (1980). Although the plasma annealing model has been useful in stimulating fundamental research, numerous papers presented in the most recent symposium on laser-solid interactions, covering measurements of charged particle emission, evaporated neutral atoms, thermally assisted photoelectric emission, space and time resolved reflectivity and transmission, phase changes, defect removal and X-ray time-resolved lattice-structure analysis, leave little doubt that the simple thermal melting model is correct (Appleton and Celler, 1982). It should also be pointed out that experimental techniques which are capable of determining the surface properties and near-surface structure of solids during the laser pulse have been developed (e.g. Appleton and Celler, 1982), and consequently, one can expect that calculations like those in Figs. 12 and 13 can be performed for a wide range of systems and checked with considerable accuracy in the future.

2. Rapid Quenching

The major advantage of utilizing scanned or pulsed laser or electron beams for mixing experiments is the rapid quenching aspects of the thermal processing. Referring again to Fig. 13, these calculations show that for a given laser energy density the solid rapidly melts to some maximum depth. Then, as the heat from the liquid is conducted away into the substrate, the melt front retreats back toward the surface. The slope of this portion of each curve in Fig. 13 shows that for these conditions the liquid-solid interface proceeds toward the surface at velocities ~ 4m s^{-1}. A rough estimate from these calculations for the time the near-surface is molten yields quench rates $\sim 10^9$–10^{10} K s^{-1}. If the laser wavelength is shifted into the ultraviolet and shorter pulse length lasers are used, these quench rates can be made even larger. It is estimated that rapid heating and cooling rates of 10^8–10^{14} K s^{-1} are within the range of existing pulsed lasers (Bloembergen, 1979).

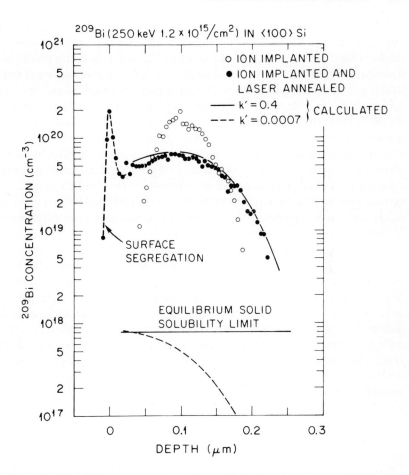

Fig. 14.   Concentrations versus depth for ion implanted and pulsed laser annealed Bi in Si illustrating the fabrication of supersaturated substitutional alloys.

3. Materials Interactions

An example which helps to identify some of the materials interactions which can occur during pulsed laser mixing is the fabrication of dilute supersaturated alloys from ion-implanted silicon. The fabrication process is illustrated by the results in Fig. 14, which show ^{209}Bi concentrations versus depth for 1.2×10^{15} Bi$^+$ cm^{-2} implanted in Si at 250 KeV before and after pulsed laser annealing (White *et al.*, 1982; Appleton *et al.*, 1979). As a consequence of ion implantation the Si was turned amorphous to a depth of ~ 0.19 μm, in the same manner as discussed for Fig. 5. Following laser annealing with a single pulse (~ 1.5 J cm^{-2}, 25 ns) from a ruby laser, the Bi depth profile was transformed into that shown by the filled circles. The interactions leading to this profile proceed as follows. The laser pulse is absorbed and the near surface melts to a depth ~ 0.6 μm. During the time the surface is molten, the Bi is redistributed by diffusion in the liquid. As the sample cools the liquid-solid interface proceeds toward the surface at a velocity ~ 4 ms^{-1}. Even at these extremely rapid regrowth velocities the silicon resolidifies by liquid-phase epitaxial growth into a defect-free single crystal. At each instant of time the amount of Bi incorporated into the solid at the rapidly moving interface or rejected into the liquid is mediated by the interfacial distribution coefficient k'. At low growth velocities under conditions of local equilibrium, k' is the same as the equilibrium distribution coefficient k_0, and the maximum concentration of Bi that can be accommodated in substitutional lattice sites is the equilibrium solid solubility limit for Bi indicated in Fig. 14. However, under these extremely rapid cooling rates, conditions at the interface are far from equilibrium and $k' \gg k_0$. Using the method of a finite difference solution to the mass diffusion equation discussed earlier, the dopant redistribution in Fig. 14 can be understood on the basis of redistribution by diffusion in the liquid, provided k' is treated as a fitting parameter (White *et al.*, 1980, 1982). Several striking features arise from an analysis of the results indicated in Fig. 14. Ion channeling shows that, following pulsed laser annealing, the Bi is totally incorporated into substitutional lattice sites at all depths $\gtrsim 0.02$ μm of the surface. Some surface segregation is observed. The total concentration of Bi incorporated into the lattice is ~ 500 times the maximum equilibrium solid solubility limit. This is emphasized in Fig. 14 by contrasting the two calculated profiles using the equilibrium (dashed line, $k' = 0.0007$) and best fit (solid line, $k' = 0.4$) values for k'. It is possible to form these supersaturated substitutional alloys because the solute atoms are trapped in the solid as a consequence of the rapid solidification. The maximum substitutional solubility concentrations which can be achieved in these dilute Si alloys by rapid quenching are limited by three mechanisms; lattice strain; instabilities created at the liquid-solid interface, which leads to segregation of the dopants; and fundamental thermodynamic considerations. Nevertheless, all these effects can be manipulated by varying the regrowth velocity (White *et al.*, 1982). A final consequence of these supersaturated alloys worth mentioning is that they can result in unique lattice alterations which lead to new materials and surface properties (Appleton *et al.*, 1979; Eastman *et al.*, 1982). It is clear that a wide range of rapid crystal growth and fundamental materials interaction phenomena, which were not possible with conventional techniques, can now be studied by utilizing pulsed laser processing. This is emphasized by the recent activity in this field (Appleton and Celler, 1982; White *et al.,* 1982).

As the quenching rate is increased through the use of other wavelengths and shorter laser pulses, several other materials interactions of fundamental interest become possible. One example is the amorphous-to-crystalline phase change in Si. Using ultra-violet radiation and 10–30 ps lasers Lie *et al.* (1979) and Tsu *et al.* (1979) turned the near surface region of single crystalline Si amorphous. In this case, solidification from the melt is so rapid that epitaxial growth is not possible and the amorphous phase is quenched. More recently, Cullis *et al.* (1982) were able to form amorphous Si by using a frequency-doubled ruby laser with 2.5 ns pulse length. The quenching in this case is intermediate between the picosecond case, where amorphous Si is produced, and the undoubled nanosecond ruby laser annealing discussed in the previous paragraph, where epitaxial regrowth occurs. As discussed in Chapter 2, Section V, from experiments such as these, it should be possible to establish critical quenching rates and relate them to calculations of the kinetics of regrowth (e.g. Spaepen and Turnbull, 1979). In fact, this concept has recently stimulated considerable study into the phase transitions in amorphous and crystalline silicon (Spaepen and Turnbull, 1979; Bagley and Chen, 1979; Fan and Anderson, 1981; Kokorowski *et al.,* 1982; Baeri *et al.,* 1981). Bagley and Chen (1979) suggested that amorphous Si could melt > 300K below the melting temperature of crystalline Si, and Baeri *et al.* (1981) reported measurements which showed such a reduction. However, Korokowski *et al.* (1982) have reported that the amorphous phase can be heated very close to the melting temperature of crystalline Si, using cw lasers, without changing phase. This controversy is as yet unresolved. From a review of the models and stability conditions in amorphous systems (Duwez, 1979; Cottril, 1976; Grant, 1981), it is clear that ion bombardment and pulsed laser processing are valuable tools for future studies in semiconductors and doped metals.

III. MATERIALS ALTERATIONS INDUCED BY ION BEAM AND PULSED LASER PROCESSING

In this section selected applications of ion beam and laser techniques used for inducing materials interactions will be presented. The presentation is neither comprehensive nor chronological. Emphasis will be on comparing ion beam and pulsed laser mixing where possible; on identifying the dominant mixing or quenching mechanisms where possible; and on highlighting new materials properties produced by these processing techniques. Several recent papers cited below review various materials interactions resulting from ion beam mixing, pulsed laser mixing, thermal annealing (solid-phase reactions), and scanned cw and electron-beam processing and the reader is referred to these original sources for complete details.

Most ion beam and pulsed laser mixing experiments are performed using thin film composite targets. Often a so-called unlimited-supply sample is used. This consists of sufficient amounts of each material so that, when mixing is induced at the interface, the materials interactions freely determine the ultimate composition. In other situations, evaporated thin films are used to limit the supply of materials for mixing and to force the composition to the desired value. Both kinds of experiments are discussed here. The first system discussed, the metal–semiconductor system, will be presented with more detail about the modification and analysis techniques used than later systems. Although specific examples will be chosen to represent trends in particular classes of materials, the reader is cautioned that exceptions are common. At various places in the text and figures, IBM and PLM are used as short notations for ion beam mixing and pulsed laser mixing, respectively.

A. Metal–Semiconductor Systems

1. Metal–Semiconductor Eutectic System

The phase diagrams for the four metal-semiconductor eutectic systems chosen for comparison are shown in Fig. 15. These eutectic systems were selected for a variety of reasons. Eutectics are simple systems with no stable phases; consequently, metastable phases initiated by ion beam or laser mixing will be less complicated to identify. The four have fairly similar phase diagrams, and cross comparisons of ion and laser mixing effects can be made on similar systems. All ion mixing bombardments were done with 300-450 keV Xe^+ in high vacuums. Most bombardments were done at room temperature, but some systems were ion mixed and ion beam analyzed *in situ* at temperatures from 4-350K, or ion mixed and then thermally annealed prior to analysis. All laser processing was done with a Q-switched ruby laser with $\sim$25 ns pulse length. The samples were analyzed using high resolution ion scattering, X-ray diffraction, and selected analysis by TEM and electrical resistivity.

(a) Au–Si. The Au-Sa eutectic was among the first to be studied systematically (e.g. Tsaur *et al.*, 1980c; Lau *et al.*, 1980a, 1981b; von Allmen, 1980). Figure 16 shows an ion-scattering analysis of a Au film vacuum deposited on Si (111) and bombarded at room temperature with 300 keV Xe^+ at doses of 2, 5 and 9 $\times$ 10^{14} Xe^+ cm^{-2}. A mixture of Au-Si of definite composition is seen to form at the interface, and the mixed layer increases in thickness

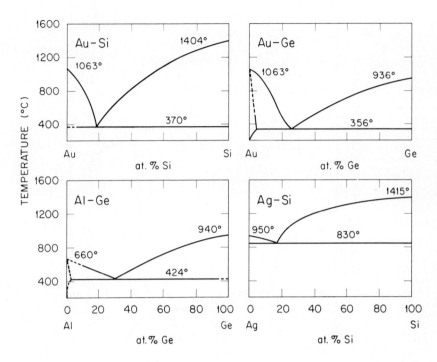

Fig. 15.   Partial equilibrium phase diagrams for Au–Si, Au–Ge, Al–Ge and Ag–Si eutectic system.

as the square root of the dose increases, but always at the same composition. From the relative heights of the ion scattering yields from Au and Si at the interface, the mixture was determined as Au-Si(28%), or $Au_{72}Si_{28}$. Annealing to $\sim 200°C$ resulted in no change in stoichiometry as measured using ion scattering. The microstructural character of the films at each stage of mixing and annealing was determined from TEM and X-ray scattering (Tsaur *et al.,* 1980c; Lau *et al.,* 1981b). The as-deposited Au films were fine grained polycrystalline; the ion mixed $Au_{72}Si_{28}$ layers were amorphous; annealing of the amorphous mixtures to $\sim 100°C$ for 30 min transformed the mixture into a metastable crystalline phase of the same composition (Au_5Si_2); and annealing to $\sim 200°C$ resulted in the decomposition of the metastable phase into an equilibrium Au–Si mixture (Tsaur *et al.,* 1980c).

This sequence of transformations can be represented schematically by the flow diagram in Table I. A similar diagram will be drawn for all the metal-semiconductor systems discussed in order to maintain a convenient record

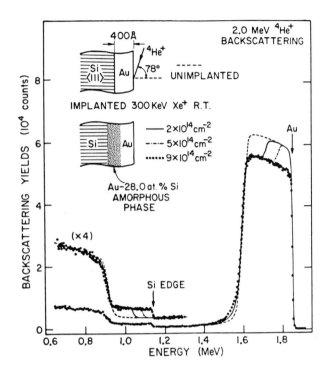

Fig. 16. Ion scattering analysis of the mixing of Au–Si induced by various doses of 300 keV Xe$^+$ at room temperature. From Tsaur *et al.* (1980c).

for reference. The last step, decomposition of the metastable crystalline phase, has been left out of Table I because it is always true that a system will progress toward the equilibrium phase when processed appropriately.

The ion beam mixing results were compared to pulsed laser mixing using the technique depicted in Fig. 17. A thin film of Si was deposited on the surface of a Au film on Si(100) so as to enhance absorption of the laser radiation. From the ion scattering analysis of Fig. 17 the effect of a single laser pulse can be seen to induce mixing at both the surface and substrate Si interfaces. From the decrease in height of the Au signal from this and similar measurements (e.g. Fig. 5 in Lau *et al.,* 1981b), the mixed composition was determined to be the eutectic composition $Au_{82}Si_{18}$; and TEM showed that the laser mixed layers were amorphous. Similar measurements by von Allmen *et al.* (1980) and Lau *et al.* (1980a), using multilayer samples to limit compositions, showed that multilayer samples covering the entire range of composition from $AuSi_{10}$ to $Au_{10}Si$ could be made amorphous mixtures by pulsed laser irradiation. Previous attempts to form such metallic glasses by liquid

TABLE I

Schematic of transformations in metal–semiconductor eutectic system.

METAL–SEMICONDUCTOR	IBM	EUTECTIC SYSTEM PLM	REF.
Au–Si	IBM: a → (TA) → mx Au$_5$Si$_2$; NEW	PLM: a → (TA(RT)) → mx Au$_5$Si$_2$; NEW	1–7
Au–Ge	IBM: a ---→ mx UNIDENTIFIED	PLM: a ---→ mx UNIDENTIFIED	5
Al–Ge	IBM: 2 PHASE MIXTURE ; LIMITED MIXING	PLM: a, ex; COMPLETE MIXING	5
Ag–Si	IBM: 2 PHASE MIXTURE ; LIMITED MIXING	PLM: a, mx; COMPLETE MIXING UNIDENTIFIED	5

IBM – ION BEAM MIXING
PLM – PULSED LASER MIXING
TA – THERMAL ANNEALING

a – AMORPHOUS
ex – EQUILIBRIUM CRYSTALLINE
mx – METASTABLE CRYSTALLINE

1. Mayer et al. (1981).
2. Tsaur et al. (1980d).
3. Lau et al. (1981a).
4. von Allmen et al. (1981).
5. Lau et al. (1981b).
6. von Allmen et al. (1980).
7. Lau et al. (1980a).

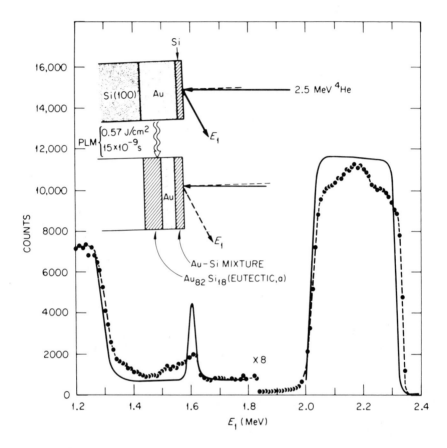

Fig. 17.   Ion scattering analysis of pulsed-laser-induced mixing in Au–Si.

quenching succeeded only near the eutectic composition. X-ray analysis and resistivity measurements led to the conclusion that amorphous Au–Si mixtures at nearly all compositions were formed during melting and rapid solidification, and that these mixtures decomposed at room temperature into the *same* metastable phase as that resulting from ion beam mixing; namely, Au_5Si_2. After longer times at room temperature, the two separate phases were observed. This sequence is also shown schematically in Table I.

   A comparison of the ion beam and laser mixing results for this system shows that both initiate amorphous mixtures with well-defined compositions. The amorphous phases almost certainly form by impurity stabilization and not as a consequence of the rapid quenching. Nevertheless, the amorphous mixtures are driven to quite different compositions in the two cases. Mixing under ion bombardment probably occurs by cascade mixing and defect enhanced migration: the systematics of the mixing (Tsaur *et al.*, 1980c) rule out contributions from thermal spikes. The composition where the ion mixed amorphous layer stabilized is the same as the composition of the metastable phase formed on annealing to 100°C; namely, Au_5Si_2. Furthermore, although some properties of the amorphous alloy formed by ion beam mixing are similar to those formed by liquid quenching, the compositions are different, and the structure of the metastable phase (Tsaur *et al.*, 1980c) is different from any of the metastable phases formed by liquid quenching (Anantharaman *et al.*, 1966; Suryanarayana and Anantharaman, 1971; Predicki *et al.*, 1965; Anderson *et al.*, 1971). This leads to the speculation that the Au_5Si_2 metastable phase was formed during ion mixing as a consequence of the (more rapid) cascade quenching, but that these local metastable phase regions were disordered by subsequent ion bombardment (Tsaur *et al.*, 1980c) only to be reformed on annealing at $\sim$ 100°C. The pulsed laser results may be more like the liquid quenched results, since the laser mixing terminates in a liquid quench, albeit much more rapid. Although all samples with unlimited supply of materials such as in Fig. 17 formed amorphous alloys at or near the eutectic composition, $Au_{82}Si_{18}$, limited supply samples were successfully used to force amorphous alloys to form at any composition (von Allmen *et al.*, 1980; Lau *et al.*, 1980a). Furthermore, upon thermal annealing at room temperature, the amorphous alloys formed a metastable crystalline phase with a hexagonal structure similar to the one found for the ion beam mixed, thermally annealed samples. The main difference between laser melt quenching and normal splat quenching experiments is that laser quenching is $\sim 10^2$ more rapid. This may explain how von Allmen *et al.*, (1980) were able to form Au–Si glass structures over a much wider range of compositions than those previously formed by liquid quenching. Pulsed laser quenching is, however, less rapid than cascade quenching.

The common element linking these sets of data is the formation of the same metastable crystalline phase from an amorphous mixture. The mixing and rapid quenching aspects are important in forming the amorphous Au–Si alloys, but the composition prior to annealing does not seem crucial. A definite preference for the $Au_{72}Si_{28}$ mixture seems to exist in the ion beam mixing results, thus supporting the idea that the metastable phase is formed during mixing. The laser mixing experiments require more careful measurements in the unlimited supply case, but the limited supply results seem to show that the metastable Au_5Si_2 phase can nucleate from a variety of starting compositions. Once in the amorphous state, the metastable crystalline phase becomes energetically favorable on annealing for thermodynamic (chemical, metallurgical) reasons, and on further annealing equilibrium conditions are reached. However, if it is true that the particular metastable phase produced by these mixing techniques cannot be produced through normal liquid quenching, it would appear that the properties of the amorphous state depend on the quenching rate which produces it, or that the "amorphous mixture" contains small quenched-in crystallites of the metastable phase which nucleate and grow on annealing. It is not inconceivable that local coordination of the atoms in the amorphous state could depend on quenching rate. A cursory analysis of the diffraction patterns of Si(100) and Si(111) made amorphous by ion implantation (see Fig. 6 for Si(100)) indicates that Si(111) shows a higher degree of disorder than Si(100). This suggests that the amorphous state can be different for different crystal orientations under identical bombardment conditions. Such observations emphasize the importance of the current controversy about, and interest in, amorphous semiconductors. In the present case, the results would suggest that rates $\sim 10^9$ K s^{-1} are sufficient to make the Au_5Si_2 metastable phase accessible on decomposition. Similarly, the concept of phase nucleation and growth is a very reasonable one, and it will be shown in later sections that this can be exploited to produce large-area samples of difficult phases.

(b) Au–Ge. The Au–Ge results are quite similar in character to Au–Si but have not been studied in sufficient detail to be interpreted unambiguously. The temperature dependence of the mixing in this system can be seen from the results in Fig. 18 and 19. These ion scattering spectra were obtained from samples ion mixed and analyzed at temperature. The series of spectra in Fig. 18 show that mixing is predominant at all temperatures from 4 to 350 K, but regions at the interface of definite composition are more obvious at room temperature and above (e.g. the step formation in the Au spectra in Fig. 18). Ion scattering analysis shows these regions of definite mixing to have compositions ranging from $\sim Au_{45}Ge_{55}$ (as in Fig. 18) to $Au_{50}Ge_{50}$ (Lau *et al.*, 1981b). The temperature dependence of the mixing shown in Fig. 18 is similar to that reported by Tsaur *et al.*, (1980c) for Au–Si, except that the Au–Ge measurements were performed at much lower temperatures, and the amount of mixing is much greater in Au–Ge than in Au–Si, even at these lower temperatures. Effects of continued mixing of Au–Ge at the higher temperatures and subsequent thermal annealing are shown on Fig. 19. Continued bombardment at 350 K to a dose of 8 × 10^{15} Xe$^+$ cm^{-2} shows that the limited supply of Au is consumed in the Ge at a composition $\sim Au_{35}Ge_{65}$. If this mixture is annealed to higher temperatures without ion bombardment, Ge–rich mixtures ranging up to $\sim Au_{15}Ge_{85}$ are formed. Analysis of the room temperature Au–Ge mixtures by X-ray diffraction within about 3 h of mixing (Lau *et al.*, 1981b) showed the presence of a metastable crystalline phase which has not yet been identified.

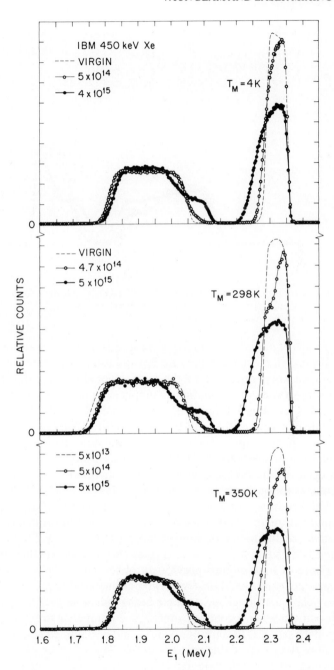

Fig. 18. Temperature dependence of ion-beam-induced mixing in Au–Ge–Al$_2$O$_3$ using 2.5 MeV He$^+$ backscattering for analysis. From Lau *et al.* (1981b).

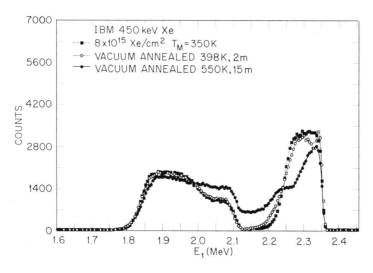

Fig. 19. Ion scattering analysis of thermal annealing effects on Au–Ge films previously mixed by ion bombardment at 350K.

The results of pulsed laser mixing were studied using a Ge–Au–Ge composite (like that discussed in Fig. 17 for Si), and using evaporated multilayer samples of Au–Ge in order to limit the composition (like those shown in Fig. 20). Laser processing of the unlimited supply samples resulted in mixtures of $\sim Au_{60}Ge_{40}$ (e.g. Fig. 7 in Lau *et al.*, 1981b), and the results of Fig. 20 show that complete mixing at the eutectic composition $\sim Au_{70}Ge_{30}$ occurred for the limited supply samples. The same unidentified metastable phase found in the ion beam mixed films was found in the laser mixed films.

Analogous to the Au–Si results, the same metastable crystalline phase forms from both ion beam and laser mixing. It is not clear in the Au–Ge results whether an amorphous mixture forms first and then decomposes at room temperature, or whether the metastable phase forms directly. Various observations, including the prominent mixing of Ge at lower temperatures compared to Si, suggest the former. It is also not known whether the metastable phase is new or one previously observed by splat quenching. Anantharaman *et al.* (1965) observed two new metastable phases in Au–Ge alloys by splat quenching, one a simple hexagonal close packed (hcp) structure (β) and the other a complex superlattice tetragonal structure (γ). The γ-tetragonal phase was the only one which could be obtained homogeneously in any alloy. Both were stable up to $\sim 100°C$. The structure of the γ phase in a $Au_{60}Ge_{40}$ alloy was in good agreement with a complex model based on two related unit cells, and the $Au_{50}Ge_{50}$ alloys showed strong preferential

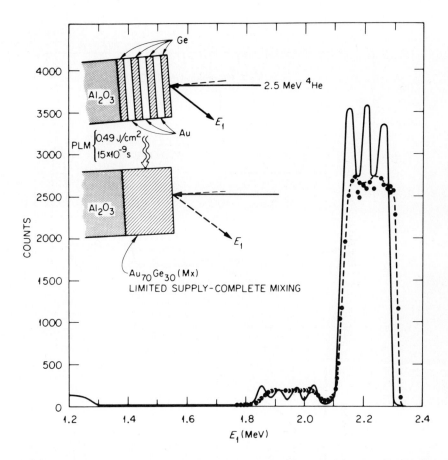

Fig. 20. Pulsed laser mixing of multi-layer Au–Ge sample with composition near the eutectic $Au_{70}Ge_{30}$. From Lau *et al.* (1981b).

orientation effects after rapid solidification. The homogeneous tetragonal phase formed in splat quenching over the alloy compositions ranging from $Au_{50}Ge_{50}$ to $Au_{64}Ge_{36}$ could easily be the same metastable phase observed in the present mixing experiments. Careful X-ray analysis is needed to clarify this point further. The more rapid quench rate in the present work, and the fact that the phase is stable up to 100°C, while the metastable phase here is formed at room temperature, makes a new metastable phase a distinct possibility. As pointed out by Anantharaman *et al.* (1965), fabrication of a homogeneous sample of the $Au_{50}Ge_{50}$ alloy which showed a marked preferential orientation would be particularly interesting because the proposed

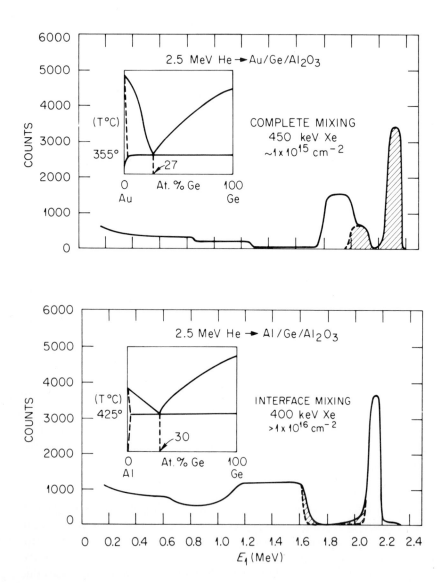

Fig. 21. Ion scattering analyses contrasting the ion beam mixing behavior of Au–Ge and Al–Ge.

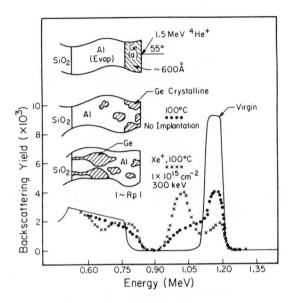

Fig. 22.   Ion scattering analysis and schematic representation of the reactions induced in Al–Ge by ion bombardment at 100°C. From Lau *et al.* (1981b).

structure is superconducting. The ion beam mixture decomposes upon thermal annealing toward a composition $Au_{15}Ge_{85}$ (Fig. 19) which is probably the Ge rich diamond-cubic phase identified in the work of Anantharaman *et al.* (1965).

(c) Al–Ge and Ag–Si. The ion beam mixing behavior of Al–Ge is contrasted to that of Au–Ge in Fig. 21. Even at doses fifteen times greater than that required to completely mix Au–Ge, Al–Ge shows only limited mixing at the interface. This is graphic evidence of the importance of materials and defect interactions in the mixing process. If the Al–Ge composite is heated to 100°C in order to encourage mixing through diffusion, results like those depicted in Fig. 22 are obtained. At 100°C without ion bombardment the Ge film decomposes and forms Ge clusters in the Al matrix. Ion bombardment accelerates the Ge transport, but phase separation still occurs (Lau *et al.*, 1981b). This is consistent with solid-phase reactions that have been reported for metal-semiconductor eutectic systems (e.g. Lau and van der Weg, 1978). Ion scattering analysis of the results of pulsed laser mixing are shown in Fig. 23. For increasing laser energy densities, increased mixing is observed at a fixed composition of $Al_{60}Ge_{40}$. X-ray diffraction shows that the rapidly quenched film forms an amorphous mixture, with some precipitated Al but no evidence of metastable crystalline phases (Lau *et al.* 1981b).

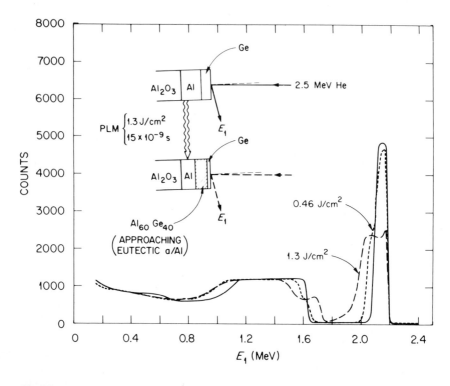

Fig. 23. Pulsed laser mixing of Al–Ge at various laser energy densities as determined from ion scattering. After Lau *et al.* (1981b).

The results of Ag–Si are very similar. Ion bombardment, even at elevated temperatures, results in limited mixing at the interface only and X-ray diffraction indicates a two-phase mixture. Pulsed laser processing is more successful in that mixing occurs and metastable crystalline phases are observed, but not identified (Lau *et al.*, 1981b). Much work remains to be done on these semiconductor eutectic systems to verify the transitions depicted in Table I. Such analysis will require low temperature X-ray analysis, TEM or some other technique so that the amorphous to metastable crystalline phase transitions can be identified.

2. Silicides

Mixing in metal–semiconductor systems which form silicides may be expected to be more complicated than the simple eutectic systems because of the many stable phases which occur. These stable phases will be effective in suppressing metastable phases of similar compositions, even under rapid quenching conditions. Some of the metal–semiconductor systems in which silicides have been formed by ion beam and pulsed laser mixing are listed in Table II. Although silicides produced by equilibrium techniques have been studied extensively, those produced by ion beam and laser mixing have not. Consequently, instead of attempting a review of the field, trends established in some of the more widely studied systems will be presented. Following the discussions of Mayer *et al.* (1981), Lau *et al.* (1980b), and von Allmen *et al.* (1981) the Pd–Si and Pt–Si systems will be reviewed.

The results for ion beam and pulsed laser mixing of Pd–Si and Pt–Si are summarized schematically and contrasted to thermally prepared silicides in Table III, and alloy composition effects on mixing are depicted in Fig. 24. Energetic ion bombardment of both Pd–Si and Pt–Si induce the formation of the stable silicides Pd_2Si and Pt_2Si respectively at the interface. The thicknesses of these silicides increase with the square root of ion dose, as with Au–Si and Ge–Si. This suggests a diffusion-like mixing process. These are also the first silicides formed by thermal annealing. Continued ion bombardment of Pd_2Si results in the formation of PdSi at the Pd_2Si–Si interface (Tsaur *et al.*, 1979). The final silicides formed by thermal annealing depend on the initial preparation of the film, annealing temperature, etc. The Pd_2Si phase forms from thermally reacted Pd–Si films at $\sim 200°C$, while PdSi nucleates at $\sim 700°C$ (Tu and Mayer, 1978). Tsaur *et al.* (1979) found that thermal annealing to $\sim 350°C$, after formation of the PdSi phase by ion mixing,

TABLE II
Ion beam and pulsed laser mixing studies in silicides

Metal	References
V	Lau *et al.* (1980b); von Allmen *et al.* (1981); Appleton *et al.* (1981); Stritzker (1982).
Cr	Mayer *et al.* (1981); Lau *et al.* (1980b).
Fe	Mayer *et al.* (1981).
Co	Mayer *et al.* (1981).
Ni	Mayer *et al.* (1981); Poate *et al.* (1979); Wittmer and von Allmen (1981); Tan *et al.* (1979).
Nb	Mayer *et al.* (1981); Poate *et al.* (1979); Sigmon (1981); von Allmen *et al.* (1981).
Mo	Poate *et al.* (1979).
Rh	Wittmer and von Allmen (1981).
Pd	Mayer *et al.* (1981); Liau *et al.* (1979); Poate *et al.* (1979); Lau *et al.* (1980b); Sigmon (1981); von Allmen *et al.* (1981); Wittmer and von Allmen (1981); Tan *et al.* (1979); Tsaur *et al.* (1979).
Hf	Mayer *et al.* (1981).
W	Tan *et al.* (1979).
Pt	Mayer *et al.* (1981); Poate *et al.* (1979); Lau *et al.* (1981a); von Allmen *et al.* (1981); Wittmer and von Allmen (1981); Tsaur *et al.* (1980b); Tsaur *et al.* (1980c).

TABLE III
Schematic of transformations in metal-semiconductor silicide system.

METAL-SEMICONDUCTOR	IBM	SILICIDE SYSTEM — PLM	REF.
Pd-Si	i) IBM → ex Pd$_2$Si → IBM → ex PdSi ii) a → TA → ex Pd$_2$Si, Pd$_2$Si	i) a → PLM → a → TA → ex Pd$_2$Si, PdSi . . . ii) PLM → ex iii) a → PLM → mx UNIDENTIFIED	1–4, 6 8, 9
Pt-Si	i) IBM → ex Pt$_2$Si → IBM → a Pt-Si a → TA → mx Pt$_2$Si$_3$, Pt$_4$Si$_9$: NEW ii) a → TA → ex Pt$_2$Si, PtSi → TA → ex PtSi	i) a → PLM → a → TA → ex PtSi, Pt$_2$Si . . . ii) PLM → ex iii) a → PLM → a → TA → mx Pt$_2$Si, Pt$_4$Si$_9$: NEW UNIDENTIFIED	1–8, 10–12

IBM – ION BEAM MIXING
PLM – PULSED LASER MIXING
TA – THERMAL ANNEALING

a – AMORPHOUS
ex – EQUILIBRIUM CRYSTALLINE
mx – METASTABLE CRYSTALLINE

1. Mayer et al. (1981).
2. Poate et al. (1979).
3. Wittmer and von Allmen (1979).
4. Lau et al. (1980b).
5. Lau et al. (1981a).
6. von Allmen et al. (1981).
7. Lau et al. (1980a).
8. Wittmer and von Allmen (1981).
9. Tsaur et al. (1979).
10. Tu and Mayer (1978).
11. Tsaur et al. (1980b).
12. Tsaur et al. (1980c).

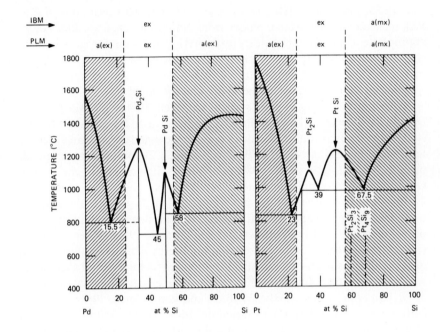

Fig. 24. Schematic summary of the ion beam mixing (IBM) and pulsed laser mixing (PLM) results induced in the Pd–Si and Pt–Si systems as a function of composition. See the discussion in the text. After Lau *et al.* (1981a); von Allmen *et al.* (1981).

resulted in the growth of PdSi at the expense of Pd_2Si, but that further annealing to $\sim$550°C resulted in a reversal to Pd_2Si. Ion bombardment of the Pt-Si system differs in that after formation of the Pt_2Si phase, further bombardment results in the formation of amorphous Pt–Si mixture (Mayer *et al.*, 1981; Tsaur *et al.*, 1980b,d). This difference has been attributed to the radiation damage sensitivity of the PtSi phase (Mayer *et al.*, 1981) and is analogous to the arguments made earlier concerning the instability of the Au_5Si_2 metastable phase under ion bombardment. There are further similarities in these two systems. When a PtSi film on Si was ion mixed (4×10^{14} Xe^+ cm^{-2}), a silicon-rich amorphous Pt–Si mixture formed; annealing ($\sim$400°C) of this amorphous alloy resulted in the formation of metastable

Pt_2Si_3. Further bombardment (5×10^{15} Xe^+ cm^{-2}) and annealing (400°C) resulted in the formation of an additional metastable phase, Pt_4Si_9 (Mayer et al., 1981; Lau et al., 1981a; Tsaur et al., 1980b,d). This technique of thermal nucleation of metastable phases from induced amorphous alloys of the appropriate composition appears extremely promising for growing and studying metastable structures. These metastable phases decompose on thermal annealing to high temperature (~ 600°C) to the stable PtSi structure, which is also the end phase in thermally reacted silicides.

Pulsed laser mixing in these systems has been studied for thin-film deposits on single crystals and multilayer samples so as to force desired compositions, and comparisons to silicides formed by scanned cw laser and e-beams have been made (Liau et al., 1979; Poate et al., 1979; Wittmer and von Allmen, 1979, 1981; Lau et al., 1980a,b, 1981a,b; Sigmon, 1981; von Allmen et al., 1980, 1981; Appleton et al., 1981; Follstaedt, 1982; Tan et al., 1979; Tsaur et al., 1979, 1980b,d; Tu and Mayer, 1978). Typical results obtained using metal layers evaporated on Si single crystals can be exemplified by Pd on Si (Lau et al., 1981a; Wittmer and von Allmen, 1981). When the Pd–Si composite is annealed with a laser pulse at energy densities sufficient to induce melting, a silicon-rich mixture of compounds is formed and a characteristic microstructure develops in the near-surface region (e.g. Poate et al., 1979; Lau et al., 1980b, 1981a; Wittmer and von Allmen, 1981). When the surface melts, Pd and Si mix by liquid diffusion. As the molten mixture solidifies, some Pd reacts with the Si and the rest is rejected into the liquid in front of the rapidly moving liquid-solid interface. Large composition gradients exist in the melt, and consequently nucleation of many compounds is possible (Wittmer and von Allmen, 1981). At sufficiently high concentrations of Pd, lateral instabilities are set up in the melt and cells are formed which consists of partially epitaxial columns of Si surrounded by thin walls of silicides and rejected metal. This cellular structure is caused by constitutional supercooling. Ion scattering analysis shows arbitrary average compositions, and X-rays reveal a mixture of phases (Lau et al., 1980b; Wittmer and von Allmen, 1981). In the case of Pd the compounds PdSi, Pd_2Si, Pd_3Si and Pd_4Si have been identified after pulsed laser mixing, and Pt showed PtSi, Pt_2Si, $Pt_{12}Si_{15}$ and Pt_3Si (Wittmer and von Allmen, 1981). This kind of mixing is described schematically by the middle regime (ii) in Table III. If these pulsed laser mixed silicides are furnace annealed, the most stable or fastest-forming phase nucleates and grows, and the surviving phase is not always the same as the end-phase in a binary reaction couple. The surviving phases for Pd–Si, Pt–Si, Ni–Si and Rh–Si which were pulsed laser mixed and then furnace annealed to 700–800°C are Pd_2Si, PtSi, NiSi, and Rh_3Si_4 respectively (Wittmer and von Allmen, 1981).

The explicit dependence of composition on pulsed laser mixing has been investigated for a number of silicides by using multilayer samples. The results for Pd and Pt are highlighted in the second half of Table III and in Fig. 24 (Lau *et al.*, 1981a; von Allmen *et al.*, 1981). These schematics indicate three definite regimes of mixing.

1. For Pd or Pt rich multilayer samples ($<$25 at. % Si), pulsed laser mixing induced an amorphous mixture which decomposed upon thermal annealing ($<$400°C) into the equilibrium silicide phases. This is indicated by (i) in Table III and at the tops of the phase diagram in Fig. 24 by a(ex).
2. For starting compositions near the major equilibrium phases (i.e. 33 and 50 at. % Si), the crystalline equilibrium phases were formed directly from the laser quenched films.
3. For Si rich alloys ($>$55 at. % Si), an amorphous mixture which resulted from mixing and thermal annealing initiated the formation of equilibrium phases in the case of Pd–Si and three metastable phases in the case of Pt–Si (Lau *et al.*, 1981a; von Allmen *et al.*, 1981).

The two metastable phases which have been identified are shown as dashed lines in Fig. 24 and are the same phases which form during thermal annealing of ion mixed Pt–Si. The third is as yet unidentified (von Allmen *et al.*, 1981).

3. Mixing and Materials Interactions

The results from the metal–semiconductor systems show that the defect and materials interactions peculiar to a particular combination of materials is the dominant factor in determining both the mixing and the ultimate materials properties. In the eutectic systems, Au–Ge and Al–Ge have very similar phase diagrams but very different ion mixing characteristics. Even allowing for kinematic differences in the cascade mixing process between Au and Al, ion beam mixing in the Au–Ge system is much more pronounced at all tempatures. This enhanced mixing is present to varying degrees in both the eutectics which form metastable phases, Au–Ge and Au–Si, and all the silicide forming systems. The term "dynamic collision cascade" mixing has been used to describe these systems because the systematics of the mixing are consistent with the diffusion-like cascade mixing process (Mayer *et al.*, 1981). Studies on Cr–Si and Nb–Si (Matteson *et al.*, 1979) show that radiation-enhanced diffusion dominates the mixing above room temperature; so it is reasonable to assume that defect mobility plays an important role in dynamic collision cascade mixing at lower temperatures in these systems.

It has been suggested by Lau et al. (1981b) that strong chemical or thermodynamic driving forces are responsible for both the efficient mixing of the Au–Si and Au–Ge system, and for the fact that they form metastable crystalline phases. In essence, if the atomic mobility provided by the ion beam mixing process makes these metastable states energetically accessible, then mixing is enhanced and phase formation occurs; if not, then neither occurs. This would also account for mixing in the silicide systems where driving forces for compound formation exist. The absence of ion beam mixing in Al–Ge and Ag–Si suggests that no strong driving force to form metastable phases exists. This is consistent with the observations that metastable phases form more easily in Au–Si and Au–Ge by liquid quenching than in Al–Ge and Ag–Si. These evaluations do not, however, identify the defect mobility mechanisms or thermodynamic driving forces; nor do they provide much information on rapid quenching effects in ion beam mixing. The dependence of amorphous mixtures on quenching rates and the growth of metastable phases from amorphous mixtures were raised earlier in section II.

The role of rapid quenching seems better defined in the pulsed laser mixing results. In the eutectic system Au–Si where no stable silicides exist it was possible to form glassy amorphous alloys over a range of compositions much greater than with splat quenching (Lau et al., 1980a, 1981a; von Allmen et al., 1980, 1981). In the silicide systems Pd–Si, Pt–Si, V–Si and Nb–Si, similar amorphous alloys could be formed at all compositions except those close to a stable phase. This effect was discussed for Pd and Pt in connection with Fig. 24 and is probably a direct result of the increased quenching rates available with laser quenching (10^8-10^{10} K s^{-1}) compared to splat quenching ($< 10^6$ K s^{-1}). At compositions near the stable phases PdSi, Pd$_2$Si, PtSi, Pt$_2$Si and V$_3$Si, von Allmen et al. (1981) found that pulsed laser mixing resulted in the formation of crystalline rather than amorphous phases. It was speculated that the stable phases could either nucleate in the liquid phase on cooling, or form from the amorphous phase at room temperature. Lau et al. (1981a) suggested that the crystalline phase was able to form because the quenching rate was slowed by heat liberated in the formation of the compounds.

B. Metal Systems

Several examples of materials interactions induced in thin-film composites or ion-implanted metal targets by ion bombardment or laser processing will be discussed in this section. Materials interactions resulting from direct ion implantation doping (so-called ion implantation metallurgy) will not be discussed. There are a number of recent articles which review the mechanisms governing the ion-implantation process, and which discuss its use of fabricating stable and metastable alloy systems, and its limitations for alloy studies (Mayer *et al.*, 1980; Liau and Mayer, 1980; Myers, 1980; Poate and Cullis, 1980; Williams and Baker, 1981; Brice, 1976; Kaufmann *et al.*, 1977).

Although ion implantation metallurgy and ion beam mixing share many of the same controlling mechanisms, there are some subtle differences. In the former case the ion which initiates the damage is also the alloying agent; thus the manner in which it comes to rest and the local metallurgy of this resting place can be very important in determining its interactions. If, for example, the ion makes a replacement collision as described in the first part of this section it can end up on a lattice site. In a review of implantation effects, Poate and Cullis (1980) showed that the preference for substitutional lattice sites of certain ion implanted impurities in Cu correlated well with the replacement collision concept. However, related work by Kaufmann *et al.* (1977) on implantation of many species in Be, in cases where replacement collisions were not possible, showed that the final lattice site for all these implants was determined by the same metallurgical parameters that govern equilibrium alloying. Ion implantation is limited to the fabrication of dilute alloys ($\sim$ 10 at. %) because of the sputtering limitation (Mayer *et al.*, 1980; Liau and Mayer, 1980); so metallurgical forces and interface effects sometimes associated with thin film systems may be absent. Both techniques, however, are subject to cascade quenching, diffusion or defect-enhanced diffusion, precipitation, defect interactions and a host of micrometallurgical effects. Consequently, both similarities and differences exist between alloys (stable and metastable) fabricated in the regime where these techniques overlap. In discussing ion beam mixing in metals, correlations will be mentioned where possible.

A selection of metals systems which have been studied by ion bombardment and pulsed laser or pulsed electron beam annealing is given in Table IV. This can be compared to a similar table in Poate and Cullis (1980), where metastable ion implanted alloys and references are given. Unfortunately, Table IV is not a complete list. The discussions in the next section on superconducting alloys and compounds will show that many ion-bombardment studies in that field are absent, and studies of surface alloys fabricated using scanned lasers (not to mention splat cooling, melt spinning, sputter deposition, vapor deposition, etc.) are also omitted. Other notable omissions are the use of ion implantation and ion bombardment in general for studies of defect-assisted segregation and precipitation (Marwick and Piller, 1981), and for investigations of amorphous metals (Grant, 1981).

The first class of materials listed in Table IV (Ni–Al, Pd–Al and Pt–Al) was chosen for comparison to the silicides already discussed (Mayer *et al.*, 1981). Ion beam mixing of these thin ($\sim$ 200 Å) metal films on Al at room

TABLE IV

Ion beam, laser and electron beam processing of metals systems.

System	Process	Results	Reference
Ni–Al	IBM	$Al_3Ni\,(\xrightarrow{TA} Al_3Ni)$	1
Pd–Al	IBM	$AlPd_2\,(\xrightarrow{TA} Al_3Pd)$	1
Pt–Al	IBM	$Al_2Pt\,(\xrightarrow{TA} Al_4Pt)$	1
Ag–Cu	IBM	Single-phase fcc, mss, $T_d \sim 175°C$	1, 2, 3
Au–Ni	IBM	Single-phase fcc, mss, $T_d \sim 300°C$	1, 4
Au–Co	IBM	Single-phase fcc, mss, amorphous $Au_{25}Co_{75}$ (LN_2), $T_d \sim 320°C$	1, 3, 4
Cu–Co	IBM	Single-phase fcc, mss	1
Au–Fe	IBM	Au-rich fcc, mss; Fe-rich bcc, mss. $Au_{38}Fe_{62}$ fcc + bcc. $T_d \sim 300°C$	4
Au–V	IBM	Au-rich fcc, ss; V-rich bcc, ss $Au_{40}V_{60}$ fcc + bcc; amorphous $Au_{40}V_{60}$ (LN_2)	3, 4
Ag–Ni	IBM	2 phases, Ag-rich and Ni-rich fcc	1, 5
Ag–Co	IBM	phase separation, Ag fcc and Co hcp	1
Au–Cu (S.C.)	IBM	ss	6
Pd–Cu (S.C.)	IBM	ss	6
Ag–Ni	PLM	ss	7
Au–Ni	PLM	ss	7
Pd–Ni	PLM	ss	7
Ta–Ni	PLM	ss	7
Ni–Au–Ni	PLM	2 phase mixture	8
Au——> Cu (S.C.)	PEBA	mss	9
Ag——> Cu (S.C.)	PEBA	mss	9
Ta——>Cu (S.C.)	PEBA	Ta precipitates	9
Au——>Ni (S.C.)	PLM	mss	10, 11
Ag——>Ni (S.C.)	PLM	mss, non-substitutional Ag	10, 11
Ta——>Ni (S.C.)	PLM	mss	10, 11
Pd——>Ni (S.C.)	PLM	lpe	10, 11
Sn——>Ni (S.C.)	PLM	lpe	10, 11
Al (S.C.)	PLM	lpe, lid, quenched-in vacancies	12
Zn——>Al (S.C.)	PLM		12
Sb——>Al (S.C.)	PLM	AlSb	12
Cd——>Al (S.C.)	PLM		13
Mo——>Al (S.C.)	PLM		13
Ni——>Al (S.C.)	PEBA	mss	18
Sn——>Al (S.C.)	PEBA	mss	18
Ga——>Al (S.C.)	PEBA	sa	14
Ni (S.C.)	PLM	lpe, depends on crystal orientation; lid	10, 11, 15
Pd (S.C.)	PLM	lpe, depends on crystal orientation; lid	15
Rh (S.C.)	PLM	lpe, lid	15
Mo (S.C.)	PLM	lpe, lid	15
Nb (S.C.)	PLM	lpe, lid	15
W (S.C.)	PLM	lpe, lid	15

TABLE IV—continued

System	Process	Results	Reference
Fe (S.C.)	PLM	lpe, lid	15
Be (S.C.)	PLM	—	15
Ti (S.C.)	PLM	—	15
Re (S.C.)	PLM	—	15
NbN (S.C.)	PLM	lpe, lid, surface damage	16, 17
V_3Si (S.C.)	PLM	lpe, lid, surface damage	16, 17
V_3Ge (S.C.)	PLM	lpe, lid	16, 17
Nb_3Ir (S.C.)	PLM	lpe, lid	16, 17
Ni	PLM	lpe, lid	16, 17
Cu	PLM	lpe, lid	16, 17
Au	PLM	lpe, lid	16, 17
Pt	PLM	lpe, lid	16, 17

IBM	—ion beam mixing	hcp	—hexagonal close packed
PLM	—pulsed laser mixing	sa	—substitutional alloy
PEBA	—pulsed electron beam annealing	mss	—metastable solid solution
TA	—thermal annealing	ss	—solid solution
S.C.	—single crystal	lpe	—liquid phase epitaxy
fcc	—face-centered cubic	lid	—laser induced defects
bcc	—body-centered cubic	T_d	—decomposition temperature

1. Mayer *et al.*, 1981.
2. Tsaur *et al.*, 1980a.
3. Lau *et al.*, 1981a.
4. Tsaur *et al.*, 1981.
5. Tsaur and Mayer, 1980.
6. Mayer *et al.*, 1980.
7. Draper *et al.*, 1980.
8. Pronko *et al.*, 1981.
9. Hirvonen *et al.*, 1980.
10. Buene *et al.*, 1981a.
11. Buene *et al.*, 1980.
12. Wampler *et al.*, 1981.
13. Battaglin *et al.*, 1981.
14. Hussain *et al.*, 1980.
15. Buene *et al.*, 1981b.
16. Appleton *et al.*, 1980.
17. Appleton *et al.*, 1981.
18. Picraux *et al.*, 1981.

temperature with 300 keV Xe^+ at doses $\sim 10^{15}$ cm^{-2} showed definite mixing and compound formation, as listed in the table. Only Ni on Al formed the same stable phase as thermal annealing. This in itself is interesting, since it indicates that the nucleation and growth sequences of stable and high temperature phases, as well as metastable phases, can be altered and studied by rapid quenching techniques. The next eight thin-film binary couples listed in Table IV, starting with Ag–Cu and ending with Ag–Co, were studied by ion beam mixing multiple layer samples of controlled thickness to give average compositions ranging from 10 to 90 at. % (Mayer *et al.*, 1981; Tsaur *et al.*, 1980a, 1981; Tsaur and Mayer, 1980; and original references therein). The mixing was done at room temperature or liquid nitrogen temperature with 100-300 keV Xe ions. This series of noble metals provides a cogent test of ion beam alloying techniques for several reasons. First, many of the same systems have been fabricated by high dose ion implantation, as well as by ion beam mixing, and most have been evaluated by splat quenching techniques. This provides a convenient benchmark for evaluating the alloying techniques relative to each other. The various binary couples pair face centered cubic (fcc) metals (Au, Ag, Cu, Ni and Pd) with each other and with hcp (Co) and body centered cubic (bcc) (Fe, V) structures. This allows an assessment of the effects different crystal structures have on alloy formation by ion beam mixing. The equilibrium phase diagrams vary from simple systems like Au–Cu, which form a continuous solid solution, to simple eutectics like Ag–Cu, which have no intermediate stable phases; to the four transition-metal couples (Ni, Co, Fe, and V), which exhibit a range of immiscibilities, and each type has different equilibrium phase structures. The Ag–Cu system is a good example for comparing the various techniques. It was the pioneering development of splat quenching by Duwez et al. (1960) which showed that rapid quenching techniques could be used to form a continuous series of metastable solid solutions from the eutectic Ag–Cu system. These metastable Ag–Cu alloys were shown to be single phase, with lattice parameters which varied linearly with composition. This is analogous to the behavior of the equilibrium Ag–Au ideal solid solutions. Using high-dose ion implantation, Poate et al. (1977) were able to produce metastable substitutional solid solutions of up to 16 at. % Ag by implanting Ag into Cu, and Hirvonen et al. (1980) showed that melting and rapid recrystallization of such ion-implanted samples formed metastable solid solutions in which the Ag remained highly substitutional (see Table IV). Similarly, ion beam mixing studies by Tsaur et al. (1980a) produced a continuous series of metastable Ag–Cu solid solutions by ion beam mixing. These metastable alloys were single fcc phases which decomposed into two-phase structures of Ag and Cu on annealing to $\sim 175°C$. These combined observations show that metastable Ag–Cu alloys can be produced by all the rapid quenching techniques.

Although Au–Ni, Au–Co, and Cu–Co have differing equilibrium phase diagrams, all form single phase fcc metastable solid solutions over the whole range of compositions (Tsaur et al., 1981, and references therein). The equilibrium phase diagram shows that Au and Ni are immiscible, but supersaturated solid solutions have been formed by splat quenching, vapor deposition, and sputtering, as well as by ion beam mixing. Au–Co is more complex, with very little mutual solubility below 500°C, and involves two structures, Au (fcc) and Co (hcp). Nevertheless, metastable solid solutions over a wide range can be produced by ion beam mixing and splat quenching, and an amorphous $Au_{25}Co_{75}$ alloy is observed.

The equilibrium phase diagrams for Au–Fe and Au–V are much more complex, with ordered phases and different crystal structures dominating at various compositions. The effects of this can be seen in the ion beam mixing results listed in Table IV. For Au-rich compositions, single phase fcc Au–Fe solutions can be obtained by ion beam mixing, while for Fe-rich compositions, single phase bcc solutions result. Simultaneous fcc and bcc phases are found at $Au_{38}Fe_{62}$, and the metastable solid solutions decompose at $\sim 300°C$. Au–V shows similar behavior (see Table IV), and an amorphous alloy is found at the same composition as the mixed phase, $Au_{40}V_{60}$.

The main conclusions to be drawn from the ion beam mixing results in metals is that metastable solid solutions can be formed over a much wider range of compositions than is possible with splat quenching, and this is most likely due to the very rapid quenching rate simulated by ion bombardment. In some cases, this rapid quench can produce metastable–amorphous phases not attainable by splat quenching. The final metastable alloy compositions are influenced by the presence of stable phases, but even in cases like Au–V, where the equilibrium phase diagram is complex, ion beam mixing results are often surprisingly simple.

The pulsed laser and electron beam annealing results listed in Table IV are too extensive to review in detail, but some general trends should be noted. The pulsed laser results usually involve a more rapid quench than pulsed electron beams, because the laser pulse duration is shorter and the energy loss processes deposit the laser energy in a much shallower surface layer than is the case for electrons. Nevertheless, many of the systems studied by both techniques have been shown to form metastable solid solutions, substitutional alloys, precipitates, quenched-in vacancies, etc., which are characteristic of quenching rates more rapid than splat quenching. Many of the systems studied were ion-implanted single crystals such as the Ag–Cu case already discussed.

Several of the studies in Table IV involved pulsed laser or electron beam processing of single crystal metals or compounds. It appears that many metals can undergo liquid-phase epitaxial regrowth following surface melting, but most also have quenched-in defects or surface damage to varying degrees. An example is shown in Fig. 25, which compares ion scattering/channeling measurements on a V_3Si (100) single crystal after 0.7 and 1.1 J cm^{-2} pulses from a Q-switched ruby laser (Appleton et al., 1980, 1981). It was found that, with increasing laser energy density, the channeling minimum yield increased, indicating an increase in lattice disorder. Transmission electron microscopy showed that microcracks developed in the surface, with no plastic zones associated with them. In this particular case the stress-strain behavior of V_3Si at high temperatures suggests that as a consequence of rapid quenching the surface did not remain above $1300°C$ long enough for dislocations to form (Appleton et al., 1981). In general, some form of laser-induced defects was observed for most single crystal metals reported in Table IV. This is probably a result of similar severe mechanical stresses established at the surfaces by the large thermal gradients.

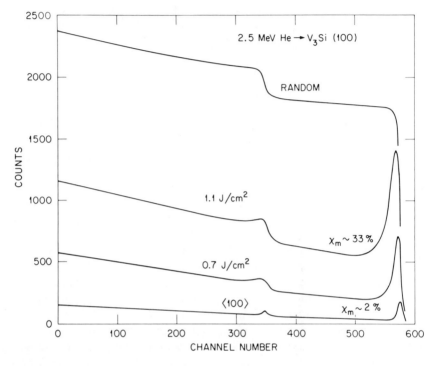

Fig. 25. Ion channeling evaluation of the disorder induced in $V_3Si(100)$ single crystals induced by pulsed laser processing. From Appleton *et al.* (1981).

C. Superconducting Materials

Superconducting materials are particularly well suited for ion beam and pulsed laser mixing investigations, for a variety of reasons. First, alterations of materials properties to the superconducting state are often marked by a change in the superconducting transition temperature T_c; and these changes can be monitored *in situ* by simple techniques such as measuring electrical resistivity versus temperature. Also, since so many superconducting systems have been studied extensively, *in situ* resistivity measurements can often be used to identify well-known phase changes which can be induced by mixing. A discussion of the Te–Au system, which illustrates this point, will be given later. Usually, only a shallow surface layer of the order of the coherence length for superconductivity (<0.05 μm) is all that need be altered in order to detect a change of state. This is quite compatible with the near-surface character of ion beam and laser processing. It is a common pattern that improved superconducting properties usually result from the application of some non-equilibrium or metastable materials processing technique. This is particularly true for high T_c materials. The reasons for this are discussed in a number of recent articles and reviews on superconducting materials (Meyer, 1980; Bernas and Nedellic, 1981; Stritzker, 1982), but, in general, both theory and experiment show that T_c can be increased if materials can be made with a high density of electronic states near the Fermi surface, N(0), or with enhanced phonon softening. Since these manipulations are not easily achieved using equilibrium processing techniques, non-equilibrium methods such as splat quenching, vapor deposition, co-sputter deposition and chemical vapor deposition have been widely utilized. For example, the material with the highest known transition temperature ($T_c \simeq$ 23.2K) is the metastable A-15 phase Nb_3Ge, which is produced by co-sputter deposition (Gavaler, 1973). In this case, sputter deposition leads to a well-ordered phase with high N(0) and correspondingly high T_c. It is not surprising then that the techniques of ion implantation doping, ion bombardment, and ion beam and laser mixing (to a lesser extent) have been used with great success for fabricating or altering superconducting materials.

The techniques which have been most utilized are ion implantation doping and ion bombardment. Ion implantation can alter electronic properties such as N(0) by introducing atomic species selected to increase the electronic density of states. We have seen that metastable alloys and extended solid solutions can be formed by ion implantation doping, and these can result in new superconducting properties. This area is adequately summarized in several recent review articles (Meyer, 1975, 1980a,b; Stritzker, 1978; Bernas and Nedellec, 1981). These articles cover a tremendous body of data and present such a comprehensive account that it is neither possible nor necessary to review ion implantation results here. However, the reader is encouraged to read these articles, because they provide invaluable insights into how implantation can be used to manipulate materials properties.

In many instances it is not the electronic or compositional changes introduced by the implanted species which are important for achieving beneficial superconducting properties but the structural alterations to the material resulting from radiation damage. Such effects are sometimes referred to as ion bombardment or radiation effects for distinction. In addition to the review papers already mentioned which discuss such effects, a summary of radiation effects on superconductivity can be found in the papers and references from the proceedings of an international conference on this subject (Brown et al., 1978). Radiation damage can change the crystal structure of a material and thereby alter the phonon spectrum of the system, which, in turn, can increase T_c. An example of such a radiation effect is the recent work on the metal Pd (Stritzker, 1979; Meyer and Stritzker, 1982). This metal has a high density of states at the Fermi surface N(0) and a phonon spectrum favorable for superconductivity, but it shows no superconductivity for temperatures as low as 1.7 mK. However, low temperature irradiation with inert He^+ transforms Pd into a superconductor with $T_c \sim$ 3 K (Stritzker, 1979). Recent experiments by Meyer and Stritzker (1982) have shown that the disorder introduced by the He^+ irradiation reduces the susceptibility of Pd by more than an order of magnitude and initiates the observed superconductivity.

The ultimate form of disorder is the amorphous phase of a material; and ion implantation/ion bombardment is very effective in achieving this state. In many materials, increased disorder enhances the electron-phonon coupling and increases T_c. The two important factors in ion implantation which lead to the amorphous state are the rapid cascade quenching effect and the chemical nature of the implanted species. Although the rapid quenching is important, only two pure metals (Ga and Bi) have been successfully prepared in the amorphous state by rapid quenching. Most metallic amorphous systems contain at least two different kinds of atoms. This emphasizes that the chemical or electronic nature of impurities is extremely important for stabilizing the amorphous state. A discussion of amorphous materials and the various stability conditions is given by several authors, and the amorphous condition as perceived through superconducitivity is particularly revealing (Meyer, 1980a,b; Stritzker, 1978, 1982; Bernas and Nedellec, 1981). For example, Stritzker (1982) points out that condensation of Ge on to a substrate at room temperature destroys long-range order and forms an apparent "amorphous" film, but in fact the local short-range order remains the same as in the crystalline state, and the film is semiconducting. However, quenching of Ge vapor on to a substrate at 4 K, along with 30 at. % Cu, drastically alters the bonding and a liquid-like amorphous state is formed which becomes superconducting at about 50 at. % Cu. This is reminiscent of the metal–semiconductor amorphous mixtures formed by ion beam and laser mixing (see section III,A) which resulted in metastable phase formation. One of these metastable phases, Pt_2Si_3 (formed from thermal annealing of ion mixed Pt–Si and pulsed laser annealing of Pt–Si films), was in fact superconducting, with a $T_c \sim$ 3.6 K (Tsaur et al., 1980d).

Since ion-implantation and ion-bombardment results have been thoroughly evaluated in the reviews already cited, the primary emphasis in this section will be on pulsed laser processing of superconducting materials and comparisons to correlated ion-bombardment results (Appleton et al., 1980, 1981; Stritzker, 1982; Stritzker et al., 1982). Initial studies of the effects of pulsed laser processing were made on materials which were already good superconductors (Appleton et al., 1980). It was observed, for example, that pulsed laser melting of the near-surface region of superconducting Nb_3Ge films (initial $T_c \sim$ 22-23 K) resulted in a decrease in T_c and formation of the stable Nb_5Ge_3 phase in the laser quenched surface layer. Similar decreases in T_c were observed in V_3Si samples. These effects can be attributed to lattice disorder induced by the rapid laser quenching. As already discussed in connection with Fig. 25, pulsed laser processing introduces defects in crystalline V_3Si. Since both Nb_3Ge and V_3Si are well-ordered A-15 superconductors with high N(0), any decrease in crystal structure can be expected to decrease T_c. A further complication in Nb_3Ge is that the high T_c phase is metastable, and any thermal processing will tend to encourage nucleation of the stable phase. These effects can, however, be turned to advantage. In more recent experiments on Nb–Ge superconducting films it was found that controlled pulsed laser processing could be used to increase the critical current density, J_c (Braginski et al., 1981). Using Ge-rich Nb–Ge films, finely dispersed precipitates of the stable Nb_5Ge_3 phase could be produced by short laser pulses, and these acted as flux pinning sites which increased J_c. A similar technique was used to nucleate the superconducting δ phase, with $T_c \sim 12K$, from amorphous Nb–C–N films by pulsed laser heating. These results support other results discussed previously which show that nucleation of metastable and stable phases from amorphous mixtures appears to be a general phenomenon. It is not clear whether this particular superconducting phase was metastable or impurity stabilized (Appleton et al., 1980).

The use of ion beam and pulsed laser mixing for fabricating superconducting materials is demonstrated in Fig. 26 for V_3Si (Appleton et al., 1981; Stritzker et al., 1982). The ion scattering analysis in Fig. 26 shows that the multilayer V-Si samples used were designed to limit the composition near V_3Si and consisted of four V layers separated by four Si layers prior to mixing. Mixing was induced by either bombardment with 4×10^{15} Xe^+ cm^{-2} or a single 15 ns pulse from a ruby laser at 0.9 J cm^{-2}. In both instances the ion scattering shows complete mixing, and this was confirmed by cross-section TEM analysis. The mixture was amorphous, with a composition $V_{2.8}Si$ and was not superconducting. Thermal annealing to only 500°C resulted in the nucleation of the superconducting A-15 phase from this amorphous mixture (Appleton et al., 1981). In the case of ion beam mixing the superconducting character of the film was as good as high-temperature thermally processed V_3Si, with $T_c \sim 16K$. This confirms an earlier ion beam mixing result for V_3Si, which was reported by Lau et al. (1980b). On the other hand, the pulsed laser mixed films had $T_c \sim 10-12K$, and as the companion results in Fig. 27 show, even when the laser mixed samples were thermally annealed to temperatures as high as 925 K, their T_c's were always less than multilayer samples (not laser annealed) thermally prepared at the same temperature. This is related to laser induced defects, which are much more difficult to anneal than ion induced damage. These results and the effects associated with multiple laser pulses, pulse length, etc., are discussed further by Appleton

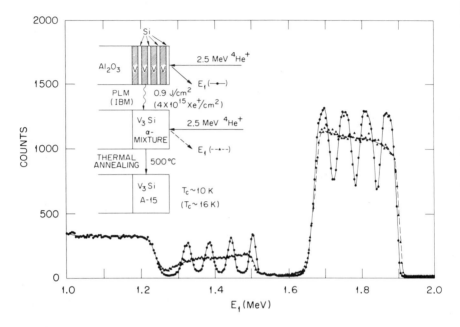

Fig. 26. Ion scattering analysis and schematic representation of the fabrication of superconducting V_3Si by ion beam and pulsed laser mixing. After Appleton *et al.* (1981).

et al. (1981). The whole question of defects in A–15 superconductors is also interesting, and the reader is referred to the discussion and references given by Appleton *et al.* (1981).

A final example for consideration is the behavior of the Te–Au system under ion bombardment and pulsed laser quenching (Meyer and Stritzker, 1982a; Stritzker *et al.*, 1980). This example is valuable for several reasons. First there are three distinct solid phases in $Te_{1-x}Au_x$ which have been studied by both liquid quenching and vapor deposition; thus a basis for comparison with ion beam and laser quenching exists. Second, each of these phases can be identified from simple resistivity versus temperature measurements, so that *in situ* alterations and evaluations may be made easily. Finally, one phase of this system is superconducting; this signifies a definite state of the material. Ion bombardment showed the following modifications (Stritzker, 1982; Meyer and Stritzker, 1982b). Irradiation at 4 K with He^+ ions transformed Te–Au films into the amorphous semiconducting state. This has also been produced by vapor deposition. Thermal annealing resulted in a transformation to the simple cubic superconducting phase at 250 K, with T_c ∿2.5K, and to the equilibrium metallic (non-superconducting) phase at

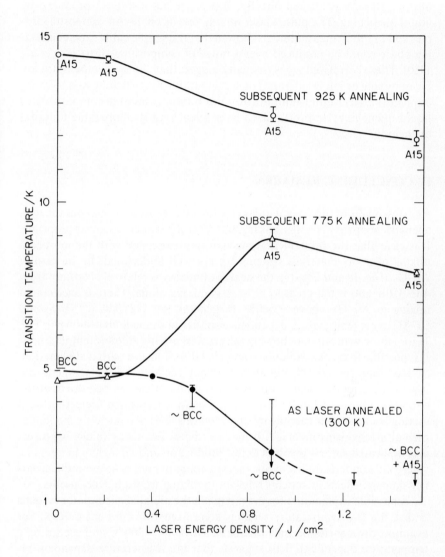

Fig. 27.   Thermal annealing effects on as deposited multilayer V–Si samples and those previously mixed by pulsed laser processing to various laser energy densities. From Appleton *et al.* (1981).

∿400K. When equivalent films were ion bombarded at 250K, the superconducting phase was formed directly; this phase has also been produced by liquid quenching. The pulsed laser mixing results on Te–Au composite samples and *in situ* T_c measurements showed that the simple cubic superconducting phase could be produced over a range of compositions (Stritzker *et al.*, 1980). These correlated measurements suggest that: (i) low-temperature ion beam mixing or ion bombardment is comparable in quenching rate to vapor deposition; (ii) higher-temperature ion bombardment is comparable to liquid quenching; and (iii) pulsed laser quenching is comparable to liquid quenching.

IV. CONCLUDING REMARKS

As assessments of the several areas considered are given throughout the text, a lengthy summary is not necessary; but several comments seem appropriate. It is clear that the fundamental mechanisms associated with the ion beam mixing of many materials systems are not well understood. In the case of Au–Ge (Fig. 18 and Fig. 19), the degree of mixing is relatively constant from 4 to 350K and is too great to be atomic mixing alone. There is accelerated mixing in Au–Ge above ∿500K. In general, Au–Ge, Au–Si, Nb–Si and Cr–Si have a temperature dependence similar in shape to that shown in Fig. 11 for Nb–Si with Au–Ge showing the greatest mixing at lower temperatures. It is possible to invoke radiation-enhanced diffusion as a partial explanation, as was done for Nb–Si, but this does not account for the temperature-independent region, where mixing is substantial. One can beg the question concerning the actual mechanisms with semantic terms like "defect-induced mixing" or "dynamic cascade mixing", but this does not elucidate the fundamental mechanisms involved. It may not be so surprising that this process is complicated since it involves defect production and annealing in a regime where little understanding exists. Investigations of high-dose ion-induced lattice damage effects in systems relevant to mixing would be very useful.

A possible explanation for the mixing in the metal-semicondutor systems is that the two temperature regimes arise from two different defects. For example, divacancies become mobile in silicon at ∿200°C and are strongly temperature dependent. This suggests that the temperature-dependent region could be associated with such vacancy motion. Interstitial defects in Si, on the other hand, are relatively independent of temperature; they are known to be highly mobile in the lattice and effective at displacing impurity atoms at temperatures as low as 4 K. Interstitials in most metals are similarly mobile at very low temperatures. This suggests that mixing in the temperature-independent region of the metal–semiconductor systems could result from the huge increase in interstitial defects produced during ion bombardment.

Because of the complexity of this problem, detailed understandings like those which exists for pure metals are not possible, but qualitative trends and mechanisms should be identifiable. An additional complication in achieving this goal is the strong dependence of the degree of mixing on the combination of materials. The metal–semiconductor systems are particularly complicated, as is evident from the difference in the mixing behavior of Au–Ge and Al–Ge (Fig. 21), but they are particularly interesting, as is shown by the glassy-metal mixtures, superconducting alloys, and metastable phases which can be produced. Even the processes by which silicon and germanium become amorphous under ion bombardment are conceptually simple but intrinsically complicated. The blessing is that, because of this complexity, ion beam mixing offers many challenging fundamental research problems and is a welcome new materials processing technique.

The mixing mechanisms associated with pulsed laser mixing are, in contrast, quite simple. Mixing under melting conditions occurs by diffusion in the liquid state. The interesting materials science usually results from the short duration of this melt and the rapidity with which solidification occurs. From a materials processing point of view this rapid cooling results in a quenching rate of $\sim 10^2$ times greater than splat quenching. Even rapid (surface) heating and cooling without melting can be a useful processing tool, as the Nb_3Ge, T_c-enhancement experiment showed. From a fundamental studies perspective, a new time regime is possible for investigations of rapid crystal growth, formation of amorphous structures, solute trapping, solid and liquid phase epitaxy, solute–liquid interactions, precipitate formation in the liquid state, and many more.

It is interesting to contrast the role of the electron–phonon interaction in the pulsed laser and ion beam mixing processes. The energy of the laser pulse is absorbed into the electronic system of the solid and rapidly transferred to lattice phonons via this interaction in times $< 10^{-11}$s. Conversely, the energy of a bombarding ion is rapidly transferred to the atoms within its damage cascade in the form of phonons in times $\sim 10^{-13}$s. Since the dissipation of this energy by lattice conduction is relatively slow ($\sim 10^{-10}$s), it is possible that some of this energy is transferred to the electronic system through the phonon-electron interaction. This could, for example, provide an alternate mechanism for dissipating energy from a thermal spike. These fundamental considerations are important for understanding ion (laser)–solid interactions and for assessing the role of cascade quenching in materials interactions. Furthermore, many of the ion beam and laser processing techniques discussed in this chapter could be turned to investigate these processes.

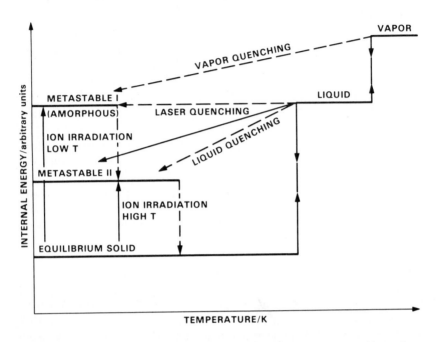

Fig. 28. Schematic comparison of the rapid quenching regimes of liquid quenching and vapor deposition to ion bombardment and pulsed laser quenching. After Meyer and Stritzker (1982b); Stritzker (1982).

An evaluation of the rapid quenching aspects of ion beam and pulsed laser mixing can be summarized by generalizing the scheme used by Meyer and Stritzker (1982b) and Stritzker (1982) to explain their results on Te–Au alloys. Following their lead, Fig. 28 is a schematic representation of the internal energy versus temperature for an imaginary system. Starting from the right-hand side of the figure, if the high internal energy of the vapor phase is reduced by slowly cooling, the system passes through the liquid phase, and possibly several high temperature phases, on its way to the equilibrium solid phase. This essentially is the process for normal equilibrium solidification. The concept behind rapid quenching techniques is that sufficiently rapid cooling to the solid state may freeze-in some of the materials properties associated with these intermediate phases, thus forming metastable phases. Thus, as indicated in Fig. 28, vapor quenching can lead to the metastable I or amorphous phase, while the slower liquid quenching leads to some metastable II phase, with lower internal energy. The time scales associated with cascade quenching are nearly the same as those of vapor deposition, and numerous examples were given, especially in the section on superconducting materials, which showed that many ion irradiation results at low temperatures were comparable to vapor quenching. This is shown by the solid line in Fig. 28 labelled "ion irradiation, low T". Similarly, pulsed laser quenching was shown to be analogous to, but more rapid than, splat quenching. These ideas are shown schematically in Fig. 28 by drawing the laser quenching lines above the liquid quenching line. Also, as shown in the figure, the quenching rate associated with ion irradiation can be slowed by heating the substrate to produce results analogous to liquid quenching. This was true, for example, for the Te–Au system (Stritzker, 1982; Meyer and Stritzker, 1982a). The same technique of heating the substrate can be used to alter pulsed laser quenching rates, along with varying the pulse duration, laser wavelength (absorption depth), laser power, etc. Thus, it is possible to crystallize amorphous Si by liquid-phase epitaxy on to single crystal silicon using pulsed (15 ns) 695 nm wavelength light, or to create amorphous Si layers from single crystalline Si by processing with 20 picosecond 533 nm wavelength laser light.

Having made such generalizations concerning quenching effects, it must be emphasized that materials interactions and ion beam or laser–solid interactions can play an important and often dominant role in determining the final material phase. The superconducting behavior of Pd discussed earlier is a good example. Vapor deposition of Pd has never produced the superconducting phase, while ion irradiation at 4 K has produced the superconducting phase, with transition temperatures up to 3.2 K. This has been attributed to the creation of Pd interstitials during ion bombardment (Stritzker, 1982). In fact, it is these differences, coupled with the tremendous processing flexibility, which rank ion beam and laser mixing as truly new processing techniques and assure that in the future they will become as commonplace and useful as splat quenching and vapor deposition.

ACKNOWLEDGMENTS

I wish to acknowledge that many of the observations presented here grew from interactions with my colleagues and collaborators. I particularly thank my ORNL associates, O. W. Holland, J. Narayan, T. S. Noggle, O. S. Oen, J. M. Williams and F. W. Young, for clarifying discussions; Susan Thomas for typing and editing; and M. T. Robinson for a critical reading of the manuscript.

Research was sponsored by the Division of Materials Sciences, U.S. Department of Energy under contract W-7405-eng-26 with Union Carbide Corporation.

REFERENCES

Adda, Y., Beyeler, M., and Bubec, G. (1975). *Thin Solid Films* **25**, 107.
Albany, J. H., ed. (1979). "Defects and Radiation Effects in Semiconductors." Institute of Physics, Bristol.
Anantharaman, T. R., Luo, H. L., and Klement, W., Jr. (1965). *Trans of Metall. Soc. of AIME* **233**, 2014.
Anantharaman, T. R., Luo, H. L., and Klement, W. (1966). *Nature* **210**, 1040.
Andersen, H. H. (1979). *Appl. Phys.* **18**, 131.
Andersen, H. H., and Bay, H. L. (1974). *J. Appl. Phys.* **45**, 953.
Andersen, H. H., and Bay, H. L. (1975). *J. Appl. Phys.* **46**, 2416.
Andersen, H. H., and Bay, H. L. (1982). *In* "Sputtering by Ion Bombardment." (Topics in Applied Physics, 47) (R. Behrisch, ed.). Springer-Verlag, Berlin.
Andersen, G. A., Bestel, J. L., Johnson, A. A., and Post, B. (1971). *Materials Science Engineering* **7**, 83.
Appleton, B. R., and Celler, G. K., eds. (1982). "Laser and Electron Beam Interactions with Solids." North Holland, New York.
Appleton, B. R., and Holland, O. W. (1982). Unpublished results.
Appleton, B. R., Larson, B. C., White, C. W., Narayan, J., Wilson, S. R., and Pronko, P. P. (1979). *In* "Laser-Solid Interactions and Laser Processing, 1978". (S. D. Ferris, H. J. Leamy and J. M. Poate, eds.), p. 291. American Institute of Physics, New York.
Appleton, B. R., White, C. W., Stritzker, B., Meyer, O., Gavaler, J. R., Braginski, A. I., and Ashkin, M. (1980). *In* "Laser and Electron Beam Processing of Materials" (C. W. White and P. S. Peercy, eds.), p. 714. Academic Press, New York.
Appleton, B. R., Stritzker, B., White, C. W., Narayan, J., Fletcher, J., Meyer, O., and Lau, S. S. (1981). *In* "Laser and Electron Beam Solid Interactions and Materials Processing", (J. F. Gibbons, L. D. Hess and T. W. Sigmon, eds.), p. 607. North Holland, New York.
Aronin, L. R. (1954). *J. Appl. Phys.* **25**, 344.
Baeri, P. (1982). *In* "Laser and Electron Beam Interactions with Solids" (B. R. Appleton and G. K. Celler, eds.), p. 151. North Holland, New York.
Baeri, P., Campisano, S. U., Foti, G., and Rimini, E. (1978). *Appl. Phys. Lett.* **33**, 137.
Baeri, P., Foti, G., Poate, J. M., Campisano, S. U., and Cullis, A. G. (1981). *Appl. Phys. Lett.* **38**, 800.
Bagley, B. G., and Chen, H. S. (1979). *In* "Laser-Solid Interactions and Laser Processing, 1978" (S. D. Ferris, H. J. Leamy and J. M. Poate, eds.), p. 97. American Institute of Physics, New York.
Battaglin, G., Carnera, A., Della Mea, G., Mazzoldi, P., Jain, A. K., Kulkarni, V. N., and Sood, D. K. (1981). *In* "Laser and Electron Beam Solid Interactions and Materials Processing" (J. F. Gibbons, L. D. Hess and T. W. Sigmon, eds.), p. 615. North Holland, New York.
Bergmann, G. (1976). *Physics Rep.* **276**, 161.
Bernas, H., and Nedellec, P. (1981). *Nucl. Instrum. Methods* **183**, 845.
Biersack, J. P., and Haggmark, L. G. (1980). *Nucl. Instrum. Methods* **174**, 257.
Billington, D. S., and Crawford, J. H., Jr., eds. (1961). "Radiation Damage in Solids." Princeton University Press, Princeton, New Jersey.
Blewitt, T. H., and Coltman, R. R. (1952). *Phys. Rev.* **85**, 384.
Bloembergen, N. (1979). *In* "Laser-Solid Interactions and Laser Processing, 1978" (S. D. Ferris, H. J. Leamy and J. M. Poate, eds.), p. 1. American Institute of Physics, New York.
Bloembergen, N., Kurz, H., Liu, J. M., and Yen, R. (1982). *In* "Laser and Electron Beam Interactions with Solids" (B. R. Appleton and G. K. Celler, eds.), p. 1. North Holland, New York.

Braginski, A. I., Gavaler, J. R., Kuznicki, R. C., Appleton, B. R., and White, C. W. (1981). *Appl. Phys. Lett.* **39**, 277.

Brice, D. K. (1975). "Ion Implantation Damage and Energy Deposition Distribution", Vol. I. IFI/Plenum Data Company, New York.

Brice, D. K. (1976). *Inst. Phys. Conf. Ser.* **28**, 334.

Brinkman, J. A. (1954). *J. Appl. Phys.* **25**, 961.

Brown, B. S., Freyhardt, H. C., and Blewitt, T. H., eds. (1978). "Proceedings of the International Conference on Radiation Effects on Superconductivity". *J. Nucl. Mater.* **72**.

Buene, L., Poate, J. M., Jacobson, D. C., Draper, C. W., and Hirvonen, J. K. (1980). *Appl. Phys. Lett.* **37**, 385.

Buene, L., Jacobson, D. C., Nakahara, S., Poate, J. M., Draper, C. W., and Hirvonen, J. K. (1981a). *In* "Laser and Electron Beam Solid Interactions and Materials Processing" (J. F. Gibbons, L. D. Hess and T. W. Sigmon, eds.), p. 583. North Holland, New York.

Buene, L., Kaufmann, E. N., Preece, C. M., and Draper, C. W. (1981b). *In* "Laser and Electron Beam Solid Interactions and Materials Processing" (J. F. Gibbons, L. D. Hess and T. W. Sigmon, eds.), p. 591. North Holland, New York.

Christel, L. A., Gibbons, J. F., and Myloric, S. (1981). *Nucl. Instrum. Methods* **182/183**, 187.

Corbett, J. W., ed. (1966). "Electron Radiation Damage in Semiconductors and Metals." Academic Press, New York.

Corbett, J. W., Karins, J. P., and Tan, T. Y. (1981). *Nucl. Instrum. Methods* **182/183**, 457.

Cottril, R. M. J. (1976). *Am. Scientist* **64**, 430.

Crawford, J. H., Jr., and Slifkin, L. M., eds. (1972). "Point Defects in Solids". Plenum Press, New York.

Cullis, A. G., Webber, H. C., and Chew, N. G. (1982). *In* "Laser and Electron Beam Interactions with Solids" (B. R. Appleton and G. K. Celler, eds.), p. 131. North Holland, New York.

Dienes, C. J., and Vineyard, G. H., eds. (1957). "Radiation Effects in Solids". Wiley, New York.

Draper, C. W., Preece, C. M., Jacobson, D. C., Buene, L., and Poate, J. M. (1980). *In* "Laser and Electron Beam Processing of Materials" (C. W. White and P. S. Peercy, eds.), p. 721. Academic Press, New York.

Duwez, P. (1979). *Proc. Indian Acad. Sci.* **C2**, 117.

Duwez, P., Willens, R. H., and Klement, W., Jr. (1960). *J. Appl. Phys.* **31**, 1136.

Eastman, D. E., Heimann, P., Himpsel, F. J., Reihl, B., Zehner, D. M., and White, C. W. (1982). *In* "Laser and Electron Beam Interactions with Solids" (B. R. Appleton and G. K. Celler, eds.), p. 261. North Holland, New York.

Erginsoy, C., Englert, A., and Vineyard, G. (1964). *Phys. Rev.* **133**, 595.

Fan, J. C. C., and Anderson, H. C., Jr. (1981). *J. Appl. Phys.* **52**, 4003.

Ferris, S. D., Leamy, H. J., and Poate, J. M., eds. (1979). "Laser-Solid Interactions and Laser Processing, 1978". American Institute of Physics, New York.

Follstaedt, D. M. (1982). *In* "Laser and Electron Beam Interactions with Solids" (B. R. Appleton and G. K. Celler, eds.), p. 377. North Holland, New York.

Gavaler, J. R. (1973). *Appl. Phys. Lett.* **23**, 480.

Gibbons, J. F., Hess, L. D., and Sigmon, T. W., eds. (1981). "Laser and Electron Beam Solid Interactions and Materials Processing." North Holland, New York.

Grant, W. A. (1981). *Nucl. Inst. Methods* **182/183**, 809.

Grob, A., Grob, J. J., Mesli, N., Salles, D., and Siffert, P., p. 85 and Bruel, M., Floccari, M., and Gailliard, J. P., p. 93 and references therein (1981), *Nucl. Instrum. Methods* **182/183**.

Guntherodt, H. J., and Lapka, P. (1980). *J. Physique* **41**, C8-381.

Hirvonen, J. K., ed. (1980). "Treatise on Materials Science and Technology." Academic Press, New York.

Hirvonen, J. K., Poate, J. M., Greenwald, A., and Little, R. (1980). *Appl. Phys. Lett.* **36**, 564.

Hussain, T., Geerk, J., Rotzel, F., and Linker, G. (1980). *Appl. Phys. Lett.* **37**, 298.

Jenkins, M. L., Norton, N. G., and English, C. A. (1979). *Phil. Mag.* **34**, 131.

Kaufmann, E. N., Vianden, R., Chelikowsky, J. R., and Phillips, J. C. (1977). *Phys. Rev. Lett.* **39**, 1671.

Kirk, M. A., Blewitt, T. H., and Scott, T. L. (1977). *Phys. Rev.* **B 15**, 2914.

Kirk, M. A., Blewitt, T. H., and Scott, T. L. (1978). *J. Nucl. Mater.* **69/70**, 780.

Kokorowski, S. A., Olson, G. L., Roth, J. A., and Hess, L. D. (1982). *In* "Laser and Electron Beam Interactions with Solids" (B. R. Appleton and G. K. Celler, eds.), p. 195. North Holland, New York.

Lau, S. S., and van der Weg, W. F. (1978). *In* "Thin Films: Interdiffusion and Reactions" (J. M. Poate, K. N. Tu and J. W. Mayer, eds.), p. 243. Wiley, New York.

Lau, S. S., von Allmen, M., Maenpaa, M., and Tsaur, B. Y. (1980a). *In* "Laser and Electron Beam Processing of Materials" (C. W. White and P. S. Peercy, eds.), p. 544. Academic Press, New York.

Lau, S. S., Mayer, J. W., Tsaur, B. Y., and von Allmen, M. (1980b). *In* "Laser and Electron Beam Processing of Materials" (C. W. White and P. S. Peercy, eds.), p. 511. Academic Press, New York.

Lau, S. S., Maenpaa, M., and Mayer, J. W. (1981a). *In* "Laser and Electron Beam Solid Interactions and Materials Processing" (J. F. Gibbons, L. D. Hess and T. W. Sigmon, eds.), p. 547. North Holland, New York.

Lau, S. S., Tsaur, B. Y., von Allmen, M., Mayer, J. W., Stritzker, B., White, C. W., and Appleton, B. R. (1981b). *Nucl. Inst, Methods* **182/183**, 97.

Liau, Z. L., and Mayer, J. W., (1980). *In* "Treatise on Materials Science and Technology, Vol. 18, Ion Implantation" (J. K. Hirvonen, ed.), p. 17. Academic Press, New York.

Liau, Z. L., Tsaur, B. Y., and Mayer, J. W. (1979). *In* "Laser-Solid Interactions and Laser Processing, 1978" (S. D. Ferris, H. J. Leamy and J. M. Poate, eds.), p. 509. American Institute of Physics, New York.

Lindhard, J., Scharff, M. E., and Schiøtt, H. E. (1963). *K. Dan. Vid. Selsk. Mat. Fys. Medd.* **13**, No. 14.

Littmark, U., and Hofer, W. O. (1980). *Nucl. Instrum. Methods* **168**, 329.

Liu, P. L., Yen, R., Bloembergen, N., and Hodgson, R. T. (1979). *Appl. Phys. Lett.* **34**, 864.

Manning, I., and Mueller, G. P. (1974). *Comp. Phys. Comm.* **7**, 85.

Marwick, A. D., and Piller, R. C. (1981). *Nucl. Instrum. Methods* **182/183**, 121.

Matteson, S., Roth, J., and Nicolet, M.-A. (1979). *Rad. Effects.* **42**, 217.

Matteson, S., Paine, B. M., Grimaldi, M. G., Mezey, G., and Nicolet, M.-A. (1981a). *Nucl. Instrum. Methods* **182/183**, 43.

Matteson, S., Paine, B. M., and Nicolet, M.-A. (1981b). *Nucl. Instrum. Methods,* **182/183**, 53.

Mayer, J. W., Lau, S. S., Tsaur, B. Y., Poate, J. M., and Hirvonen, J. K. (1980). *In* "Ion Implantation Metallurgy" (C. M. Preecy and J. K. Hirvonen, eds.), p. 37. The Metallurgical Society of AIME.

Mayer, J. W., Tsaur, B. Y., Lau, S. S., and Hung, L. S. (1981). *Nucl. Instrum. Methods* **182/183**, 1.

Meyer, J. D., and Stritzker, B. (1982a). *Phys. Rev. Lett.* **48**, 502.

Meyer, J. D., and Stritzker, B. (1982b). *Nucl. Inst. Methods* **183**, 965.

Meyer, O. (1975). *In* "New Uses of Ion Accelerators" (J. F. Ziegler, ed.), p. 323. Plenum Press, New York.

Meyer, O. (1980a). *In* "Treatise on Materials Science and Technology, Vol. 18, Ion Implantation" (J. K. Hirvonen, ed.), p,. 415. Academic Press, New York.

Meyer, O. (1980b). *Rad. Effects.* **48**, 51.

Moline, R. A., Reutlinger, G. W., and North, J. C. (1973). *In* "Atomic Collisions in Solids" (S. Datz, B. R. Appleton and C. D. Moak, eds.), p. 159. Plenum Press, New York.

Morehead, F. F., and Crowder, B. L. (1971). *In* "Ion Implantation" (F. H. Eisen and L. T. Chadderton, eds.), p. 25. Gordon and Breach, London.

Myers, S. M. (1980a). *In* "Ion Implantation Metallurgy" (C. M. Preece and J. K. Hirvonen, eds.), p. 51. The Metallurgical Society of AIME.

Myers, S. M. (1980b). *Nucl. Instrum. Methods* **168,** 265.

Narayan, J., and Tan, T. Y., eds. (1981). "Defects in Semiconductors." North Holland, New York.

Narayan, J. (1982). Private communication.

Nelson, R. S. (1965). *Phil. Mag.* **11,** 291.

Nelson, R. S. (1973). *In* "Ion Implantation" (G. Dearnaley, J. H. Freeman, R. S. Nelson and J. Stephen, eds.), p. 154. North Holland, Amsterdam.

Peterson, N. L., and Harkness, S. D., eds. (1975). "Radiation Damage in Metals." American Society for Metals, Metals Park, Ohio.

Peterson, N. L., and Siegel, eds. (1978). "Properties of Atomic Defects in Metals." *J. Nucl. Mater.* **69/70.**

Picraux, S. T., Eer Nisse, E. P., and Vook, F. L., eds. (1974). "Applications of Ion Beams to Metals." Plenum Press, New York.

Picraux, S. T., Follstaedt, D. M., Knapp, J. A., Wampler, W. R., and Rimini, E. (1981). *In* "Laser and Electron Beam Solid Interactions and Materials Processing" (J. F. Gibbons, L. D. Hess and T. W. Sigmon, eds.), p. 525. North Holland, New York.

Piercy, G. R. (1963). *J. Phys. Soc. Japan* **18,** Suppl. III, 169.

Poate, J. M., and Cullis, A. G. (1980). *In* "Ion Implantation Metallurgy" (C. M. Preece and J. K. Hirvonen, eds.), p. 85. The Metallurgical Society of AIME.

Poate, J. M., Borders, J. A., Cullis, A. G., and Hirvonen, J. K. (1977). *Appl. Phys. Lett.* **30,** 365.

Poate, J. M., Leamy, H. J., Sheng, T. T., and Celler, G. K. (1979). *In* "Laser-Solid Interactions and Laser Processing, 1978" (S. D. Ferris, H. J. Leamy and J. M. Poate, eds.), p. 527. American Institute of Physics, New York.

Predicki, P., Giessen, B. C., and Grant, N. J. (1965). *Transactions AIME* **233,** 1438.

Pronko, P. P., Wiedersich, H., Seshan, K., Helling, A. L., Lograsso, T. A., and Baldo, P. M. (1981). *In* "Laser and Electron Beam Solid Interactions and Materials Processing" (J. F. Gibbons, L. D. Hess and T. W. Sigmon, eds.), p. 599. North Holland, New York.

Robinson, M. T. (1981). *In* "Topics in Applied Physics, Volume 47, Sputtering by Particle Bombardment I" (R. Behrisch, ed.), p. 73. Springer-Verlag, Berlin.

Robinson, M. T., and Young, F. W., Jr., eds. (1975). "Fundamental Aspects of Radiation Damage in Metals." USERDA CONF 751006-P2. Seeger, A. K. (1958). *Proc. Second Int. Conf. Peaceful uses of Atomic Energy* **6,** 250.

Seitz, F., and Koehler, J. S. (1956). *Solid State Phys.* **2,** 307.

Sigmon, T. W. (1981). *In* "Laser and Electron Beam Solid Interactions and Materials Processing" (J. F. Gibbons, L. D. Hess and T. W. Sigmon, eds.), p. 511. North Holland, New York.

Sigmund, P. (1974). *Appl. Phys. Lett.* **25,** 169.

Sigmund, P. (1977). *In* "Inelastic Ion-Surface Collisions" (N. H. Tolk, J. C. Tully, W. Heitland and C. W. White, eds.), p. 121. Academic Press, New York.

Sigmund, P., and Gras-Marti, A. (1981). *Nucl. Instrum. Methods* **182/183,** 25.

Sizmann, R. (1978). *J. Nucl. Mater.* **69/70,** 386.

Spaepen, F., and Turnbull, D. (1979). *In* "Laser-Solid Interactions and Laser Processing, 1978" (S. D. Ferris, H. J. Leamy and J. M. Poate, eds.), p. 73. American Institute of Physics, New York.

Stritzker, B. (1978). *J. Nucl. Mater.* **72,** 256.

Stritzker, B. (1979). *Phys. Rev. Lett.* **42,** 1769.

Stritzker, B. (1982). *In* "Laser and Electron Beam Interactions with Solids (B. R. Appleton and G. K. Celler, eds.), p. 363. North Holland, New York.

Stritzker, B., Appleton, B. R., White, C. W., and Sekula, S. T. (1980). Unpublished data. Reviewed in Stritzker (1982).

Stritzker, B., Appleton, B. R., White, C. W., and Lau, S. S. (1982). *Solid State Commun.* **41,** 321.

Suryanarayana, C., and Anantharaman, T. R. (1971). *Materials Science Engineering* **13,** 73.

Tan, T. Y., Tsu, R., Ho., P. S., and Tu, K. N. (1979). *In* "Laser-Solid Interactions and Laser Processing, 1978" (S. D. Ferris, H. J. Leamy and J. M. Poate, eds.), p. 533. American Institute of Physics, New York.

Tsaur, B. Y., and Mayer, J. W. (1980). *Appl. Phys. Lett.* **37,** 389.

Tsaur, B. Y., Matteson, S., Chapman, G., Liau, Z. L., and Nicolet, M.-A. (1979a). *Appl. Phys. Lett.* **35,** 825.

Tsaur, B. Y., Lau, S. S., and Mayer, J. W. (1979b). *Appl. Phys. Lett.* **35,** 225.

Tsaur, B. Y., Lau, S. S., and Mayer, J. W. (1980a). *Appl. Phys. Lett.* **36,** 823.

Tsaur, B. Y., Mayer, J. W., Graczyk, J. F., and Tu, K. N. (1980b). *J. Appl. Phys.* **51,** 5334.

Tsaur, B. Y., Mayer, J. W., Nicolet, M.-A., and Tu, K. N. (1980c). *In* "Ion Implantation Metallurgy" (C. M. Preece and J. K. Hirvonen, eds.), p. 142. The Metallurgical Society of AIME.

Tsaur, B. Y., Mayer, J. W., and Tu, K. N. (1980d). *J. Appl. Phys.* **51,** 5326.

Tsaur, B. Y., Lau, S. S., Hung, L. S., and Mayer, J. W. (1981). *Nucl. Instrum. Methods* **182/183,** 67.

Tsu, R., Hodgson, R. T., Tan, T. Y., and Baglin. J. E. E. (1979). *Phys. Rev. Lett.* **42,** 1356.

Tu, K. N., and Mayer, J. W. (1978). *In* "Thin Films: Interdiffusion and Reactions" (J. M. Poate, K. N. Tu and J. W. Mayer, eds.). Chapter 10. Wiley, New York.

Van Vechten, J. A. (1980). *In* "Laser and Electron Beam Processing of Materials" (C. W. White and P. S. Peercy, eds.), p. 53. Academic Press, New York.

von Allmen, M., Lau, S. S., Maenpaa, M., and Tsaur, B. Y. (1980). *Appl. Phys. Lett.* **36,** 207.

von Allmen, M., Affalter, K., and Wittmer, M. (1981). *In* "Laser and Electron Beam Solid Interactions and Materials Processing", (J. F. Gibbons, L. D. Hess and T. W. Sigmon, eds.), p. 559. North Holland, New York.

Wampler, W. R., Follstaedt, D. M., and Peercy, P. S. (1981). *In* "Laser and Electron Beam Solid Interactions and Materials Processing" (J. F. Gibbons, L. D. Hess and T. W. Sigmon, eds.), p. 567. North Holland, New York.

Wang, J. C., Wood, R. F., and Pronko, P. P. (1978). *Appl. Phys. Lett.* **33,** 455.

Watkins, G. D. (1963). *J. Phys. Soc. Japan* **18,** Suppl. II, 22.

White, C. W. and Peercy, P. S., eds. (1980). "Laser and Electron Beam Processing of Materials." Academic Press, New York.

White, C. W., Narayan, J., and Young, R. T. (1979a). *Science* **204,** 461.

White, C. W., Pronko, P. P., Wilson, S. R., Appleton, B. R., Narayan, J., and Young, R. T. (1979b). *J. Appl. Phys.* **50,** 3261.

White, C. W., Wilson, S. R., Appleton, B. R., and Young, F. W., Jr. (1980). *J. Appl. Phys.* **51,** 738.

White, C. W., Appleton, B. R., and Wilson, S. R. (1982). *In* "Laser Annealing of Semiconductors" (J. M. Poate and J. W. Mayer, eds.), p. 112. Academic Press, New York.

Williams, P., and Baker, J. E. (1981). *Nucl. Instrum. Methods* **182/183,** 15.

Winterbon, K. B. (1975). *In* "Ion Implantation Damage and Energy Deposition Distribution," Vol. II. IFI/Plenum Data Company, New York.

Wittmer, W., and von Allmen, M. (1979). *In* "Laser-Solid Interactions and Laser Processing, 1978 (S. D. Ferris, H. J. Leamy and J. M. Poate, eds.), p. 539. American Institute of Physics, New York.

Wittmer, M., and von Allmen, M. (1981). *In* "Laser and Electron Beam Solid Interactions and Materials Processing" (J. F. Gibbons, L. D. Hess and T. W. Sigmon, eds.), p. 533. North Holland, New York.

Wood, R. F., and Giles, G. E. (1981). *Phys. Rev.* **B 23**, 2923.

CHAPTER 8

High-Dose Implantation

D. G. BEANLAND

Royal Melbourne Institute of Technology
Melbourne, Australia

ION IMPLANTATION
AND BEAM PROCESSING
ISBN   0 12 756980 4

I. INTRODUCTION

Since there is no convenient absolute method of defining the high-dose domain, an arbitrary definition is usually employed. In this chapter, implants with doses greater than 1×10^{15} cm^{-2} are considered to be high-dose implants. High-dose implantation is obviously associated with a large amount of radiation damage and high dopant concentrations (see Chapter 2, Section II). Both damage and dopant concentration depend upon the energy of the implant, and the damage also depends upon a number of other implant parameters, such as the mass of the implant species, the mass of the substrate, the dose rate, the scanning strategy used and the implantation temperature.

It is sufficient, at this stage, to note that high-dose implants are usually associated with high damage rate effects, ion beam heating during implantation and amorphous layer formation, which is a function of the implant species and the implant temperature (Morehead and Crowder, 1970). However an amorphous layer (Mazey *et al.*, 1968) will not always be created by implants above 1×10^{15} cm^{-2}.

This chapter concentrates on high-dose implants into silicon, and the discussion will be directed towards implants into silicon unless it is stated otherwise. These high-dose implants are becoming increasingly important in the microelectronics industry and their growing significance has paralleled the increased ion beam current capability of modern implanters, a development which has enabled high-dose implants to be undertaken economically. The successful application of low-dose implants in the fabrication of microelectronic devices has led to benefits in doping accuracy, profile control, repeatability and uniformity. This result has also generated a need to achieve the same benefits in the processes which require high doping concentrations. This has not proved to be as straightforward as the low-dose domain, because there are many more factors that affect the behavior of high-dose implants. Our understanding of the interaction of these parameters in high-dose implantation conditions is incomplete. Therefore, it has been necessary to establish experimentally the implantation conditions that give suitable results and to maintain them constant unless further testing is to be undertaken.

There are two general categories of problems associated with high-dose implants:

(i) those resulting from damage to the target; and

(ii) those resulting from changes in target temperature.

As discussed in previous chapters, the damage and its resultant effects arise from the dissipation of the kinetic energy of the ions into displacement and excitation of atoms in the target (wafer). With high-dose implants, damage to the target is severe and, if the aim is to produce electrically active dopant atoms, this damage must be appropriately annealed (Chapter 2, Section III).

High-dose implants also result in a significant rise in the temperature of the substrate, as a consequence of the energy dissipation of the impinging ions. Temperature rise depends on the wafer-scanning techniques utilized (Section V,C.) and the wafer-cooling method employed (Section V,E.). During implantation the temperature rise can produce variations in the damage generated by the implant, both across the wafer (depending on the scanning technique), and between wafers (depending on the exact implantation conditions). The damage created by a high-dose implant depends upon the thermal history of the substrate during implantation. The amount of damage that can be removed during subsequent annealing may also be affected by the thermal history during implantation (Chapter 2, Section III). Since the temperature of the wafer during implantation is an important parameter when considering the behaviour of high-dose implants, beam heating and wafer cooling are considered in detail in Section II,B.

High-dose implants are usually undertaken with high dose rates in order to minimize the duration of the implant. This means that during implantation the temperature can rise as much as a few hundred °C. Consequently, the behaviour of high-dose implants is made more complex by the damage generation and annealing processes, as they are affected by rises in temperature during implantation. In addition, the thermal effect may not be uniform over the implanted target.

II. IMPLANTING AT HIGH DOSES

A. Applications of High-Dose Implantation

The technology of the microelectronics industry has advanced rapidly, with improved lithographic techniques leading to progressive reductions in device dimensions. This has necessitated associated advances in doping processes. As the size of the devices used has been reduced, it has been necessary to find ways of making the doped layers shallower and improving their lateral definition. In addition, the trend towards larger and more complex circuitry has necessitated improved doping accuracy and uniformity in order to achieve reasonable yields from the fabrication processes. These requirements have resulted in the adoption of ion implantation as the doping technique for the high-dose sections of microelectronic devices, in addition to its already established use for the low-dose sections such as MOS channel implants (see, for example, Namba, 1978; Shannon, 1981).

The most common high-dose implantation stages in microelectronic device fabrication are:

1. Drain/source doping of MOS devices (see, for example, Murase and Harada, 1979, using As^+ at approximately 1×10^{16} cm^{-2}).
2. Emitter doping (see, for example, Koji et al., 1979, using P^+ at 1×10^{16} cm^{-2}).
3. Buried layer doping (see, for example, Beyer et al., 1977, and Sanders, 1976, using As^+ at 1×10^{16} cm^{-2}).
4. Isolations (see, for example, Lam et al., 1981, using O_2^+ at 300 keV to 6×10^{17} cm^{-2}).
5. Pre-deposition for diffusion (see, for example, Seidel et al., 1976b, using B^+ at 5×10^{14} cm^{-2}).
6. Gettering of impurities (see, for example, Beyer and Yeh, 1978, using Ar^+, O^+, Si^+ and Xe^+ at 1×10^{16} cm^{-2}).

Other high-dose implantation applications which have potential, but which are not yet widely utilized, include:

1. SiO_2 formation by implanting O^+ (see, for example, Hayashi et al., 1980, using 2.4×10^{18} cm^{-2}).
2. Si_3N_4 formation by implanting N^+ (see, for example, Tsujide et al., 1980, using 3×10^{17} cm^{-2}).
3. Deposition of surface layers by ion beams of very low energy for conductors or contacts (see, for example, Glaser et al., 1977; Freeman et al., 1976).
4. Contact formation and alloy/metal creation (see, for example, Hiraki et al., 1976, using Cu^+ at 3×10^{17} cm^{-2}).
5. Hard-type photomask formation by ion implantation of photo-resist (see, for example, Okuyama et al., 1978, using P^+, Ar^+, etc. at 3×10^{15} cm^{-2}).
6. Radiation enhanced etching (see, for example, Moriwaki et al., 1980, using Ar^+ at 5×10^{15} cm^{-2}).

Non-microelectronic applications of high-dose implantation include:

1. Modification of surface properties of metals: friction, wear, hardness, corrosion, roughness, reflectivity, etc.
2. Creation of amorphous metals or metastable phases.
3. Ion beam mixing (see Chapter 7).
4. Special property modification: superconductivity, magnetic, optical, acoustic propagation, catalytic coefficients, etc.

B. Ion Beam Heating

The energy of the ion beam is dissipated and ultimately converted into heat. This causes the temperature of the target to rise. If the target has a high thermal capacitance, the increase in temperature will be negligible. However, semi-conductor wafers have a small thermal capacity; thus significant temperature rises can occur.

A convenient parameter to use when considering beam heating is irradiance. This was introduced and defined by Freeman *et al.*, (1975) as:

$$\text{irradiance} = IE/A \text{ (in W m}^{-2}\text{)} \tag{1}$$

where I is the ion beam current in amperes,
E is the ion energy in electron volts, and
A is the area (in m^2) scanned by the beam.

For wafers which are clamped to a metal surface in a vacuum, there is effectively no heat transfer by conduction, although there may be localized heat conduction in the vicinity of the clamp. All heat dissipation is by radiation from the front and back surfaces of the specimen. The thermal power, P, removed by radiation is given by:

$$P = \varepsilon A_t \sigma (T_T^4 - T_0^4) \tag{2}$$

where ε is the thermal emissivity of the surface,
A_t is the surface area of the target,
σ is the Stefan–Boltzmann constant (5.67×10^{-12} W cm^{-2} K^{-4}),
T_T is the temperature of the target in K, and
T_0 is the temperature of the surroundings in K.

Consequently, the equilibrium temperature rise of the wafer is given by:

$$T_T - T_0 = (irradiance_w/2\varepsilon\sigma)^{1/4} \tag{3}$$

assuming that the ion beam is scanning the entire area of the target. The *irradiance$_w$* is that experienced by the wafer. The result is plotted in Fig. 1, from Freeman *et al.* (1975), who obtained experimental results corresponding to an average total emissivity of approximately 0.45 for an entire Si specimen continuously scanned. Parry (1976) obtained an emissivity of 0.75 for the Si wafer's front surface. He also showed that it is effectively reduced by a closed-back wafer holder; i.e., where the wafer is radiating to a nearby surface.

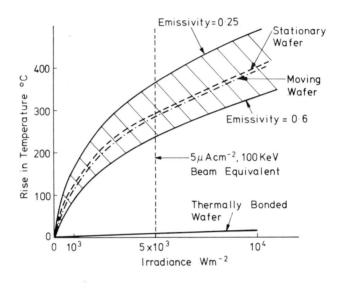

Fig. 1. Temperature rise for Si targets as a function of ion beam irradiance. After Freeman *et al.* (1975).

Fig. 1 shows that when a beam current of 720 µA and an overscan of 20% at a beam energy of 100 keV (i.e. irradiance = 5 × 10³ W m⁻²) is used, the maximum temperature rise in a 10 cm diameter wafer is approximately 300°C.

It follows that there are basically two approaches that can be used to minimize the temperature rise of implanted specimens, since it is not economical to use low dose rates (ion beam currents). Firstly the irradiance can be reduced by increasing the scan area. The most convenient way of achieving this is to have multiple scanning of a wafer by using some form of mechanical system to aid the movement of the wafer through the ion beam. This approach was pioneered by Freeman *et al.* (1970) and it has subsequently been applied in various forms to all commercial ion implanters capable of producing high beam currents (>1 mA).

The various approaches to increasing the scan area in practical ion implantation systems are shown schematically in Fig. 2. They may be classified as either one-directional or two-directional mechanical systems. The one-directional mechanical systems use electrostatic or electromagnetic scanning in the first direction, combined with a mechanical motion, such as a rotating drum (Fig. 2b) or rotating disc (Fig. 2a), in the second. The two-directional

(a)

(b)

(c)

(d)

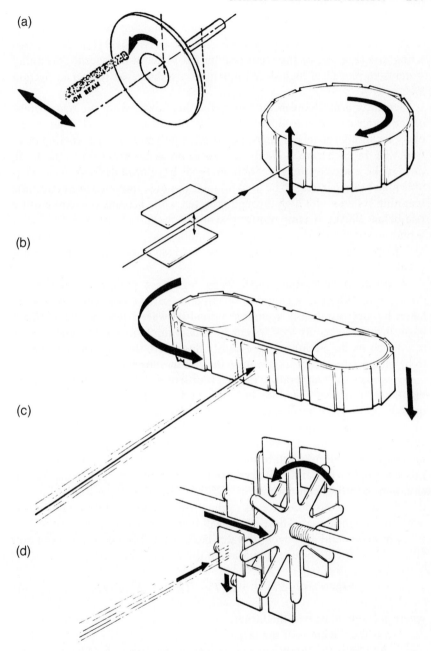

Fig. 2.   Schematic representation of some scan systems utilized in high dose implanters. After Freeman (1976).

mechanical systems combine a linear motion in the first direction with various motions, such as the carousel (Fig. 2c), the ferris wheel (Fig. 2d), the rotating disc (Fig. 2a) or the reciprocating flat plate, in the second. Scanning systems employed in high-dose implanters are discussed further in Section V,C.

Secondly, a mechanism for conducting heat away from the rear surface of the wafer can be introduced. A variety of approaches have been developed, including elastic polymers, liquid-filled polymers and gas cooling (Section V,E). In each case, a clamp is used to press the wafer on to the solid, or to make a seal for the gas. These methods have been devised so as to enable high beam currents to be used for medium-dose implants in electrostatic scanning systems with high throughput rates, while keeping the temperature rise below 100°C. A temperature rise of this magnitude permits the use of a photoresist material as an ion-implantation mask. Such cooling methods also help to minimize the temperature rise associated with high-dose implants.

A prime consideration when using high-dose implants is the wafer throughput. Whereas medium-dose implants can be conveniently undertaken by electrostatically scanning individual wafers fed on a continuous basis through a vacuum lock system, high-dose implants must be undertaken in a batch mode, because as previously described, the scanned area needs to be increased in order to minimize the rise in temperature.

Obviously the temperature rise is a transient which occurs during the implantation process. The dose build-up and the damage build-up consequently occur as a complicated function of temperature, which is dependent upon the scanning geometry and rate, the beam power, the wafer cooling system, the total dose and the dose rate. The effects of this complex situation have not yet been fully established, since only controlled conditions with a limited number of variables have been studied. In practical implants, the situation is further complicated by localized thermal effects and variations in the instantaneous dose rate, as distinct from the average dose rate, which is normally considered. These points will be elaborated later.

A more general approach to wafer heating has been described by Parry (1976). He gives the heating equation in differential form as:

$$EI\Delta t = \rho A_t l C \Delta T_T + \varepsilon \sigma A (T_T^4 - T_0^4)\Delta t + Ka(\Delta T/\Delta x) \tag{4}$$

where ρ is the density of the target,
l is the thickness of the target,
$\Delta T/\Delta x$ is the temperature gradient in the direction of heat conduction,

C is the specific heat of the target,
K is the thermal conductivity across the target, and
a is the cross-sectional area.

This states that in time Δt the power input from the beam is equal to the energy absorbed, plus the energy radiated, plus the energy conducted away. Equation (4) gives:

$$\Delta T = \Delta t [EI - \alpha(T_T^4 - T_0^4) - \beta(T_T^4 - T_{wh}^4) - H(T_T - T_{wh})]\rho A_t / C \qquad (5)$$

where
$$H = Ka/\Delta x \qquad (6)$$

$$\alpha = \sigma A_t \varepsilon_w \varepsilon_s / [\varepsilon_s + \varepsilon_w (1 - \varepsilon_s)] \qquad (7)$$

$$\beta = \sigma A_t \varepsilon_w \varepsilon_{wh} / [\varepsilon_{wh} + \varepsilon_w (1 - \varepsilon_{wh})] \qquad (8)$$

and T_{wh} is the temperature of the wafer holder, ε_{wh} is the emissivity of the wafer holder, ε_s is the emissivity of the surroundings, and ε_w is the emissivity of the wafer surface.

Considering the right-hand terms of eqn. (5): the first term is the ion beam power absorbed by the wafer; the second term is the power radiated from the front of the wafer and the fraction scattered back from the surroundings; the third term is the power radiated from the back of the wafer to the wafer holder and the fraction scattered back; and the fourth term is the power conducted from the wafer to the wafer holder.

Unfortunately H, ε_s and T_s are unknowns. H depends on the contact area of the small number of points where the silicon wafer and the wafer holder will contact. Depending upon how the irregularities of the two surfaces juxtapose, this contact area can vary widely from implant to implant (Parry, 1976). For contact to a metal surface without a means of increasing the thermal conductivity, the value of H is almost zero. However, small localized variation in H will exist (Parry, 1978).

When using a repetitive scan technique to implant a batch of many wafers the calculations used to measure temperature rise must include the effects of cooling between the scans. Also, the thermal conditions may vary for different wafers and across individual wafers (see Section III,B). Parry (1976) obtained an approximate time constant of 40 seconds for the wafer cooling cycle when using a solid-backed wafer holder. He also determined that the lateral conduction time constant of a Si wafer was approximately 20 seconds.

Measurements of the rise in temperature of electrostatically scanned wafers by Bruel et al. (1979) have indicated that the apparent emissivity of the wafer rises as a function of the implantation temperature. These authors believe that the emissivity is modified by the free carriers generated during the implantation process itself. The emissivity is also wavelength dependent.

C. Damage Generated in High-Dose Implants

The electrical behaviour of high-dose implants is basically determined by the residual damage after annealing. Furthermore, the damage after annealing is a function of both the annealing process and the damage generated during implantation. The dependencies of damage generation are now briefly reviewed. (This subject has been discussed in detail in Chapter 2.)

Implanted ions create zones of gross disorder in the region where the ion deposits its kinetic energy. The zones are vacancy rich in the centre and are surrounded by interstitial atoms. During high-dose implants, these zones may overlap and create a continuous amorphous layer. The energy deposition is approximately Gaussian in its depth distribution, so that the disorder is non-uniform in depth. The amorphous layer will initially become continuous at some depth below the surface. As the dose increases during the implantation process, the amorphous layer will increase in width. It follows that a high-dose implant may produce either a buried amorphous layer, or an amorphous layer which is continuous to the surface (Fig. 3). A buried amorphous layer is thus more likely to result from lower mass and higher energy implants, but the characteristics of the amorphous layer formed also depend on the dose, dose rate and implantation temperature (see Section III).

The dose at which the amorphous zones overlap and become continuous is known as the amorphous threshold. However, this dose is difficult to quantify accurately as its determination depends upon the measurement method used. The various measurement techniques involve the detection of saturation in a damage-related variable to identify the amorphous threshold. Since the effects examined are depth sensitive and therefore correspond to differing amounts of zone overlap, different measurement techniques give different doses for the amorphous threshold.

D. Damage Annealing of High-Dose Implants

Since the electrical activity of the implanted ions is usually of prime importance, post-implantation annealing must be used in order to achieve substitutionality of the dopant atoms and the removal of the implant-generated damage. Removal of damage depends not only on the annealing process used (e.g. furnace annealing, pulse laser annealing), and the annealing con-

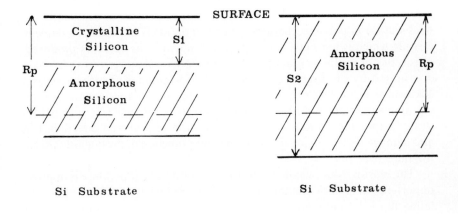

Fig. 3.   Schematic representation of amorphous layer formation. After Beanland (1977).

ditions (e.g. furnace temperature and time, laser pulse energy and duration), but also upon the implant conditions. The total annealing history of the wafer comprises the sum of the post-implantation annealing, the dynamic annealing (occurring in the collision cascade region: see Section II,E and Chapter 2) and, if the implant temperature is high enough, the direct thermal annealing during implantation. The post-implantation annealing process has been fully discussed on Section III of Chapter 2 and will not be considered here. However, it should be noted that for high-dose implants the solid-phase regrowth of amorphous layers has been shown to be dose (Tamminga and Josquin, 1978), orientation (Csepregi *et. al.*, 1978), energy density (Beanland and Williams, 1977) and species (Christodoulides *et. al.*, 1978) dependent.

What is of relevance here, however, is that, for annealing processes dependent upon the solid-phase epitaxial regrowth mechanism, the residual damage will depend on the implant conditions. When annealing occurs via ultra-rapid regrowth from the liquid phase (Chapter 2, Section IV) the post-annealing damage is not significantly affected by the implantation conditions. Consequently these methods allow the effects of high-dose implants to be more predictable. However, such methods are often inapplicable to the fabrication of microelectronic devices in silicon. In high-dose implants the temperature during implantation, which is not constant and which is affected by many other implant conditions, is a critical parameter in determining the residual damage after annealing. This point is often overlooked, but it will be developed and explained throughout much of this chapter.

E. Dynamic Annealing

As discussed in previous chapters, whenever an ion is implanted, a damage cascade which is ion mass and energy dependent in its extent is produced. This series of events is immediately followed by a damage-recovery phase dominated by the higher diffusion rate of vacancies (Tsuchimoto and Tokuyama, 1970). This phase is the primary mechanism for dynamic annealing (damage removal during implantation). It is enhanced by higher substrate temperatures and may not be uniform in each crystal direction. It is also damage-density dependent and may be a function of the dopant concentration.

The sensitivity of dynamic annealing to substrate temperature is of prime importance in high-dose implants. A convenient means of expressing this relationship is by the temperature dependence of the amorphous threshold. This relationship has been calculated by Morehead and Crowder (1970) using a simplified model (Fig. 4).

For doses below the amorphous threshold, "cigar-shaped" damage zones of individual ions are reduced in size or eliminated by the dynamic annealing process. For post-amorphous threshold doses, the thickness of the amorphous layer can be reduced at both the top and bottom of the layer. If a semiconductor has had its surface layer pre-amorphized, the thickness of the amorphous layer may be reduced by the dynamic annealing process (Beanland and Chivers, 1978a).

Seidel et. al., (1976a) showed that, in at least some cases, a heavily damaged layer consisting of crystalline defects is generated below the amorphous layer. Although no model for its formation or minimization has been prescribed we do know that it is difficult to anneal this layer by subsequent thermal annealing. A similar heavily damaged layer is not observed above the amorphous layer, presumably because of the relative proximity of the surface, which acts as a damage sink.

The sensitivity of the dynamic annealing process to substrate temperature explains why the damage associated with high-dose implants is significantly affected by the implant temperature (and any implant condition which modifies it).

III. EFFECT OF IMPLANT TEMPERATURE ON DAMAGE

A. Effects of Implantation Temperature

Early studies of the effect implant temperature has on residual damage (after annealing) in Si, rapidly established that, although less damage was created by high-temperature implantation, was more difficult to anneal. The experi-

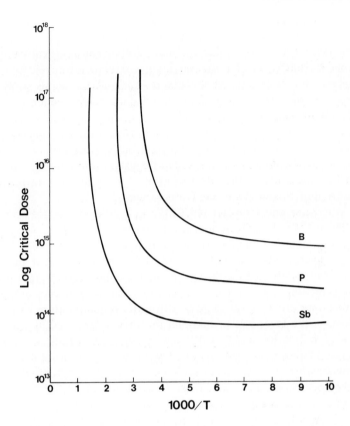

Fig. 4. Theoretical relationship between amorphous threshold and temperature for B^+, P^+ and Sb^+ into Si. After Morehead and Crowder (1970).

ments conducted (Davies, 1969; Eriksson *et. al.*, 1969; Mayer *et. al.*, 1967; Shannon *et. al.*, 1970) concentrated on the temperature range 400–600°C, where the creation of an amorphous phase is prevented. It was shown that the development of an amorphous layer upon a relatively defect-free under-lying crystal greatly assisted post-implantation annealing.

There have been relatively few studies of the effects of the rise in wafer temperature normally encountered during high-dose implantation at high currents. These increases may typically range up to 400°C. Picraux *et. al.* (1969) showed that the disorder created by 40 keV Sb^+ implants at doses 1.5×10^{13} to 2×10^{14} cm^{-2} reduced as the implant temperature increased from 20° to 200°C. Picraux and Vook (1971) showed that the lattice reorder-ing that occurs during implantation increases rapidly with implantation tem-perature. They also showed that much higher post-implantation anneal temperatures are required in order to achieve a reduction in disorder equivalent to a 100°C increase in implantation temperature.

The behaviour of Si implanted with 40 keV P^+ at constant temperatures in the range 20–300°C, which is the usual range of temperature rise for high-dose implants, has been studied (Beanland et. al., 1978). In this study the specimens were physically and thermally bonded to a controlled temperature heat sink. Unfortunately, a practical method of achieving this bonding for a high wafer throughput has not yet been established, although wafer cooling methods do rely on improving the conduction to the back surface of the Si wafers. It should be noted that the study of constant-temperature implants is only a tool for studying the effect of implant temperatures: in practice, implants are undertaken at varying temperatures.

The Morehead and Crowder (1970) thermal diffusion model proposes that for 280 keV P^+ the critical dose for the creation of a continuous amorphous layer becomes infinite if the implantation temperature exceeds 157°C. The other experiments (Beanland et. al., 1978) have indicated that the amorphous layer created by a 40 keV P^+ implant into (111) Si reduced in thickness as the implantation temperature (and thus the efficiency of the dynamic annealing process) was increased from room temperature to 167°C, at which stage the layer was of minimal thickness. These results were obtained for both 2×10^{16} and 2×10^{15} cm^{-2} P^+. The sheet resistances of the "as implanted" specimens were measured by the four-point probe technique. The results obtained are shown in Fig. 5. The 40 keV 2×10^{16} cm^{-2} P^+ specimens were isochronally annealed at 300, 500, 700, 900 and 1100°C and were shown to undertake the sheet resistance variations depicted in Fig. 6. Sheet resistance is an indicator of the combined effect of electrical activity and mobility, and it is a good indicator of the damage. Fig. 6 shows that above room temperature modest increases in the implantation temperature can produce significant changes in the resultant damage, even after annealing to high temperatures. It is also interesting to note that, in addition to the initial damage being lower for the specimens implanted above 167°C, their subsequent annealing produced the lowest damage, with the exception of the room-temperature implant annealed at 1100°C.

While the epitaxial recrystallization process most efficiently reduces the sheet resistance of the room temperature implants, the implants at temperatures below 167°C, which have thinner amorphous layers, anneal less effectively. This is because the epitaxial recrystallization of the amorphous layers of these specimens commences from disordered silicon crystals which have been effectively, but not perfectly, annealed during the implantation process, rather than from relatively undamaged silicon crystals (Csepregi et. al., 1976). These observations do not imply that the annealing is perfect or complete for the sample implanted at room temperature.

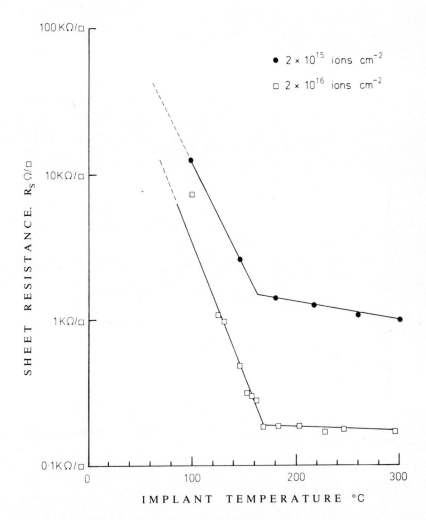

Fig. 5. As implanted sheet resistance as a function of implantation temperature for 40 keV P$^+$ implants 2×10^{15} and 2×10^{16} cm^{-2}. After Beanland *et al.* (1978).

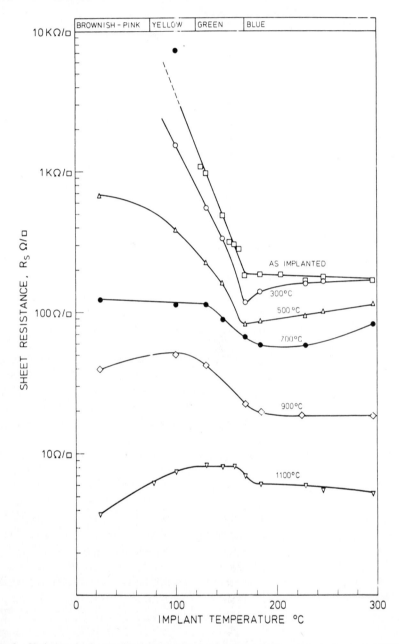

Fig. 6. Variations in sheet resistance following isochronal annealing at temperatures to 1100°C of specimens implanted with 2×10^{16} cm^{-2} 40 keV P^{+} ions at temperatures 20°–300°C. After Beanland *et al.* (1978).

The specimens implanted above 167°C annealed steadily as the anneal temperature increased, and for implant temperatures $\geq$ 180°C they exhibited a relatively constant sheet resistance, which was independent of the implant temperature, for annealing at and above 900°C. The achievement of post-annealing behaviour which was relatively independent of implantation temperature in the range 170–300°C is an interesting result which follows from the dominance of the dynamic anneal process in these conditions.

Tamura et. al. (1978a) studied Si implanted with 3 × 10^{16} cm^{-2} P$^+$ and confirmed the reduction in disorder and increase in electrical activity for implantation temperatures up to 850°C. Another interesting study is that of Tamura (1973), who used TEM to examine the secondary defects of 5 × 10^{14} cm^{-2} P$^+$ implanted Si annealed with temperatures of 500–1200°C, after implantation at temperatures ranging from room temperature to 700°C. He found that an increase in implantation temperature resulted in a general increase in the size of the secondary defects.

A further important observation was made by Servidori and Vecchi (1981). They used TEM to examine (100) Si implanted with 2 × 10^{15} cm^{-2} P$^+$ 100 keV at room temperature and at 77K. Implantation at very low temperatures created deep amorphous layers which annealed at temperatures above 650°C and produced crystal free from detectable crystallographic defects. It follows that because the production of damage is affected by the implantation temperature, for implants undertaken with significant beam heating, non-uniform or non-reproducible sheet resistances and electrical activities may be obtained. This may be an important factor in explaining the variety of results obtained by groups undertaking implants under different implantation conditions.

B. Colour-Band Generation

The amorphous silicon layer created by high-dose implants has a milky appearance and associated hues which can be readily observed (Mazey et. al., 1968). The refractive index of amorphous Si differs from that of crystalline Si. Optical interference results in hues which are generally indistinct because the amorphous–crystalline interface is not perfectly planar. However, these interference colours may become quite distinct following some high-dose implants, as an abrupt interface is produced. If the thermal conditions vary across the wafer, then various colours may become evident in distinct bands.

Colour-bands on ion-implanted Si were first reported by Freeman et. al. (1975) when studying the degree of uniformity in sheet resistance among high-dose implants undertaken using high beam currents. They showed that the different colour-bands resulted from variations in temperature across the wafer during implantation and that the coloured regions were associated with crystalline surface layers.

Csepregi *et. al.* (1976) qualitatively associated the thickness of the surface crystalline layers with visual colour changes. Seidel *et. al.* (1976) quantitatively correlated the thickness of the surface crystalline layer with "optical-thicknesses" derived from peaks in the visible optical reflectance spectrum. They also correlated the thicknesses of thicker (mostly buried) amorphous layers with peaks in the near infrared reflectance spectrum.

Visible interference colours may be generated when there is a surface layer of amorphous Si above crystalline Si, or one of crystalline Si above amorphous Si (Beanland, 1977). Colours become bright and clearly visible when there is an abrupt interface between the amorphous and crystalline layers, and this effect usually occurs when the implantation temperature is increased during implantation. The observed colours are the result of light reflected from the surface interfering with that reflected from the subsurface interface; i.e., the point at which the refractive index changes. The particular wavelength attenuated, λ, is dependent on the depth of the surface layer, d, and is given by

$$\lambda = [(4-n)/(2k-1)]d \qquad (9)$$

where $k = 0, 1, 2, 3, \ldots$, and n is the refractive index of surface layer.

Since the interference is subtractive, the colour observed is the complement of the wavelength attenuated. Using $n = 3.865 - j\,0.14$ for crystalline Si and $n = 4.25 - j\,0.45$ for amorphous Si, which is consistent with experimental results reported by other workers, the colours likely to be observed have been calculated for both amorphous and crystalline Si surface layers of various depths (Fig. 7). These depths must be considered approximate, because the damage variation throughout the surface layers can cause the optical constants of the layers to be non-uniform. Furthermore, phase shifts (Csepregi *et al.,* 1976) can result in an error of approximately 25% for the first-order coloured layers.

Colour assessment is also somewhat subjective and depends on the light source. It is also determined by the absorption of the surface layer, particularly for amorphous surface layers. The colours associated with surface crystalline layers are usually brighter and more distinct. It is difficult to assess the order of the interference colour, but colours up to fourth order have been observed. However, if an approximate damage profile is known, the depth of the damage peak is a convenient reference point for wafers which show colour-bands in addition to having a "clear" crystalline region on the wafer; the colour at the interface between the colour-band and the "clear" Si represents the depth of the damage peak.

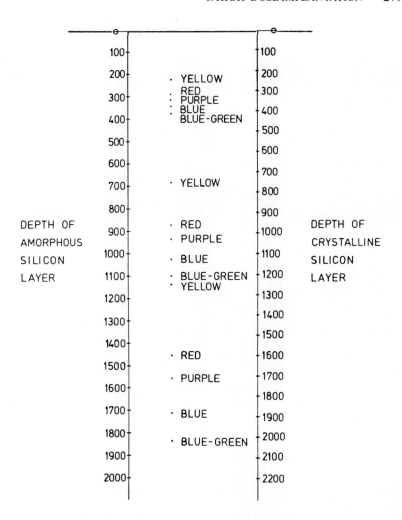

Fig. 7. Interference colours as a function of depth for amorphous and crystalline Si surface layers (1st, 2nd and 3rd order). After Beanland and Chivers (1978b).

The colour-bands studied by Seidel *et al.* (1976a) were created by placing a heat sink on the edge of a Si wafer in order to produce non-uniform cooling across the wafer. Colour-bands are only evident on implanted specimens when the thermal conditions are not identical at all points on the specimen. Since electrostatically scanned wafers experience uniform thermal conditions, they do not exhibit colour-bands unless a thermal gradient is established by non-uniform cooling (such as contact points behind the wafer or by clamping points), or as a result of non-uniform doping.

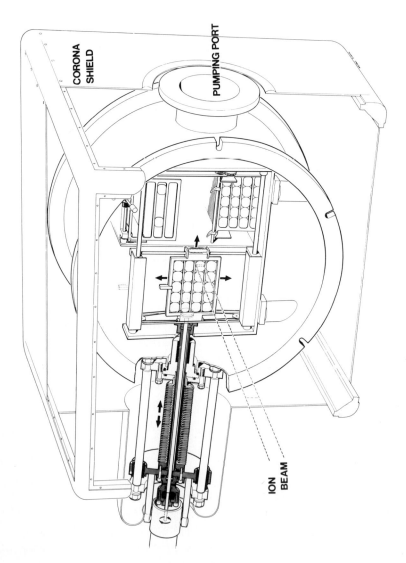

CORONA SHIELD

PUMPING PORT

ION BEAM

Fig. 8. Target chamber of MK VI Harwell–Lintott ion implanter. After Freeman *et al.* (1970).

TOP

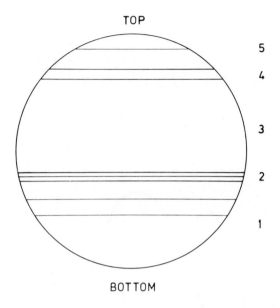

5

4

3

2

1

BOTTOM

Fig. 9.   Schematic diagram of colour bands formed on a Si wafer implanted to high dose using 2-axis mechanical scanning. After Beanland and Chivers (1978b).

Unfortunately, the mechanical scanning systems which have been derived to minimize the rises in temperature of the substrates during implantation have the disadvantage of producing non-uniform thermal conditions across the wafer during implantation. Mechanical scanning systems do have the advantage of improving dose uniformity, however, they produce non-uniform damage as a consequence of the non-uniform thermal conditions.

The thermal conditions which give rise to colour-bands on one particular type of target stage are now described (from Beanland and Chivers, 1978b), as they give insight into the effects which will be observed with other types of mechanical systems. The scanning system studied was the double-axis mechanical scanning system (Freeman *et al.*, 1970) of the Mk IV Harwell–Lintott implanter (Fig. 8). The typical colour-bands resulting from this type of scanning system are shown schematically in Fig. 9. The relationship between equilibrium temperature rise and irradiance (Fig. 1) assumes that the ion beam is scanning the entire area of the target. In the Mk IV Harwell–Lintott separator, a 3 cm high beam is used to scan progressively across a silicon wafer of 5 cm diameter. The area being scanned is thus a function of the relative location of the ion beam's centre line and the wafer. It increases to a maximum when the ion beam is scanning the centre of the wafer (Fig. 10). The beam power transmitted to the wafer is proportional to the

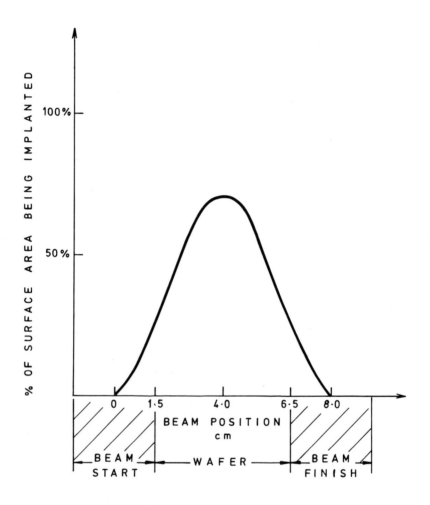

Fig. 10.   Percentage of wafer implanted as a function of ion beam centreline position. After Beanland and Chivers (1978b).

area of the wafer being scanned. The heat deposited into the wafer is conducted through it with a time constant of approximately 20 sec (Parry, 1976). Heat dissipation only occurs by radiation from the entire surface area, since conduction to the mounting plate is negligible. If it is assumed that the lateral conduction time constant is negligible compared to the total time taken by the implantation cycle, the "equilibrium" temperature rise as a function of the position of the ion beam's centre line can be calculated as a percentage

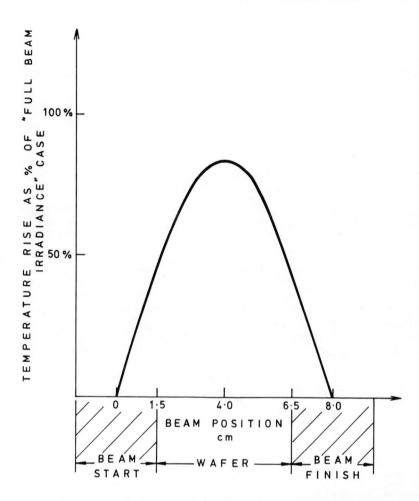

Fig. 11. "Equilibrium" temperature rise as a function of ion beam centreline position. After Beanland and Chivers (1978b).

of the temperature predicted in Fig. 10 (when complete scanning of the wafer occurs). The result is shown in Fig. 11. Each horizontal strip on the wafer has a unique temperature–time profile as the scan proceeds across it. Strips at the bottom are initially at a low temperature, with an increasing temperature during implantation; strips at the centre have high and relatively constant temperatures during implantation; while strips at the top of the wafer have an initially high temperature which decreases as the implantation cycle

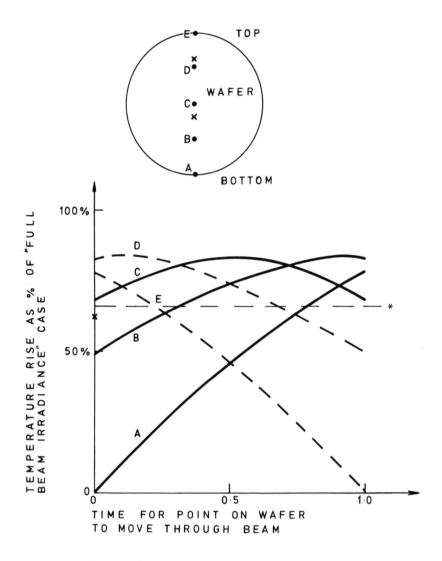

Fig. 12.   Temperature variation of horizontal strips across the wafer during implantation calculated with no thermal capacitance. After Beanland and Chivers (1978b).

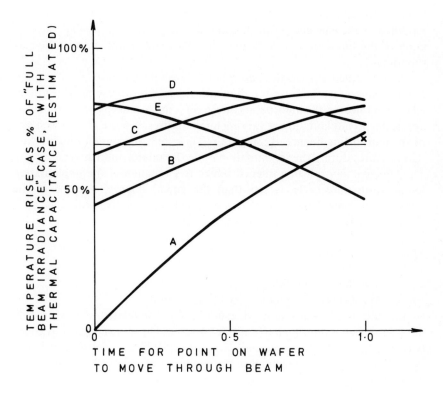

Fig. 13. Temperature variation of horizontal strips across the wafer during implantation calculated with estimated thermal capacitance. After Beanland and Chivers (1978b).

progresses. This temperature variation during implantation is shown in Fig. 12 for some points on the wafer. However, these results assume that implantation has proceeded sufficiently slowly for lateral heat conduction to maintain a uniform temperature across the wafer and that the wafer has negligible thermal capacity so that cooling is equally efficient. Wafer cooling has an appreciable time constant, and this effect has been estimated so as to determine the more realistic temperature variation curves of Fig. 13.

The thermal conditions of a wafer scanned by such a mechanical scanning system are thus seen to vary in a continuous manner during implantation if beam heating is significant. Each horizontal strip of the wafer has a unique thermal behaviour during implantation. The temperatures attained, in addition to being determined by the ion beam irradiance, are also modified by the efficiency of the thermal contact with the mounting, the duration of the implantation cycle, and the efficiency of radiation to the surroundings.

As was noted earlier, the amorphous threshold increases with implantation temperature because the dynamic annealing process becomes more efficient. However, the amorphous threshold is not a concept which is readily applicable to implantation at varying temperatures. A more general concept of an amorphizing fluence, ϕ_{am}, is required in order to account for the varying temperatures during the implantation cycle (Beanland and Chivers, 1978b). The effective amorphizing fluence, which is a function of the implantation temperature–time cycle, is less than the actual fluence, because of the temperature–time dependent dynamic annealing. It can be written as:

$$\phi_{am}(T,t) = \int_0^\phi [1 - k\ (\phi,\ T,\ t)]d\phi \qquad (10)$$

where ϕ is the fluence.

   t is time,

   T is the temperature,

and $k(\phi,T,t)$ is the dynamic annealing function.

In addition, the amorphous threshold should be related to a volumetric disorder density rather than to a surface fluence. Thus, since the competition between damage production and dynamic annealing is complex, it is not possible to model the dependence on temperature accurately. A simplified discussion of colour-band generation, based on amorphous threshold variation, is therefore presented.

In the Mk IV Harwell–Lintott separator, the current density is approximately constant along the height of the line beam. Therefore, as the sweep proceeds, the fluence increases proportionally with time. From the temperature–time relationship already established (see Fig. 12), the temperature–fluence relationship can be readily derived for the various horizontal strips of the wafer. These are plotted for points A–E in Fig. 14 by using a logarithmic scale for the fluence. The numerical scale is for a 2×10^{16} cm^{-2} 40 keV P$^+$ implant at 500 μA. Also plotted in Fig. 14 is the variation of amorphous threshold with implantation temperature (solid curve) for 280 keV P$^+$ implants, using the electron spin resonance (ESR) data of Morehead and Crowder (1970). Even though this data cannot be expected to predict the amorphous threshold accurately, they exhibit the expected relationship with temperature.

Although the approach illustrated in Fig. 14 is only an approximation, some interesting trends are indicated. For implants which commence at low temperatures (point A at the bottom of the wafer) it is relatively easy to generate an amorphous layer. An amorphous layer is certainly generated when

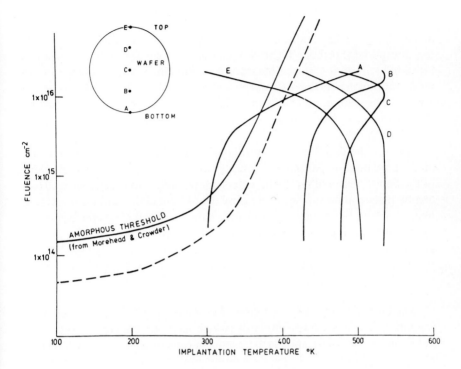

Fig. 14. Fluence variations of horizontal strips across the wafer as a function of implantation temperature (with no thermal capacitance); cf. amorphous threshold data from Morehead and Crowder (1970) for 280 keV P^+ (solid curve) and (dotted curve) "effective amorphous threshold". After Beanland and Chivers (1978b).

a temperature–time cycle crosses the amorphous threshold curve from a lower temperature. An amorphous layer will be generated at a dose lower than that predicted by the amorphous threshold curve because as the implantation proceeds the damage is cumulative. For a point such as B, an amorphous layer may be established as the temperature increases if the cumulative damage is sufficiently high. The damage occurring before the temperature increases significantly is the determining factor. For point C on the wafer, the temperature is too high during the entire implant for an amorphous layer to be created. Amorphousness could be created at D, but this is unlikely since the majority of the damage is generated at high temperatures and the amorphous threshold curve is approached with much less damage than a constant temperature implant. However, it is likely that amorphousness is created at point E as the wafer cools.

Since the amorphous threshold is a constant implant temperature concept, a lower "effective amorphous threshold" (depicted by the broken line in Fig. 14) is a more realistic indication of when the total damage reaches the amorphous threshold. It can be seen that the steepness of the amorphous threshold variation with temperature is of fundamental importance in determining the generation of amorphous regions of varying thickness across a wafer. The generation of the amorphous layer is primarily determined by the behaviour of the wafer during the lowest temperature phases of the implantation process.

Because the depth of the amorphous–crystalline interface is effected by all the implantation parameters, infinite variations in the position and colour of the bands observed on the Si wafers are possible. However, the bands do exhibit a general form (Fig. 9). Because the bottom of the wafer is implanted first, at a low, but rising, temperature, a deep amorphous layer extending to the surface will probably be generated. The depth of the amorphous layer is reduced in the successive horizontal strips of the wafer, as they are implanted at progressively higher temperatures. This corresponds to region 1 in Fig. 9. The colours are relatively diffuse and changes in colour indicate layers of reducing depth.

The diffuse band is usually followed by a narrow, brightly coloured band (region 2). For low-energy implants (which have the damage density peak at the surface) this corresponds to a region of rapid reduction in the thickness of the amorphous layer. Depending on the implant conditions, region 3 may either have a thin amorphous layer or be heavily damaged but crystalline Si. In this region, the implant temperature is high but relatively constant, and uniform colours are likely when a thin amorphous layer results. For high-energy implants (which have a peak energy deposition density some distance below the surface) region 2 is a narrow, more brightly coloured band in which the order of colours is reversed. This is the region in which the amorphous layer is buried below a layer of crystalline Si. The colours are brighter owing to the greater optical transparency of crystalline Si. The colour order is reversed because the depth at which the colours are generated now increases as the implantation temperature is increased. For such implants, region 3 is then crystalline Si.

Regions 4 and 5 may not be evident if insufficient cooling of the wafer occurs. When they are evident, region 4 is a bright band and is less distinct than region 2, possibly because it has been formed on cooling and because the amorphous–silicon interface is apparently less abrupt. Region 5 is similar to region 1 and exhibits diffuse colours which result from deep amorphous layers being continuous to the surface.

C. Examples and Consequences of Damage Non-uniformity

The non-uniform thermal conditions which exist during high-dose implantation undertaken using a mechanical scanning technique lead to non-uniform damage variations that may be visible. However, as the wafers will undergo subsequent annealing, the damage non-uniformity will be reduced and may be eliminated. Consideration is now given to observations of the damage non-uniformity after thermal annealing.

The experimental analysis of colour-banded wafers outlined here is based on work reported in Beanland and Chivers (1978b, 1978c). Again, sheet resistance was used as a convenient means of assessing the magnitude of damage variations across wafers implanted at higher doses. Following 30 min isochronal anneals at temperatures to 1100°C, the sheet resistance (R_s) variation across the diameter of the implanted wafers, in a direction normal to the colour-bands, was measured using the four-point probe technique. The four-point probe under-estimates the abruptness of the resistance change, since it averages the resistance in the region being measured.

Case (i): P^+, 2×10^{16} cm^{-2}, 40 keV, 500 μA

The results are shown in Fig. 15, together with the colour-bands on the "as implanted" wafer. A large R_s variation existed across the (111) silicon wafer after implantation because the amorphous layers were deeper in the high R_s regions at the top and bottom of the wafer. This variation was maintained throughout the annealing cycle, but was reduced to a maximum variation of 14% after annealing to 1100°C. The central section of the wafer, which was implanted at approximately 200°C, exhibited the lowest R_s after each annealing cycle.

It should also be noted that at different parts of the wafer the changes in R_s varied dramatically during annealing. The annealing characteristics for points A, B, and C (Fig. 15), are shown in Fig. 16. Curve D was obtained on a wafer implanted using the same implantation parameters, but with the temperature increasing from room temperature to 220°C during implantation. Also included in Fig. 16 is the result Shannon et al. (1970) obtained following implantation at room temperature. It will be seen that during the epitaxial regrowth phase at approximately 600°C, the room-temperature implant annealed more efficiently but the annealing of damage for the implant at approximately 200°C was much more efficient than for the implants which were undertaken over a range of temperatures from room temperature to 200°C. It appears that under the conditions associated with curves B, C, and

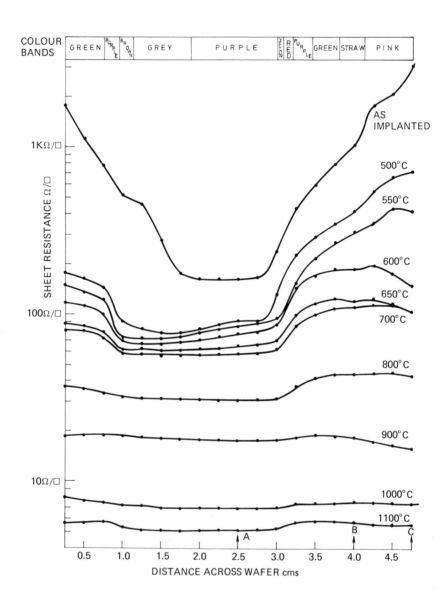

Fig. 15. Sheet resistance profiles across wafer implanted with 2×10^{16} cm^{-2} P^{+} at 40 keV, 500 μA and isochronally annealed. Bottom of wafer at the right. After Beanland and Chivers (1978b).

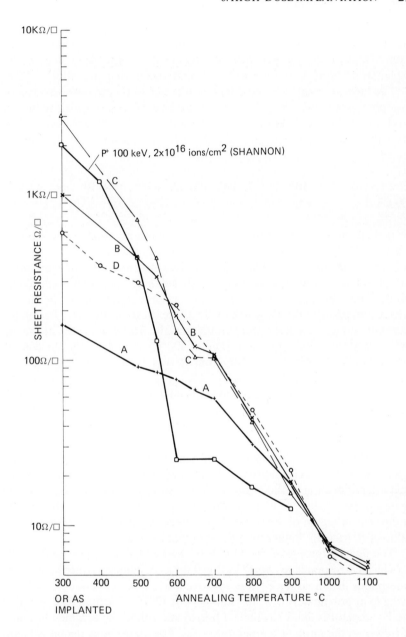

Fig. 16. Isochronal anneal characteristic of sheet resistance for 40 keV P^+ implant to 2×10^{16} cm^{-2} at 500 μA with varying implant temperature conditions. After Beanland and Chivers (1978b).

D, the dynamic annealing, which reduced the depth of the amorphous layer, has produced crystalline disorder which remains in the deep, subamorphous layers. This disorder was generated during the low-temperature phase of the implantation process, and it is difficult to remove during annealing.

The measurements are consistent with the colour-band observations for amorphous layers which are continuous to the surface and which reduce in depth for the "hotter", central part of the wafer. The results are also consistent with the data of Fig. 6, although the thermal conditions are different of course.

Case (ii): B^+, 1×10^{15} cm^{-2}, 25 keV, 100 μA + F^+, 1×10^{15} cm^{-2}, 43 keV, 100 μA

A dual implant was chosen in order to obtain an appropriate damage density, and it also allowed a suitable low-mass, electrically active species to be used. Because the ion masses and doses were lower the damage is obviously less than in the previous example. The damage was mainly caused by the fluorine. The electrical activity of the boron was measured, and the results of annealing in the range 400–1100°C are shown in Fig. 17. The colours after implanting were noticeable, but not bright. Those indicated at the top of Fig. 17 were visible after annealing at 400°C, at which stage the colours were particularly bright. The minimum R_s was at the clear-blue interface. As the wafer was annealed at successively higher temperatures up to 650°C, the region of minimum R_s moved towards the bottom of the wafer. (The colour bands disappeared after annealing to 650°C.) The colour bands were relocated after each anneal sequence, with the minimum R_s always coinciding with the top edge of the blue region. Obviously, the colour bands generated by this implant differ from those generated by the P^+ implant. Once again, however, a thermal history of the implantation temperature was evident after annealing to 1000° and 1100°C. The lowest sheet resistances were again associated with the highest implantation temperatures, which occurred in the central region of the wafer. After annealing at 1100°C, the maximum value of R_s was 11% higher than the minimum value.

The damage profile of the 43 keV F^+ had a peak at approximately 400 Å (which corresponds to "blue" in Fig. 9 for a crystalline surface layer). The amorphous threshold for F^+ was approximately 2×10^{14} ions cm^{-2} at 20°C, rising to approximately 1×10^{15} ions cm^{-2} at 100°C. It is therefore seen that the F^+ implant is likely to create a buried amorphous layer which becomes narrower as the implant temperature rises. The amorphous region is below a crystalline silicon layer of increasing thickness as the implant temperature increases. This explanation is consistent with the R_s observations plotted in

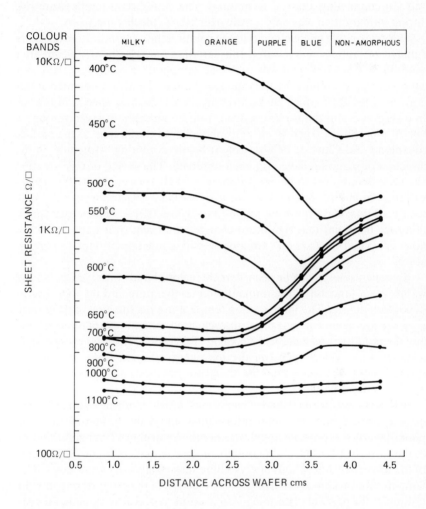

Fig. 17. Sheet resistance profiles across wafer implanted with 1×10^{15} cm^{-2} B$^+$ at 25 keV + 1×10^{15} F$^+$ at 43 keV, 100 μA and isochronally annealed. Top of wafer at the right. After Beanland and Chivers (1978c).

Fig. 17. The R_s reduced for the regions where the amorphous layer was thinnest and the crystalline layer was thickest. This has been confirmed by TEM and ion channeling analysis techniques. The equilibrium temperature rise during implantation was only a little over 100°C for this specimen.

It is reasonable to conclude that the colour-bands are indicative of severe damage variation across a wafer; this variation may also be significant after solid-phase epitaxial regrowth and high-temperature annealing. An indication of the abruptness of the damage change across an implanted wafer is given in the Rutherford backscattering and channelling spectra of Fig. 18. In less than 3 mm the wafer changed from no amorphous layer, through a buried amorphous layer, to an amorphous layer continuous to the surface (Beanland and Chivers, 1978b). Colour-bands exhibiting "structure" in the direction of scanning have also been observed. The period of this structure has been determined to be equivalent to a 50 Hz (power supply frequency) variation in any of the ion beam or scan mechanism parameters, although such variations have not been found to be within 0.01%. These observations reinforce the point that significant changes can occur over quite small distances and that they are an extremely sensitive function of implant temperature.

In conclusion, it can be seen that the colour-bands observed on silicon wafers are a function of the implantation temperature and the total energy deposition density. The implantation temperature is a function of the ion energy, the ion beam current, the scan cycle used in the implantation process, and the radiative and conductive cooling of the wafer. The total energy deposition density is dependent on the ion energy, the ion dose, and the ion species. With so many variables, there are obviously many possible variations of colour-bands.

Colour-bands formed under conditions which result in significant rises in temperature provide useful information about the formation of amorphous layers. It is possible to tell whether the amorphous layer is continuous to the surface or buried, and to obtain an approximate estimate of the depth of the respective amorphous or crystalline surface layers. A knowledge of the temperature variations occurring in each section of the wafer during implantation, for the particular scanning system employed, is advantageous in assisting such interpretation.

If the thermal behaviour varies across the wafer, temperature rises of 200°C or more from room temperature during implantation will generate colour-bands on high-dose implants of medium mass ions. The colour-bands indicate variations in damage across the wafer, and, even after annealing to high temperatures, non-uniform electrical activity may result. For applications where a high degree of implant uniformity is required across the wafer,

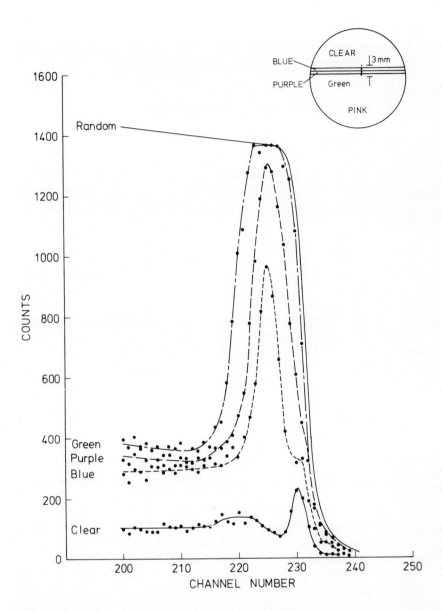

Fig. 18. Rutherford backscattering data for areas of colour-banded wafer implanted with 2×10^{15} cm^{-2}, 80 keV P^{+} at 500 μA. After Beanland and Chivers (1978b).

care should be taken to avoid implant conditions which generate colour-banded wafers. If R_s measurements are made on a colour-banded wafer, or if TEM specimens are examined, depending on the area of the wafer being examined, the experimental results can vary considerably.

IV. BEHAVIOUR OF HIGH-DOSE IMPLANTS

A. Damage Observations

Although the damage resulting from high-dose implants may be useful in applications such as gettering, the usual objective is to minimize the residual damage that follows the annealing process. It is widely appreciated that such damage has a negative effect on the behaviour of electronic devices. As has been noted previously, the damage depends on almost every implant parameter. The purpose of this section is not to review all the available literature pertaining to the residual damage of high-dose implants, but rather to draw some conclusions about the general behaviour observed and provide some appropriate examples.

Various methods have been used to study and quantify the damage associated with high-dose implants. Each method has particular advantages and limitations, so that an adequate representation of the damage behaviour can only be established when a number of complementary methods are used.

The damage measurements of high-dose implants are consistent with the observations discussed in Section III,A. In summary, the thickness of the amorphous layer created by high-dose implants is determined by the dose, species and implant temperature. Depending upon the implant energy and species used, the layer may be buried in the wafer or continuous to the surface. The quality of the recrystallized silicon is seen to decrease when the quality of the underlying material upon which it grows deteriorates. The experiments of Christodoulides et al. (1977) with Pb^+ implants at increasing doses are an interesting example of this. The remnant disorder of the annealed layers continued to increase linearly when the dose was increased beyond the amorphous threshold. They considered that, although the increasing amount of insoluble Pb^+ might have affected regrowth, the structural changes within the bulk lattice underlying the amorphous layer arose from accumulated stresses and were the most likely cause of increased disorder. This explanation is consistent with the observed increase in residual disorder arising from high-dose implants at elevated temperatures (Csepregi et al. 1976), as discussed previously. For further discussion of regrowth effects the reader is referred to Chapter 2.

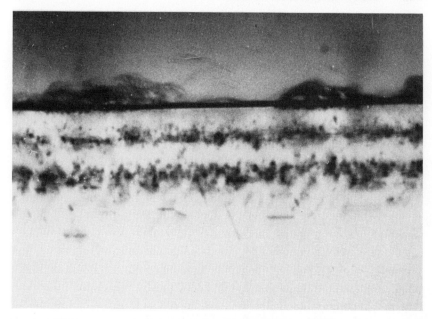

Fig. 19.   TEM cross-section of damage resulting from implantation of 68 keV BF$^+$ at 1 × 10^{15} cm^{-2}, with annealing at 800°C. After Beanland (1978).

A particularly useful method of analysing the damage resulting from the high-dose implantation process is cross-sectional TEM. The cross-section specimens of an implanted layer enable the damage to be viewed as a function of depth (Fletcher, 1973). Sadana *et al.* (1977) reported an application of this method to 120 keV P$^+$ 5 × 10^{14} cm^{-2} implanted Si. Under these conditions, a buried amorphous layer is generated after implantation, and following annealing (950°C) the residual damage is seen to be confined within two discrete damage layers. The depth of these layers at 950 and 1900 Å correlates well with measured reductions of mobility, of approximately 30% below maximum, at depths of 750 and 1900 Å, thus confirming that the observed defects in the damage layers result in scattering of electrical carriers.

The cross-sectional TEM of a wafer implanted to 1 × 10^{15} cm^{-2} with BF$^+$ at 65 keV and annealed to 800°C is given in Fig. 19. The peak damage densities, which occurred at 590 and 1300 Å, can be compared with a peak dopant range of 950 Å. The amorphous layer created by the implant was again buried and it should be noted that it regrew during annealing from both the surface crystalline Si and the underlying crystalline Si.

A cross-sectional TEM study of colour-banded Si (see Section III,B and C) was undertaken by Sadana *et al.* (1980b) to ascertain that the damage

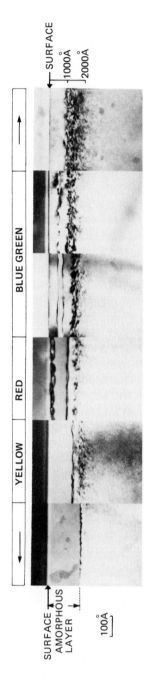

Fig. 20. Cross-sectional TEM damage corresponding to colour bands on high dose-rate implanted wafer 160 keV As$^+$ implanted (100) Si to 2.5 + 10^{15}[cm^{-2} at 2 × 10^{15}] ions cm^{-2}sec^{-1}. After Sadana (1976).

as measured by channelling (e.g. Fig. 18) correlates well with depth of the damage-layer obtained by the TEM method. Fig. 20 shows the cross-sectional TEM damage observed by Sadana (1976) across a colour-banded wafer after implantation. It shows the variation from the surface amorphous layer (left) to buried amorphous layers (centre) and no amorphous layer (right) as a consequence of the wafer temperature–dose cycle.

When high-dose specimens are annealed using a laser or electron beam to cause melting, the damage non-uniformities which exist after implantation are removed (Sadana et al. 1980a; Williams et al. 1981).

B. Dose-Rate Observations

Although dose-rate effects have been reported by various authors over a long period (see, for example, Blamires, 1971), an adequate study of the effects has not been made. As discussed in Chapter 2, it is known that a localized increase in the damage density in the collision cascade volume will result in increased damage. This has been established from sputtering and implantation studies in which comparable atomic and molecular ions were used (see, for example, Thompson et al. 1977).

Dose-rate effects, however, are difficult to explore because of the need to maintain constant temperatures, use comparable scan rates and use identical doses. The dose-rate effects must be associated with the localized conditions during the implantation. It is not the average dose rate which is of relevance, but the instantaneous ion flux density as the wafer is scanned. The average dose rate is a rather meaningless function of the scan geometry and cycle times, although it is usually the parameter quoted if the dose rate is considered. In their studies of variations in dose rates Tamura et al. (1978a) used ion beam currents of 1–5 mA at a dose of 3×10^{16} cm^{-2} P$^+$ implanted Si at 25 keV. Deep amorphous layers were generated in each case, and no subsequent changes in the amount of damage were observed after annealing. However, it has been shown previously that high-dose implants can also often produce amorphous layers of different depths. In these cases the damage observed will be a function of the dose rate.

As noted in Chapter 2, experimental studies of both Si and GaAs have shown that (at constant temperature) an increased dose rate gives increased damage, since there is a balance between dynamic annealing and damage production at target temperatures at which dynamic annealing is efficient.

Localized damage in high-temperature implanted high-dose wafers was studied by Parry (1978) when measuring the enhanced etching of ion-implanted silicon nitride in buffered HF. He found that 1×10^{16} cm^{-2} 30 keV P$^+$ implants produced fifteen times more etching when undertaken at

0.5 mA than at 3 mA. Substrate temperature models are unable to explain this effect, and Parry concluded that the high dose-rate case produced greater localized annealing in the atomic collision region; however, the effects may be brought about from "localized" rises in temperature.

C. Electrical Activation

Some examples of the measurement of electrical activity for high-dose implants have already been discussed in Sections III,A and C. A comprehensive experimental study of 1×10^{15} cm^{-2} implants of B$^+$, P$^+$, As$^+$ and Sb$^+$ at 40 keV with different beam currents, using a particular double-axis mechanical scanning configuration has been reported by Smith et al. (1980). This study includes both one-step anneals to various temperatures up to 1200°C, and various sequential anneals. At the dose considered, it is not surprising that specimens implanted with B$^+$ had the best electrical uniformity and the least dependence upon dose rate. In terms of increased activity and better uniformity, for P$^+$, As$^+$ and Sb$^+$ there was a clear advantage to be gained by employing single-step annealing to 1200°C, although under these implant conditions there was little advantage in annealing above 950°C for B$^+$. Annealing at lower temperatures was found to remove fewer damage variations.

Considering a dose of 6.2 $\times$ 10^{15} cm^{-2} As$^+$ at 150 keV, Lietoila et al. (1981) showed that thermal annealing which is just sufficient to remove the amorphous layer (4 min at 560°C in this case), is able to produce electrically active concentrations in excess of the solid solubility limits. For greater anneal times, the electrically active concentration decays. These results are consistent with the impurity atoms moving to substitutional sites during the solid-phase epitaxy process and subsequently relaxing from the metastable state. Such metastable solid solutions, electrical activity and mobility for high-dose implants are discussed more fully in Chapters 2 and 9.

D. Surface Sputtering

An important effect associated with all implantation, but of special significance in the high-dose regime, is that of surface sputtering. Carter et al. (1972) showed that for implantation at very high doses the dopant concentration peak moves towards the surface as implantation and sputtering proceeds. This results in a flat-topped dopant profile continuing to the surface and achieving an equilibrium maximum dopant concentration.

A simple model to determine the maximum achievable concentration has been developed by Liau and Mayer (1978). It is assumed that efficient atomic mixing by the implanted ions occurs over a depth W. Precipitation (Marwick and Piller, 1978) and surface cone formation (Whitton and Grant, 1981) are ignored.

Conservation of atoms requires:

$$W(dNa/dt) = J_i - J_A \tag{11}$$

where N_A is the concentration of the implanted species,
J_i is the flux of incident ions (species A),
J_A is the flux of species A sputtered from the target.
At steady state $J_i = J_A$.
The total sputtering yield (S) is given by:

$$S = (J_A + J_B)/J_i \tag{12}$$

where J_B is the flux of B (substrate) atoms sputtered from the target. Therefore, at steady state:

$$J_B = (S - 1)J_A \tag{13}$$

If we assume that the probability of species A being sputtered is different from that of species B:

$$J_B/J_A = r(N_B/N_A) \tag{14}$$

where r is the ratio of probability for a B atom near the surface to be sputtered to that for an A atom near the surface.
Consequently the (maximum) achievable steady state concentration is given by:

$$N_A/N_B = r/(S - 1) \tag{15}$$

This model has been applied to a number of systems (Liau and Mayer, 1978) with quite satisfactory results. Since the preferential sputtering tends to be higher for low mass elements, higher concentrations of heavy elements can be achieved. Preferential sputtering effects are discussed in detail in chapter 6.

It should be noted that wafer contamination can also result if sputtered material from beam-line components, apertures, wafer holders, etc., reaches the target (Hemment, 1979).

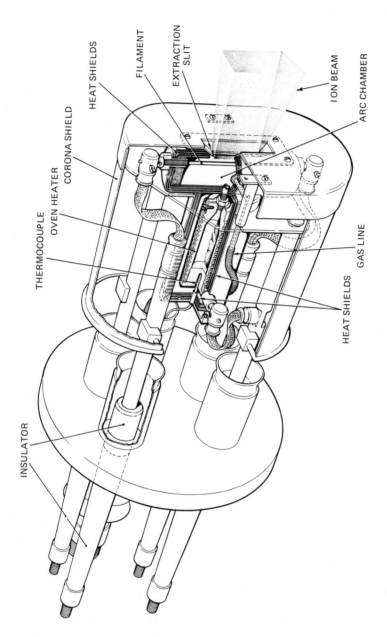

Fig. 21.   Sectioned drawing of the Freeman Ion Source. After Freeman (1969).

SEPARATOR ION SOURCE

HEAT SHIELDS

FILAMENT

EXTRACTION SLIT

CORONA SHIELD

OVEN HEATER

THERMOCOUPLE

INSULATOR

ION BEAM

ARC CHAMBER

GAS LINE

HEAT SHIELDS

IV. HIGH-DOSE ION IMPLANTERS

A. Requirements

The requirements of a high-dose implanter are fairly obvious, but they have a fundamental effect upon the design of the implanter. The unique high-dose requirements are:

(a) high current source (> 1 mA) in order to achieve the doses required in reasonable time.

(b) batch scanning of wafers in order to reduce the temperature rise on the wafers and still provide reasonable wafer throughput.

As for all implanters, the scanning system must provide good uniformity, neutral beam error minimization and dose accuracy. The requirements for appropriate voltage, wafer size, dopant types and automatic control are also common to all implanters. The historical development of implanters has been reviewed effectively by Wegmann (1981), who indicates that there has been and will continue to be a rapid rise in the number of high-dose implanters required.

High-dose implants may be susceptible to the build-up of a carbonaceous contamination layer up to approximately 100 Å thick. This layer can inhibit etching and contact formation. It results from using vacuum pump oil and may be prevented by using perfluorinated polyether diffusion pump oil (Tsai *et al.,* 1979), oil-free high-vacuum pumping systems, or by the use of cold shields.

B. High Beam Currents

The fundamental requirement for high-dose implantation is a high beam current source so that an appropriate range of ion species may be used. The source must provide an acceptable degree of beam control and perform reliably.

The source developed at Harwell by Freeman (1969) has proved to be the most suitable for high beam currents. It is shown in Fig. 21. It has been adopted, with various minor modifications, for all commercial high-current implanters. The source is of the hot cathode type, with the filament parallel and close to the ion extraction slit. It can produce highly focused high-current beams from gas, vapor or solid feed material. To increase the beam current, the slit geometry can be scaled up and beam currents over 20 mA have been achieved.

When high beam currents are used, it is imperative to avoid electrostatic focusing or deflection elements as they result in a loss of space-charge neutralization of the ion beam and consequent "blow-up" of the beam (Dearnaley *et al.*, 1973).

C. Scanning Systems

In order to avoid loss of space-charge neutralization it is therefore essential to choose magnetic or mechanical scanning systems for high current implantation. Electromagnetic scanning systems have not been widely used, but for beam currents to 10 mA Hanley (1981) recently described a hybrid system which combined magnetic scanning with a rotating disc system. The scan frequency employed is typically 0.1 Hz. A second magnet with an equivalent field is used to remove the angular variation of the beam introduced by the first magnet.

Most high-dose implanters use two-axis mechanical scanning (Ryding, 1981). As noted earlier, the carousel (Aitken, 1976), the ferris wheel (Ryding *et al.*, 1976) and the disc (Robertson, 1975) provide the basic mechanisms employed in practical mechanical scan systems. The disc system has a number of advantages, and it is becoming increasingly common in commercial machines.

The disc generally rotates at a constant speed of approximately 1000 RPM, and the scan rate in the radial direction is varied as a function of the radius and the beam current. A linear motion is applied to the rotating disc, with the required velocity being determined by a small on-line computer.

The double-axis mechanical scanning systems employed in high-dose implantation have uniformly distributed neutral beams and result in no scanning geometry errors and no space-charge blow-up. During implantation they will produce a wafer-temperature rise depending on the scan area and the method used to cool the wafers. All such systems produce non-uniform thermal conditions across the wafer during implantation (see Section III,B). The most obvious way to eliminate the effects of non-uniform temperatures is to use multiple scans of much higher frequency in the second axis direction. However, current machines, being somewhat constrained by the need to move a high mass in a controlled manner, generally employ only one sweep of very low velocity for the second axis motion.

The various scan systems used in high-dose implantation build up the ion dose gradually. The number and magnitude of the dose increments, and the time between them, will differ for the various implanters and for various implant conditions. Consequently, the implant conditions of nominally equal implants are always different on implanters with different scan systems; differences exist in the thermal conditions of the implant and the dose build-up cycle and the dose rate.

D. Measurement of Dose Uniformity

It is necessary for users of ion implanters to be able to quantify the dose uniformity across the silicon wafers. It is normally quoted at the 1 s level, as a percentage of the average dose. This can be calculated for particular scanning geometries and a particular number of beam sweeps across a wafer (see, for example, Temple *et al.*, 1981), but a convenient measurement method is also required. A convenient and common method used for demonstrating dose uniformity has been the measurement of sheet resistance at a matrix of points on a wafer using the four-point probe (e.g. Smith and Stephen, 1977) or a contactless method (Miller *et al.*, 1976). These methods measure an average electrical activity; both dose and mobility variations with depth are effectively averaged. As was noted in Section III, C, this is also a function of the damage structure after annealing, which is determined by the damage created during implantation. However, as noted earlier, this damage is a sensitive function of the implantation temperature during the implant cycle, which is a function of the scan geometry and many other implant conditions. Being indirect these methods for measuring dose uniformity are quite adequate for low-dose implants, but will exaggerate dose non-uniformity for high-dose implants. They do serve to indicate the damage non-uniformity, but the coarseness of the matrix will often minimize the detail of the much larger variations which exist in the wafer (see, for example, Smith *et al.*, 1980; Hanley, 1981).

E. Cooling of Wafers

As the temperature rise during high-dose implantation of silicon wafers is a major constraint, increasing attention has been given to wafer cooling. Although thermal bonding to a large heat sink (with say water or freon cooling if necessary) would be ideal, a suitable bonding material has not been found. The cleaning process is inconvenient and almost certain to leave behind undesirable impurities.

Various approaches have been used, most of which depend on improved heat conduction from the back surface of the wafer. The heat conduction efficiency is expressed in terms of H/A, where H is the conductive heat-loss coefficient from wafer to wafer holder, and A is the area of the wafer.

The methods employed include:

1. Solid silicone rubber on the wafer backing plate so as to improve heat conduction from the wafer when the wafer is pushed on to it by a circumferential clamp. H/A is improved from 0–2 mW cm^{-2} °C^{-1} to approximately 18–24 mW cm^{-2} °C^{-1} (King and Rose, 1981).

2. Liquid-filled silicone membrane (Aitken, 1980).

3. Silicone membrane filled with silicone foam, which expands approximtely 20% in vacuum and provides a homogeneous contact between wafer and heat sink (Bayer et al., 1980) and may provide higher H/A than for a solid silicone membrane.

4. Black anodizing of the wafer holding plates has been shown by Gardner et al. (1979) to lower the temperature of the implant by a factor of three in some cases.

5. Doping of the back-surface of the wafer to be implanted with a low resistance n-diffiusion has been shown by Schmitt and Wagner (1980) to improve the wafer's back-surface radiation.

6. Gas cooling (King and Rose, 1981). The wafer is clamped around the edge and a gas is fed into the slightly recessed ($\sim 2\mu$m) wafer backing plate. The value of H/A when nitrogen gas is employed is approximately 18 mW cm^{-2} °C^{-1}. Only a modest gas flow is involved into the beam line; the major gas component enters the wafer loading ports. Gas cooling is clean and most effective. It is likely to become quite widespread for high-dose implanters if appropriate seals can be developed for the rotating disc wafer-holding system.

There is a limitation with the conductive membrane solutions for wafer cooling: an impinging high-current ion beam may result in their deterioration and outgassing.

V. SUMMARY

High-dose implants have become commercially feasible as a result of the development of ion implanter technology during the 1970s. They have found many applications in silicon device technology and in other fields (Hubler, 1981). There is no doubt that all these applications will expand significantly in future. However, there are many physical processes which occur during high-dose implantation which are poorly understood. These effects are intrinsically related to both the annealing process and the implantation process. The physical effects associated with high-dose implants are numerous, and it is a fertile field for further study. Although many of the basic processes are now well understood, the effects of implantation temperature and dose-rate are comparatively unknown. Progress is being made quite rapidly, but additional fundamental studies are required.

The data now available must be of considerable assistance to those wishing to utilize high-dose implantation. Unfortunately, a particular practical application may produce situations which are not seen in experimental studies. For example, the effects of implantation temperature, dose-rate, dose build-up and scan rate are interdependent functions of time. This complicates the interpretation of some experimental results.

Device applications which utilize high-dose implantation (e.g. buried layer implant prior to growth of the epitaxial layer) usually cannot tolerate varying damage conditions across the wafer. In these cases, attention must be given to the scanning strategy, the wafer cooling and the irradiance required to achieve satisfactory results. Gas cooling may be of particular value in this regard.

High-dose implants are associated with deep disorder, amorphous layers of varying depths, layered residual damage, mobility modification and electrical activity variations, all of which are determined by the dopant, damage, profile and dose. In addition to the high-dose effects discussed in this chapter there are additional effects (e.g. recoils when implantation is through SiO_2, surface topography and ion beam mixing) that are discussed in other chapters of this book.

REFERENCES

Adams, J. R., and Bashara, N. M. (1975). *Surface Science* **49**, 441.
Aitken, D. (1976). *Nucl. Instrum. Methods* **139**, 125.
Baranova, E. C., Gusev, V. M., Martynenki, Yu, V., and Hailbullin, I. B. (1975). *Rad. Effects* **25**, 157.
Bayer, E. H., Kranik, J. R., and Mueller, W. F. (1980). *IBM Tech. Disc. Bull.* **22**, 4073.
Beanland, D. G. (1977). *Rad. Effects* **33**, 219.
Beanland, D. G. (1978). *Solid-State Electron*, **21**, 537-549.
Beanland, D. G., and Chivers, D. J. (1978a). *In* "Proc. of 1st Conf. on Ion Beam Modification of Materials" (J. Gyulai, T. Lohner and E. Pasztor, eds.) p. 267. C.R.I. for Physics, Budapest.
Beanland, D. G., and Chivers, D. J. (1978b). *J. Electrochem. Soc.* **125**, 1331-1338.
Beanland, D. G., and Chivers, D. J. (1978c). *J. Vac. Sci. and Tech.* **15**, 1536.
Beanland, D. G., and Williams, J. S. (1978) *Rad. Effects* **36**, 15.
Beanland, D. G., Temple, W., and Chivers, D. (1978). *Solid-State Electron.* **21**, 357.
Beyer, K. D., and Yeh, T. H. (1978). *J. Electrochem. Soc. Extended Abstracts.* **78-2**, 552.
Beyer, K. D., Poponiak, M. R., and Yeh, T. H. (1977). *IBM Tech. Disclosure Bull.* **20**, 1003.

Blamires, N. G. (1971). *In* "Proc. 2nd Int. Conf. on Ion Implantation" (I. Ruge and J. Graul, eds.), p. 119. Springer, Berlin.

Brodsky, M. H., Title, R. S., Weiser, K., and Pettit, G. G. (1970) *Phys. Rev. B* **1**, 2632.

Bruel, M., Berthet, B., Floccari, M., and Michaud, J. F. (1979). *Rad. Effects* **44**, 173.

Carter, G., Baruah, J. N., Grant, W. A., and Whitton, J. L. (1972). *Rad. Effects* **16**, 101.

Christodoulides, C. E., Grant, W. A., and Williams, J. S. (1977). *App. Phys. Lett.* **30**, 322.

Christodoulides, C. E., Baragiola, R. A., Chivers, D., Grant, W. A., and Williams, J. S. (1978). *Rad. Effects* **36**, 73.

Csepregi, L., Kennedy, E. F., Lau, S. S., Mayer, J. W., and Sigmon, T. W. (1976). *App. Phys. Lett.* **29**, 645.

Csepregi, L., Kennedy, E. F., Mayer, J. W., and Sigmon, T. W. (1978). *J. Appl. Phys.* **49**, 3906.

Davies, E. D. (1969). *Appl. Phys. Lett.* **14**, 227.

Dearnaley, G., Freeman, J. H., Nelson, R. S., and Stephen, J. (1973). "Ion Implantation." North Holland, Amsterdam.

Eriksson, L., Davies, J. A., Johansson, N. G. E., Mayer, J. W. (1969). *J. Appl. Phys.* **40**, 842.

Fletcher, J. (1973). *Metals and Mat.* **1**, 530.

Freeman, J. H. (1969). *A.E.R.E. Report* R-6138.

Freeman, J. H. (1976). *In* "Application of Ion Beams to Materials, 1975" (G. Carter, J. S. Colligon and W. A. Grant, eds.) p. 340. Inst. of Phys., London.

Freeman, J. H., Caldecourt, L. R., Done, K. C. W., and Francis, R. J. (1970). *A.E.R.E. Report* R-6496.

Freeman, J. H., Chivers, D. J., Gard, G. A., Hinder, G. W., Smith, B. J., and Stephen, J. (1975). *In* "Ion Implantation in Semiconductors" (S. Namba, ed.), p. 555. Plenum, New York.

Freeman, J. H., Temple, W., Beanland, D. G., Gard, G. A. (1976). *Nucl. Instrum. Methods* **135**, 1.

Gardner, J. A., Lever, R. F., and Michel, A. E. (1979). *IBM. Tech. Disc. Bull.* **21**, 4526.

Glaser, P., Herman, P., Gy, V. (1977). *Vacuum* **27**, 197.

Hanley, P. R. (1981). *In* "Ion Implantation Equipment and Techniques" (C. M. McKenna, P. J. Scanlon and J. R. Winnard, eds.), p. 227. North Holland, Amsterdam.

Hayashi, T., Okomoto, H., and Homma, Y. (1980). *Jpn. J. Appl. Phys.* **19**, 1005.

Hemment, P. L. F. (1979). *Vacuum* **29**, 439.

Hiraki, A., Iwami, M., Shuto, K., Saegusa, T., Gamo, K., and Namba, S. (1976). *In* "Ion Implantation in Semiconductors" (F. Chernow, J. A. Borders and D. K. Brice, eds.), p. 57. Plenum, New York.

Hubler, G. K. (1981). *In* "Ion Beam Analysis" (J. R. Bird and G. J. Clark, eds.), p. 101. North Holland, Amsterdam.

King, M. and Rose, P. (1981). *In* "Ion Implantation Equipment and Techniques" (C. M. McKenna, P. J. Scanlon and J. R. Winnard, eds.), p. 169. North Holland, Amsterdam.

Koji, T., Tseng, W. F., Mayer, J. W., and Suganuma, T. (1979). *Solid-State Electron.* **22**, 335.

Lam, H. W., Pinizziotta, R. F., Yuan, H. T., and Bellavance, D. W. (1981). *Electron. Lett.* **17**, 356.

Liau, Z. L., and Mayer, J. W. (1978). *J. Vac Sci. Technol.* **15**, 1629.

Lietoila, A., Gold, R. B., Gibbons, J. F., Sigmon, T. W., Scovell, P. D., and Young, J. M. (1981). *J. Appl. Phys.* **52**, 230.

Marwick, A. D., and Piller, R. C. (1978). *In* "Proc. of 1st Conf. on Ion Beam Modification of Materials" (J. Gyulai, T. Lohner and E. Pasztor, eds.), p. 1849. C.R.I. for Physics, Budapest.

Mayer, J. W., Marsh, O. J., Shifrin, G. A., and Baron, R. (1967). *Can. J. Phys.* **46**, 4073.

Mazey, D. J., Nelson, R. S., and Barnes, R. S. (1968). *Phil. Mag.* **17**, 1145.

Miller, G. L., Robinson, D. A. H., and Wiley, J. D. (1976). *Rev. Sci. Instrum.* **47**, 799.

Morehead, F. F. and Crowder, B. L. (1970). *Rad. Effects* **6**, 27.

Moriwaki, K., Masuda, N., Aritome, H., and Namba, S. (1980). *Jpn. J. Appl. Phys.* **19**, 491.
Murase, K., and Harada, H. (1979). *Trans. Inst. Electron and Commun. Eng. Jpn. Sect. E* **E62**, 709.
Namba, S. (1978). *In* "Proc of 1st Conf. on Ion Beam Modification of Materials" (J. Gyulai, T. Lohner and E. Pasztor, eds.), p. 887. C.R.I. for Physics, Budapest.
Okuyama, Y., Hashmoto, T., and Koguchi, T. (1978). *J. Electrochem. Soc.* **125**, 1293.
Parry, P. D. (1976). *J. Vac. Sci. Tech.* **13**, 622.
Parry, P. D. (1978). *J. Vac. Sci. Technol.* **15**, 111.
Picraux, S. T., and Vook, F. L. (1971), *Rad. Effects* **11**, 174.
Picraux, S. T., Westmoreland, J. E., Mayer, J. W., Hart, R. R., and Marsh, O. J. (1969). *Appl. Phys. Lett.* **14**, 7.
Robertson, G. I. (1975). *J. Electrochem. Soc.* **122**, 796.
Ryding, G. (1981). *In* "Ion Implantation Equipment and Techniques" (C. M. McKenna, P. J. Scanlon and J. R. Winnard, eds.), p. 239. North Holland, Amsterdam.
Ryding, G., Wittkower, A. B., and Rose, P. H. (1976). *J. Vac. Sci. Technol.* **13**, 1030.
Sadana, D. K., Fletcher, J., and Booker, G. R. (1977). *Electron. Lett.* **13**, 632.
Sadana, D. K., Wilson, M. C., Booker, G. R., and Washburn, J. (1980a). *J. Electrochem. Soc.* **127**, 1589.
Sadana, D. K., Strathman, M., Washburn, J., and Booker, G. R. (1980b). *App. Phys. Lett.* **37**, 234.
Sanders, I. R. (1976). *Microelectron. and Reliab.* **16**, 75.
Schmitt, A., and Wagner, H. (1980). *IBM Tech. Disc. Bull.* **22**, 4600.
Seidel, T. E., Pasteur, G. A., Tsai, J. C. C. (1976a). *App. Phys. Lett.* **29**, 648.
Seidel, T. E., Payne, R. S., Moline, R. A., Costello, W. R., Tsai, J. C., and Gardner, K. R. (1976b). *IEEE Trans. Electron. Devices* **ED-24**, 717.
Servidori, M., and Vecchi, I. (1981). *Solid-State Electron.* **24**, 329.
Shannon, J. M. (1981). *Nucl. Instrum. Methods* **182/183**, 545.
Shannon, J. M., Ford, R. A., and Gard, G. A. (1970). *Rad. Effects* **6**, 217.
Smith, B. J., and Stephen, J. (1977). *Rev. Phys. Appliquée* **12**, 493.
Smith, B. J., Stephen, J., Chivers, D., Fisher, M. (1980). *A.E.R.E. Report* R-9868.
Tamminga, Y., and Josquin, W. J. M. J. (1978). *App. Phys. Lett.* **32**, 13.
Tamura, M. (1973), *App. Phys. Lett.* **23**, 651.
Tamura, M., Yagi, K., Sakudo, N., Tokiguti, K., and Tokuyama, T. (1978a). *In* "Proc. of 1st Conf. on Ion Beam Modification of Materials" (J. Gyulai, T. Lohner and E. Pasztor, eds.), p. 515. C.R.I. for Physics, Budapest.
Tamura, M., Yagi, K., Sakudo, N., Tokiguchi, K., and Tokuyama, T. (1978b). *Jap. J. Appl. Phys.* **17**, Supplement 1, 193.
Temple, W., Beanland, D. G., and Bridgewater, A. N. (1980). *AERE Report* R-9586.
Thompson, D. A., Walker, R. S., and Davies, J. A. (1977). *Rad. Effects.* **32**, 135.
Tsai, M. Y., Streetman, B. G., Blattner, R. J., and Evans C. A., Jr. (1979). *J. Electrochem. Soc.* **126**, 98.
Tsuchimoto, T., and Tokuyama, T. (1970). *Rad. Effects* **6**, 121.
Tsujide, T., Nojira, M., and Kitagawa, H. (1980). *J. Appl. Phys.* **51**, 1605.
Wegmann, L. (1981). *In* "Ion Implantation Equipment and Techniques" (C. M. McKenna, P. J. Scanlon and J. R. Winnard, eds.), p. 1. North Holland, Amsterdam.
Whitton, J. L., and Grant, W. A. (1981). *Nucl. Instrum. Methods.* **182/3**, 287.
Williams, J. S., Pogany, A. P., Beanland, D. G., Chivers, D. J., Kenny, M. J., Rose, A., and Scott, M. D. (1981). *In* "Laser and Electron Beam Solid Interactions and Materials Processing" (J. F. Gibbons, L. V. Hess and T. W. Sigmon, eds.), p. 169. North Holland, Amsterdam.

CHAPTER 9

Trends of Ion Implantation in Silicon Technology

H. S. RUPPRECHT AND A. E. MICHEL

IBM, Thomas J. Watson Research Center
Yorktown Heights, New York, USA

I. INTRODUCTION

Of all the semiconductors, silicon has evolved as the most technologically advanced and the one best understood. It has the simplicity of being a single element material and its chemical purity and crystalline perfection are easier to control. This is evident when it is compared with binary compounds of the III–V type, and especially so when compared with higher order mixtures of III–V material which are made up of ternary and quartenary compounds. However, this material simplicity also has certain disadvantages. The choice and variety of applications had to be more limited, as the essential electrical parameters are clearly restricted to a smaller range.

ION IMPLANTATION
AND BEAM PROCESSING
ISBN   0 12 756980 4

In the fabrication of switching devices such as bipolar and field-effect transistors, the electrical characteristics of silicon have proven over the years to be an excellent match to desired device performance. With the persisting trend towards greater levels of integration and a higher degree of performance of functional circuits, the interest in materials with even more favorable electrical properties has steadily increased. Those new materials are expected to provide a greater latitude in terms of available applications and functions. So far, silicon has met most of the challenges from other materials by the refining and tightening of its technology, by allowing for smaller and shallower structures, and consequently by providing improved device performance.

Ion implantation has played a major role as a method of simultaneously providing shallow impurity distributions and precise control of doping concentration. As the trend continues towards shallower devices, one can foresee the point at which even statistical phenomena such as range straggling of implanted dopants will become a limitation to the abruptness of the impurity profiles required for future devices. Epitaxial techniques, such as molecular beam epitaxy (MBE), may be an alternative, particularly when combined with implants of extremely low energies (Bean and Sodowski, 1982).

In this chapter, we select a few specific topics in order to outline recent trends and, in particular, we discuss some areas in silicon technology which have been influenced by ion implantation.

II. HEAVILY N-DOPED SILICON

Many device structures require heavily doped regions for optimal performance. In n-chanel FET devices, for example, the source-drain pockets should be of the lowest possible electrical resistance (R) (see n^+ regions in Fig. 1). This reduces parasitic effects, which adversely affect transconductances (g_m) and lower the overall performance of the device according to the relation

$$g_m = (dI_{SD}/dV_G) = g_m /(1 + g_m R) \qquad (1)$$

where I_{SD} is the source-drain current,
      V_G is the gate voltage, and
      g_m is the intrinsic transconductance.
For details, see Grove (1967).

Similar parasitic effects can be found for the subcollector region of bipolar transistors (Fig. 1a). In the case of a n-p-n transistor, one has to reduce the resistivity of the n^+ layer to the lowest possible value. The emitter is another vital functional element which can benefit from heavy doping.

DEVICE STRUCTURES REQUIRING
HIGH IMPURITY CONCENTRATIONS

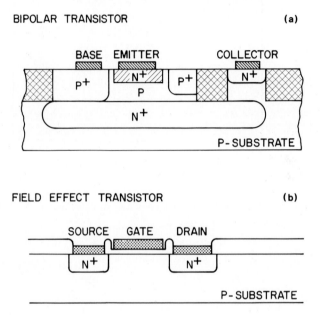

Fig. 1. Schematic cross-section of (a) n–p–n bipolar transistor; (b) FET device. The heavily N doped regions are denoted by N$^+$.

Here, however, the situation is more complex. On the one hand, a high impurity concentration reduces the hole injection from the base and therefore improves current gain; on the other hand, heavy doping leads to band-gap narrowing and counteracts the reduction of hole injection. We return to this point in section IV, when we discuss the diffusion from ion-implanted polysilicon.

Over the years, As has become the preferred n-type dopant for the above applications. According to detailed studies of the phase diagram of the Si-As system by Sandhu and Reuter (1971), As has a maximum solubility in Si under thermodynamic equilibrium conditions of about 3 at. %, which corresponds to 1.5×10^{21} As cm^{-3}. From electrical measurements (Hall effect) one finds, however, that the free electron concentration saturates at a value of 3×10^{20} cm^{-3} (see, for example, section III of Chapter 2). Fig. 2 depicts results obtained by Guerrin et al. (1982). The total As concentration has been

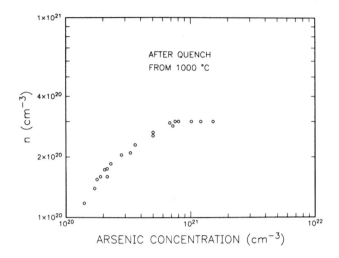

Fig. 2.   Free carrier concentration n as a funtion of total As concentration N_T. After Guerrin *et al.* (1982).

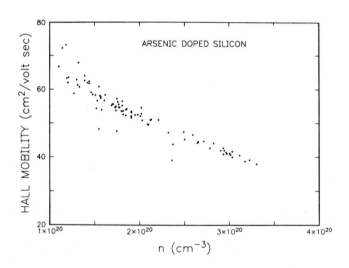

Fig. 3.   Room temperature Hall mobility as a function of total As concentration. After Guerrin *et al.* (1982).

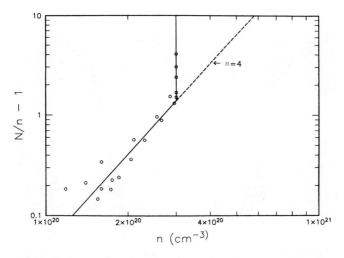

Fig. 4. Experimental relationship between $(N_T/n) - 1$ and n at room temperature; m is the number of As atoms in the cluster.

measured by neutron activation techniques. The corresponding Hall mobility is given in Fig. 3. The test samples were ion implanted, subsequently heat treated at 1000°C and then cooled rapidly. The data were obtained from incremental sectioning techniques; that is, each sample provided a multitude of correlations between Hall mobility, total As concentration and free carrier concentration. The mobility values derived from these measurements differ slightly from Irvin's (1962) data. They are about 10% smaller.

The observed saturation of the free carrier concentration has been known for some time. Schwenker *et al.* (1971) proposed a clustering model based on a simplistic model given by Fistul (1969). Assuming (i) that As can be present in atomically dispersed form and aggregates with one cluster size being predominant, and (ii) that the clustered As is electrically neutral, one can calculate the following relation between total As concentration (N_T) and measured free carrier concentration (n).

$$\log[(N_T/n) - 1] = (m - 1) \log n + constant \qquad (2)$$

where m is the number of As atoms forming the cluster.

Fig. 4 gives the experimentally determined relationship between $(N_T/n) - 1$ and n. The slope in Fig. 4 indicates a cluster factor of 4 and again confirms the experimentally observed saturation at values of $n \sim 3 \times 10^{20}$ cm^{-3}. It also makes it obvious that the proposed model is too simple, and cannot explain the saturation effect. There must be other more complex

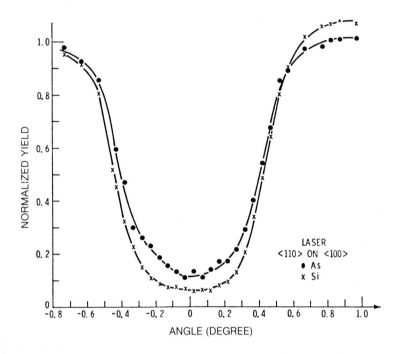

Fig. 5. Angular scan of backscattering yield for the Si and As response. The sample was laser annealed and aligned along the <110> direction (see text). After Chu and Masters (1979).

phenomena that come into play. In addition, the cluster factor of $m = 4$ observed in Fig. 4 is twice that observed by Schwenker *et al.* (1971). Possibly some of the As determined chemically is present in the form of larger precipitates and leads to an overestimate of N_T in eqn. *(1)*. N_T should be replaced by $N_T - N_{Prec.}$, where $N_{Prec.}$ denotes the total As in the larger precipitates. Such a correction would lead to a smaller cluster factor.

Chu and Masters (1979) applied Rutherford backscattering techniques in order to gain further insight into the clustering mechanism. They activated the implanted As (10^{17} cm^{-2} at 90 keV) with pulses of 100 nsec duration from a NdYAG laser and obtained total As concentrations up to 2×10^{21} cm^{-3} in Si; that is, concentrations well above the thermodynamic equilibrium solubility limit. Fig. 5 gives the angular scan along the <110> direction for the Si and As backscattering yield. The half-angle values of the rocking curves are the same for As and Si, which indicates the strict substitutionality of the As. After a furnace heat treatment, however, at 950°C for one hour, the angular backscattering yield in this particular sample (Fig. 6) indicates that about

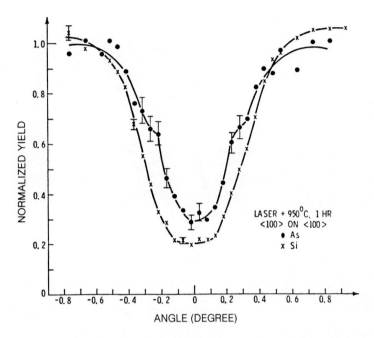

Fig. 6. Angular scan of backscattering yield for the Si and As response (aligned along the <110> direction) after the laser annealed sample was heat treated at 950°C for one hour. After Chu and Masters (1979).

50% of the As atoms were displaced by a small amount from their exact substitutional location. From the reduction in the half-angle, Chu (1981) calculated that the displacement projected on the <110> plane resulted in a 0.15 Å deviation from the exact substitutional location. Correlation with similar measurements in other crystallographic directions led Chu to conclude that the As clusters would not be of the As–As type in which As atoms occupy nearest neighbor sites with slightly changed bond length. The channeling results are in rather good agreement with the vacancy cluster model suggested by Fair and Weber (1973). A configuration of the type $As^+V^-As^+$ which lends further support to a cluster factor of 2 is depicted in Fig. 7.

Although laser annealing of As implanted Si has led to As solubilities exceeding that observed under thermal equilibrium conditions and to electrically activated centers beyond 3×10^{20} cm^{-3}, any further heat treatment at temperatures as low as 500°C reduces the conductivity remarkably. This effect, which was predictable from Schwenker's experiments, severely limits the usefulness of these metastable doping levels generated by pulsed annealing (Chu *et al.* 1980).

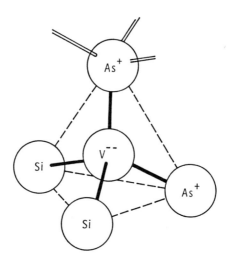

Fig. 7. A possible configuration of a cluster model compatible with RBS data depicting an As–Si vacancy–As complex. After Fair *et al.* (1973).

III. INTERACTIVE EFFECTS IN DOUBLE-IMPLANTED PROFILES

The basic advantages of double-implanted bipolar structures have been known for some time and several publications during the early 1970s reported on the improved properties of shallow emitter-base structures (Reddi, 1972; Payne *et al.* 1974). Graul *et al.* (1975) observed propagation delays as low as 550 psec in ECL circuits by using structures schematically depicted in Fig. 8. The performance enhancement is partly due to the narrow base, which decreases the total electrical charge stored in the base and therefore permits higher switching speeds.

Early attempts at using ion implantation for the fabrication of emitters showed that the resultant devices had very low current gain. Acceptable current gains were obtained only if the implanted dopant was diffused into the Si much deeper than its original implanted profile. As a consequence a two-step process must be used for the emitter, which combines ion-implanted predeposition and thermal drive-in. This heat cycle inevitably leads to the well-known interactive diffusion effects between As and B. The phenomenon was predicted by Hu and Schmidt (1967), and first observed on diffused structures by Ziegler *et al.* (1972). In addition, broadening of the first distribution can result from radiation-enhanced diffusion, as shown in Fig. 9. Both

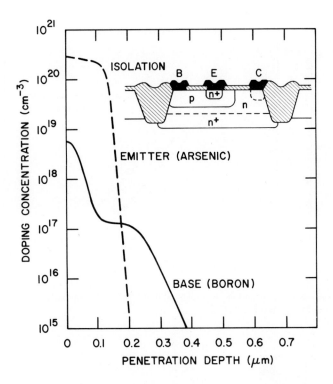

Fig. 8.   Schematic cross-section of a double implanted n-p-n bipolar structure and schematic of B and As impurity profiles. After Graul *et al.* (1975).

phenomena pose a challenge to the obtaining of narrow, well-controlled impurity profiles. Fig. 9 depicts a B distribution, implanted through a 750 Å thick SiO_2 layer. The profile after 20 min. heat treatment at 800°C clearly indicates a redistribution which is beyond that expected for normal diffusion relaxation.

Fig. 10 gives the superposition of an implanted B distribution relaxed for 20 min. at 800°C and an As implant into bare Si, following the removal of the previously deposited 300 Å SiO_2. The bare Si surface was then again capped by a 200 Å SiO_2 layer, pyrolytically deposited at 800°C for 20 min. (Fig. 11). The profiles in Figs. 11 and 12 (the latter following a further heat treatment at 950°C for 35 min.) clearly show a "dip" in the B profile at the As diffusion front. During the thermal cycle, this dip is produced by the transport of B ions in the electric field caused by the steep gradient of As ions.

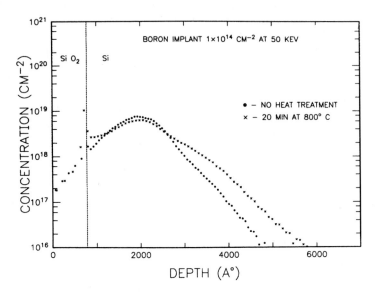

Fig. 9.   Implanted B distribution, as implanted and after heat treatment, obtained by SIMS analysis. After Michel and Kastl (1982).

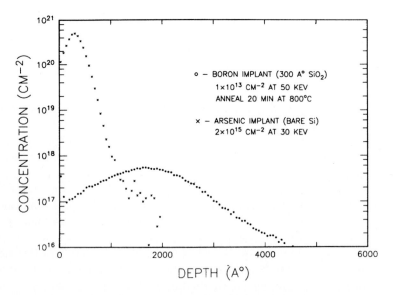

Fig. 10.   Implanted As distribution (no heat treatment) superimposed on a B distribution, obtained from SIMS analysis. After Michel and Kastl (1982).

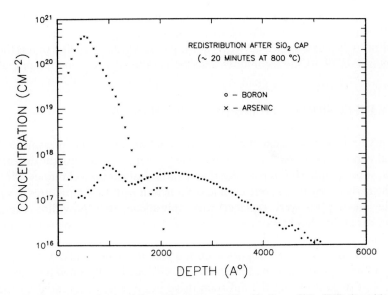

Fig. 11.   Redistribution of As and B profiles shown in Fig. 10 after a SiO_2 CVD deposition process (20 min. at 800°C). Obtained by SIMS analysis.

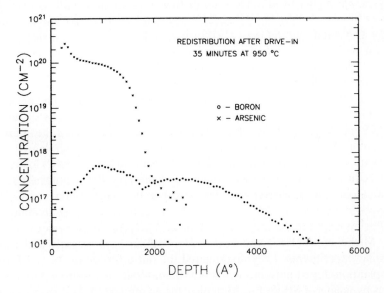

Fig. 12.   The redistributed impurity profiles of As and B (Figs. 10 and 11) after a complete As drive-in cycle (35 min. at 950°C), obtained from SIMS analysis. After Michel and Kastl (1982).

In general, double implantation into single crystalline Si is well suited for making bipolar structures with base widths of 2000 Å and above. For ultra-high-performance devices requiring base widths of 1000 Å or less (Solomon *et al.* 1979), the techniques described in the next section are preferable.

IV. DIFFUSION FROM IMPLANTED POLYSILICON

Very uniform polysilicon films are readily obtainable by low-pressure chemical vapor deposition. These can be doped either *in situ* during the deposition or, subsequently, by implantation or standard diffusion techniques. Most of the early applications were used in conjunction with FET structures in which the metal gates were replaced with polysilicon, thus providing alternate means of threshold tailoring, or, in the field area, of preventing surface inversion.

Takagi *et al.* (1973) reported on the use of highly doped polysilicon as a diffusion source for the fabrication of As-doped or P-doped emitters. The loss of dopant during the diffusion drive-in cycle was prevented by simultaneously oxidizing the polysilicon during the heat treatment.

Graul *et al.* (1976) found that the high-frequency gain of bipolar structures, which were formed by As out-diffusion from ion-implanted polysilicon layers, was higher by about a factor of 10 when compared with standard diffused bipolar devices having equal integrated base doping (Gummel number). DeGraaff and deGroot (1978) suggested that a tunnel barrier, formed in the emitter area at the interface between polysilicon and the single crystalline substrate, was responsible for the increase in gain. They concluded that the interface barrier effectively reduces hole injection into the emitter region without affecting the electron injection into the base. The net result is a higher current gain. They based their model of the emitter structure on SIMS and Auger analysis, which indicated a thin oxide layer at the interface. In a more detailed study of the hole injection into a thin ion-implanted emitter with heavily doped polysilicon contacts, Ning and Isaac (1980) found that the reduction in current was a function of the polysilicon thickness rather than an interfacial barrier. In order to explain the experimental results, they proposed a simple model involving only the difference in hole mobility and diffusion length in the mono crystalline and polycrystalline regions.

Michel *et al.* (1983) and Barson *et al.* (1982) have recently undertaken similar experiments. They investigated the out-diffusion of As and B from implantion-doped polysilicon layers and analyzed the resulting doping profiles by means of SIMS. Fig. 13 depicts the as-implanted As distribution (no heat treatment) and the implant conditions were E = 30 keV, dose 2×10^{15} cm^{-2}. The As profile is superimposed on a B implant into the composite struc-

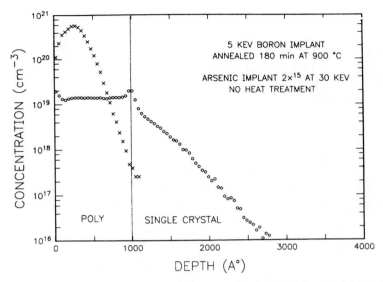

Fig. 13. A polysilicon layer deposited on single crystalline Si with B implant (○) into the polysilicon, and redistributed by heat treatment. Subsequently implanted with As (×) but no heat treatment after As implant. Profiles obtained by SIMS. After Michel *et al.* (1983).

ture which, prior to the As implant, has been heat treated at 900°C for 180 min. The B was implanted under the following conditions, E = 5keV, dose 2×10^{14} cm^{-2}. One clearly sees an increase in total boron concentration at the interface. As shown in Fig. 14, a similar increase is found for the redistributed As after an oxidation process at 900°C for 30 min. There is also an increase in As at the newly formed SiO_2-polysilicon interface owing to a "snowplough" effect during the oxidation.

Fig. 15 depicts the impurity profile after further heat treatment in N_2 atmosphere; that is, after completion of the As drive-in cycle. Further detailed studies of the diffusion behavior from these doped polysilicon films led to the following observation. The maximum As concentration at the polysilicon-single crystal silicon interface remains at the same value and does not decrease under prolonged heat treatment. This suggests that some of the As might be bound at the interface in the form of an immobile complex formed with other impurities such as oxygen, carbon and fluorine, all of which have been observed in SIMS measurements. This corroborates previous observations by deGraaff and deGroot (1978). Finally, it was observed that the interface layer acts as a diffusion barrier *per se*.

These examples demonstrate that if polysilicon is used as an intermediate layer, steeper profiles and better control of doping can be obtained by using

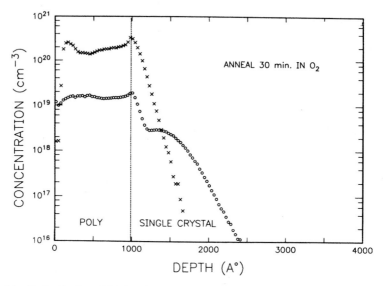

Fig. 14. Redistribution of B (○) and As (×) profiles shown in Fig. 13 during partial oxidation of polysilicon layer (900°C for 30 min. in O_2). Profiles obtained by SIMS. After Michel *et al.* (1983).

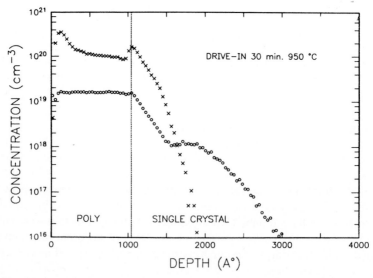

Fig. 15. Resulting impurity profiles (arsenic, ×, and boron, ○) after further heat treatment (950°C, 30 min.) in N_2 atmosphere for final drive-in cycle. Profiles obtained by SIMS. After Michel *et al.* (1983).

a combination of diffusion and ion implantation. Part of the reason is as follows. Owing to the presence of grain boundaries, the diffusivity of B and As is much higher in polysilicon than in single crystalline material. During heat treatment, the dopant is readily distributed uniformly in the polysilicon layer. The absolute amount of dopant introduced can be accurately controlled by implantation, while low-energy implantation damage is confined to the polysilicon layer. The redistribution of the dopant in the single crystalline silicon is therefore not enhanced by radiation damage. The final result is a doping process which utilizes the control of ion implantation and the steepness of profiles obtainable from "infinite" diffusion sources.

V. SUMMARY AND CONCLUSIONS

Most implantations in silicon technology require implant energies of less than 200 keV. The increasing tendency to use implantation as a predeposition process, followed by a thermal drive-in diffusion, will further decrease the energy range. In the previous sections, we have depicted a few examples which illustrate this trend. In particular the use of polysilicon as the dopant source for thermal diffusion, with the accurate control of total impurity dose being provided by implantation, is of great interest. This process has the potential of providing the shallow and steep impurity profiles which clearly are required for future high-performance device structures. However, in order to make this a usable and reliable process, a better understanding of the structure of the interface between polysilicon and single-crystal silicon, and its role as a diffusion barrier, is required.

We can conclude with the following statements. Ion implantation has become an acceptable technology and has become an integral part of silicon device manufacturing. Many of the performance advances in the bipolar, as well as in the FET area, would have been impossible without ion implantation.

ACKNOWLEDGMENTS

The authors wish to express particular appreciation to R. H. Kastl for his efforts in providing the secondary ion mass spectrometry data for the impurity profiles. They also wish to acknowledge the many enlightening discussions with W. K. Chu concerning his helium ion backscattering experiments.

REFERENCES

Barson, F., Kastl, R., Kemlage, B., and Michel, A. E. (1982). Paper given at Electrochemical Society VLSI Symposium, Detroit.

Bean, J. C., and Sadowski, E. A. (1982). *J. Vac. Sci. Technol.* **20**, 137.

Chu, W. K. (1980). *Appl. Phys. Lett.* **36**, 273.

Chu, W. K., and Masters, B. J. (1979). *In* "Laser-Solid Interactions and Laser Processing, 1978" (S. J. Ferris, H. J. Leamy and J. M. Poate, eds.), p. 305. AIP Conference Proceedings No. 50.

Chu, W. K., Mader, S. R., and Rimini, E. (1980). *In* "Laser and Electron Beam Processing of Materials" (C. W. White and P. S. Peercy, eds.), p. 253. Academic Press, New York.

DeGraaff, H. C., and de Groot, J. G. (1978). IEDM Proceedings 333.

Fair, R. B., and Weber, G. R. (1973). *J. Appl. Phys.* **44**, 273.

Fistul, V. I. (1979). "Heavily Doped Semiconductors." Plenum, New York.

Graul, J., Kaiser, H., Wilhelm W., and Ryssel H. (1975). *IEEE J. Solid State Circuits* **SC10**, 201.

Graul, J., Glasl, A., and Murrmann, H. (1976). *IEEE J. Solid State Circuits* **SC11**, 491.

Grove, A. (1967). "Physics and Technology of Semiconductor Devices." John Wiley, New York.

Guerrin, F., Michel A. E., and Kastl, R. (1982), Private communication.

Hu, S. M., and Schmidt, S. (1968). *J. Appl. Phys.* **39**, 4272.

Irvin, J. C. (1962). *Bell System Technical Journal,* **41**, 387.

Michel, A. E., and Kastl, R. (1982). (Unpublished.)

Michel, A. E., Kastl, R., and Mader, S. M. (1983). *Nucl. Instrum. Methods* **209/210**, 719.

Ning, T. H., and Isaac, R. D. (1980). *IEEE Trans Electron Devices* **ED-27**, 2051.

Payne, R. S., Scavuzzo, R. J., and Olsen, K. H. (1974). *IEEE Trans Electron Devices* **ED-21**, 273.

Reddi, V. G. (1972). *Solid State Technol.* **35.**

Sandhu, J. S., and Reuter, J. L. (1971). *IBM J. Res. Development* 464.

Schwenker, R. O., Pan, E. S., and Lever, R. F. (1971). *J. Appl. Phys.* **42**, 3195.

Solomon, P. M., and Tang, D. D. (1979), *IEEE ISSCC.* **86.**

Takagi, M.

Ziegler, J. F., Cole, J. C., and Baglin, J. E. E. (1972). *Appl. Phys. Lett.* **21**, 177.

CHAPTER 10

Implantation in GaAs Technology

F. H. EISEN

*Rockwell International Microelectronics
Research and Development Center
Thousand Oaks, California, USA*

I. INTRODUCTION

Ion implantation doping of silicon has been used in the fabrication of silicon integrated circuits for over ten years, and during that time there has been a significant increase in its application. On the other hand, the application of ion implantation to the fabrication of GaAs devices has not developed as rapidly. The reasons for this lag are that the development of implantation doping techniques in GaAs matured somewhat later, and the development of integrated circuit technologies in GaAs has only recently occurred. These integrated circuit technologies (both digital and microwave) require the reproducibility and uniformity of doping which implantation has demonstrated in silicon and represent the first widespread use of implantation in GaAs device technology.

ION IMPLANTATION
AND BEAM PROCESSING
ISBN   0 12 756980 4

There are several features of implantation in GaAs which are different from implantation in silicon. The most notable of these is the dissociation of GaAs by loss of arsenic. This occurs rapidly at the temperatures usually required for post-implantation annealing. Several methods have been used to prevent this dissociation. Because of the influence these annealing techniques may have on implantation doping results and on device processes they will be discussed in Section II. Implantation doping results will then be considered.

Both n-type and p-type implantations have been applied to the fabrication of such GaAs devices as FETs (Higgins *et al.* 1978), junction FETs (Troeger *et al.* 1979), bipolar transistors (Yuan *et al.* 1980), solar cells (Fan *et al.* 1979), and varactor diodes (Immorlica and Eisen, 1977). Since the electron mobility in GaAs is much higher than the hole mobility, high-speed majority carrier devices require n-type active layers. For this reason, n-type implantation is of considerable interest for device applications, although in some respects it is more difficult to achieve good n-type doping than it is to achieve good p-type doping of GaAs. The n-type implants can be divided rather naturally into low-dose and high-dose regions. The low-dose region includes implants which result in a maximum carrier concentration no greater than $\sim 10^{17}$ cm^{-3}, which is typical of the concentration required for the n-type active layers of high-speed devices. The activation of implants producing such maximum carrier concentrations should be approximately 100% (see Fig. 1). For equilibrium conditions this figure also shows that, as the implantation dose is raised to produce significantly higher electron concentrations, the activation can be expected to fall well below 100%. In addition, changes in the implanted substrate material during post-implantation annealing can significantly affect the results of low-dose n-type implants, whereas the doping resulting from high-dose implants is relatively insensitive to substrate changes. For these reasons low-dose and high-dose n-type implants will be considered separately (sections III and IV). Section V will be devoted to p-type implants. Examples of device applications will be given in each section.

This chapter will be devoted to a discussion of the doping effects in GaAs which are the result of the chemical or electrical nature of the implanted species. It should be mentioned that high resistivity layers can be produced in either n-type or p-type GaAs by using proton or heavier ion bombardment (Wohllenben and Beck, 1966; Steeples *et al.* 1980). This method has been used in several laboratories to fabricate experimental devices (Murphy *et al.* 1972; Speight *et al.* 1974) and is potentially useful for isolating devices fabricated in epitaxial layers. However, a disadvantage is that it may be thermally unstable, since the resistivity increase is associated with the ion bombardment damage. Further information is available in the references cited.

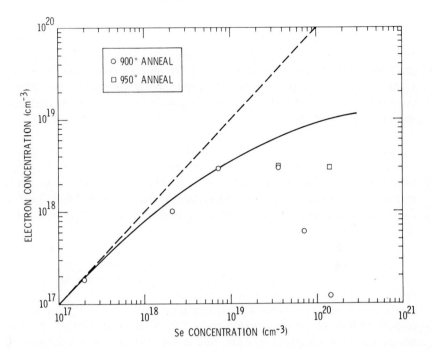

Fig. 1. Measured peak electron concentration *vs* calculated peak Se concentration in Se-implanted GaAs (Gamo *et al.*, 1977). The solid line is based on data for bulk GaAs and shows the measured electron concentration *vs* Se concentration in such material (Vieland and Kudman, 1963). The dashed line shows the relation which would be obtained for 100% activation of the Se.

II. ANNEALING TECHNIQUES

As mentioned in the introduction, the dissociation of GaAs at elevated temperatures complicates the annealing of ion-implanted GaAs. When bare GaAs is annealed at temperatures of about 600°C or higher, visible surface damage caused by a loss of As can be observed. Loss of As from implanted GaAs at annealing temperatures ≤500°C has also been observed (Picraux, 1973). Since typical annealing temperatures for ion-implanted GaAs are in the range 800°–900°C, it is necessary to encapsulate the annealed material with a suitable protective layer or to perform the anneal in an appropriately controlled ambient. As a background to the implantation results that are discussed in the succeeding sections, this section discusses the various materials that have been used as encapsulants, as well as capless annealing techniques.

In addition, some consideration will be given to the suitability of different annealing techniques for device processing.

Silicon dioxide was employed as an annealing encapsulant (cap) in early work on implantation in GaAs. The maximum electron concentrations achieved in early n-type implantation experiments were rather low (Sansbury and Gibbons, 1970; Hunsperger and Marsh, 1970). It was later realized that Ga diffuses rapidly in SiO_2 and that the loss of Ga might limit the activation of implanted n-type dopants (Gyulai et al. 1970). Subsequent research has shown that there is indeed diffusion of Ga through a SiO_2 cap (Fig. 2a). As a result the use of Si_3N_4 as a cap was investigated in a number of laboratories. When a Si_3N_4 cap containing only a very low amount of oxygen is employed, no Ga is detected on the surface of the cap (Fig. 2b). However, Si_3N_4 caps which contain appreciable oxygen do not act as effective barriers to Ga diffusion.

Other materials which have been used as encapsulants include Al (Sealy and Surridge, 1975) and AlN. The early work on AlN made use of sputtered material which contained a large amount of oxygen and it should really be called an aluminum oxy-nitride (Eisen et al. 1977; Gamo et al. 1977). Recently, interesting results have been obtained with sputter-deposited AlN containing little or no oxygen (less than 1%) (Nishi et al. 1981). For thicknesses ranging from 200 Å to 2 μm, this material shows good adherence to GaAs during annealing. This observation is consistent with the fact that the published values of the thermal expansion coefficient for AlN and GaAs are almost equal; thus, when AlN is employed as a cap, little stress should be produced in the surface of the GaAs during annealing.

A number of capless annealing techniques have been proposed for implanted GaAs. All of these techniques attempt to provide a suitable pressure of As over the surface of the annealed GaAs in order to retard the loss of As from that surface. One of the first such methods reported made use of a closed system, with the As being supplied from a GaAs melt (Malbon et al. 1976). Several laboratories have used an atmosphere of arsine in hydrogen (Kasahara et al. 1979). Finely powdered graphite containing crushed GaAs has been used to retard the loss of As from GaAs and to provide a source of As overpressure (Immorlica and Eisen, 1976). A further technique is proximity annealing, in which a polished wafer of GaAs is placed over the surface of the implanted GaAs during the anneal (Mandal and Scoble, 1979). This technique has been employed to anneal implanted GaAs in a hydrogen atmosphere or under circumstances in which an As pressure is supplied from another source, such as arsine in the hydrogen. Indium arsenide has also been used in a closed system in order to provide an As pressure over proximity-annealed GaAs wafers (Woodall et al. 1981). Successful annealing of implanted GaAs has been achieved with all these techniques, and some

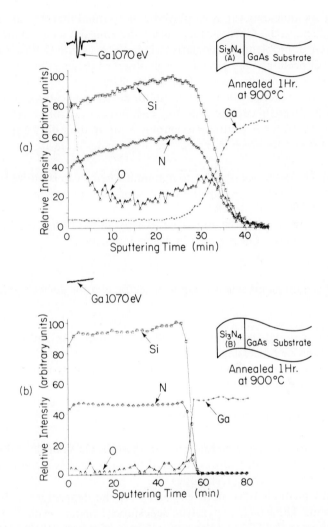

Fig. 2. Auger electron depth profiles from GaAs samples encapsulated with different Si_3N_4 layers and anealed at 900°C for 1 hr. $Si_3N_4(A)$ (Fig. 2a) contained significant O, and Ga was found on the surface of the nitride and throughout the film. No Ga was detected on the surface of $Si_3N_4(B)$ (Fig. 2b) or in the film and the O level in the film was low, barely above the detection limit of 0.1 atomic percent (Vaidyanathan *et al.*, 1977).

of them have been employed in the fabrication of GaAs discrete devices and integrated circuits (Yuan *et al.* 1980; McLevige *et al.* 1982, Hojo *et al.* 1981).

When an annealing cap is employed, it is essential that the cap material should adhere to the GaAs surface during the anneal. Good adherence has often been a problem, particularly when Si_3N_4 is used. Blistering and bubbling or peeling of the cap have been observed (Eisen *et al.* 1973). When such phenomena occur, dissociation causes damage to the surface of the GaAs and the material will not be useful for device applications. Since there are several successful capless annealing techniques available, one might ask why some laboratories continue to employ a cap in their device processing. Some of the factors which make the use of a cap desirable are:

1. A clean GaAs surface is easier to maintain when a cap is utilized.
2. Etching of selected areas of the cap can be used to provide registration of successive mask levels.
3. The dielectric cap can be employed to assist in the lifting and definition of the metalizations required in device fabrication.

Essential requirements when using a dielectric cap for device applications are:

1. The cap material should adhere well during annealing and during subsequent device processing.
2. The implantation doping profiles following annealing with a cap must meet device requirements.
3. The encapsulant material must allow pattern definition by dry etching techniques without damage to the GaAs.

The use of dry etching techniques is important in GaAs device fabrication because the very small features required for such devices cannot be made reliably using wet etching techniques.

Various methods have been employed for the deposition of dielectric encapsulants. These include pyrolytic deposition (Donnelly *et al.* 1975), sputtering (Eisen *et al.* 1977) and deposition from a rf plasma (Vaidyanathan *et al.* 1977). It is not clear whether any particular technique has strong advantages over the others. For example, each technique has been employed successfully to deposit useful Si_3N_4 caps on GaAs. However, the results obtained with caps deposited by different methods may show certain differences. For example, depending on whether a pyrolytically deposited Si_3N_4 or a reactively sputtered Si_3N_4 was used, the activation of high-dose Se implants has been observed to be quite different (Section IV).

Another kind of annealing technique which has been employed in GaAs involves the use of pulsed laser or electron beams (as discussed in Section IV of Chapter 2). While very high electron concentrations in implanted GaAs have been achieved by using either pulsed laser beams or pulsed electron beams, the electron mobility in these layers has been significantly below that expected in a material that has such electron concentrations (Eisen, 1980). Pulsed techniques have not been used successfully to anneal low-dose implants in GaAs. At present, it is not clear whether pulsed annealing techniques will have a significant impact on the processing of implanted GaAs for device fabrication.

Recently reported work on the results of short-time (~ 1–10 sec.) thermal annealing of implanted GaAs indicates that such techniques may be promising for device processing. Annealing of GaAs wafers implanted with 3×10^{12} Si^+ cm^{-2} at 70 keV with radiation from halogen lamps has shown good activation of the implanted species and little diffusion, with and without a Si_3N_4 cap (Arai et al. 1981). Light from filament lamps has been used to anneal GaAs samples implanted with high doses of Si or Zn, with good results (Davies et al. 1982). Multiply-scanned electron beams have been successfully used to activate low-dose Si implants (Bujatti et al. 1982) and both low-dose and high-dose Se implants (Shah et al. 1981). In order to evaluate these techniques for device processing applications, further work will be required, but the initial results and the simplicity of some of the equipment indicate that the effort will be merited.

III. LOW-DOSE n-TYPE IMPLANTS

As indicated in Fig. 1, an approximately 1:1 ratio of free electrons to donors is observed in bulk GaAs, up to donor concentrations of $\sim 10^{17}$ cm^{-3}. This result indicates that n-type implants with maximum donor concentrations of the order of 10^{17} cm^{-3} or lower should show $\sim 100\%$ activation of the implanted donors. Doses of n-type dopants which result in such maximum donor concentrations ($\lesssim 1$ to 5×10^{12} cm^{-2} depending on dopant and energy) will be referred to as low doses. The application of low-dose n-type implants generally involves implantation into semi-insulating GaAs. The apparent activation of such low-dose implants depends strongly on the properties of the semi-insulating substrate material. It is the purpose of this section to discuss the effects of semi-insulating substrates, the behavior of various n-type dopants in GaAs, and the properties of n-type layers produced by implantation of low doses of donors into semi-insulating GaAs. In addition, the application of low-dose n-type implants to the fabrication of GaAs devices will be reviewed.

One of the principal problems in applying low-dose n-type implants in semi-insulating GaAs to the fabrication of devices in that the semi-insulating substrate often exhibits a substantial change in surface electrical properties during post-implantation annealing (Higgins *et al.* 1978). The most extreme change observed is the formation of an n-type surface layer on semi-insulating material which has not been implanted, but which has been capped and annealed as would be done for an implanted sample. Even when an n-type conversion layer cannot be observed on annealed unimplanted material, tails may be observed on the electron concentration profile in samples implanted with low doses of n-type dopants (Fig. 3).

It is possible to identify semi-insulating GaAs which does not exhibit the thermal conversion described in the preceding paragraph. Usually test wafers are taken from each end of a boule of GaAs, and if the results of tests on these wafers are satisfactory, the remainder of the boule will also be acceptable. Several kinds of tests may be employed, and the detailed techniques may vary from laboratory to laboratory. Usually, unimplanted wafers are prepared and annealed as would be done for an implanted wafer. Following this treatment, the measured resistivity of the material must be above a specified minimum value for the material to be acceptable. Implantations similar to those which will be used in device fabrication are often employed as another test of the material. Generally the electron concentration profiles need to exhibit a sharp drop and not show the deep doping tail illustrated in Fig. 3. In addition, the profile may need to be close to an accepted standard or the doping efficiency may need to lie within a certain range. Some workers also require that the electron mobility measured in the implanted layer be above a specified minimum value.

Much of the semi-insulating GaAs which has been available to date has had Cr added to it in the growth process in order to compensate the residual donors and hence obtain high resistivity material. Recently, it has been observed that the Cr in semi-insulating GaAs redistributes during annealing (Asbeck *et al.* 1980). An example of this redistribution is shown in Fig. 4. It can be seen that the Cr concentration at the surface of the GaAs is significantly lower than in the bulk of the material. If the Cr concentration near the surface falls below that of the residual donors, those donors will not be fully compensated and an n-type surface will result.[*] The redistribution of the Cr depends on the conditions under which the GaAs is annealed. For example, it has been observed that there is significantly less outdiffusion of Cr when an AlN cap is used than when a SiO_2 cap is employed (Nishi *et al.*, 1981). It has been suggested that this is because of the similarity in expan-

---

[*] Surface depletion effects may prevent observation of this n-type surface conversion if the net sheet electron concentration is low.

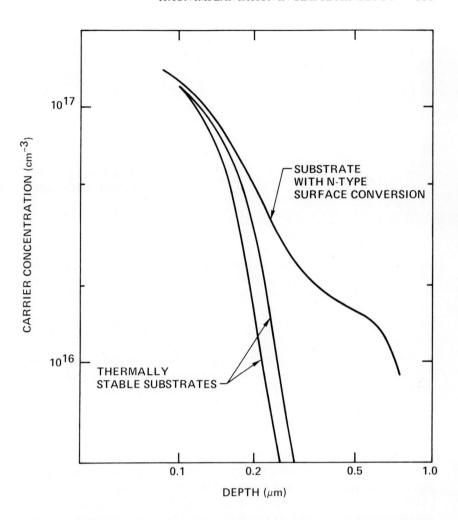

Fig. 3. Examples of electron concentration profiles measured in ion implanted, thermally stable, semi-insulating GaAs substrates and in a substrate which shows n-type surface conversion (Asbeck, 1982).

sion coefficients of AlN and GaAs; this results in a lower stress in the GaAs when it is annealed with an AlN cap than when it is annealed with a SiO$_2$ cap. The redistribution of Cr in GaAs annealed under arsine, without a cap, has been found to depend on the arsine pressure (Kasahara and Watanabe, 1980).

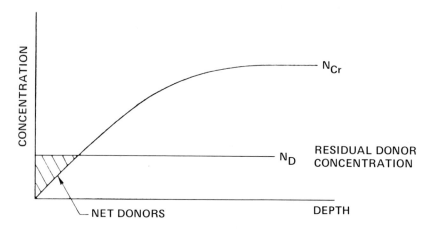

Fig. 4.   Surface conversion mechanism resulting from redistribution of Cr in Cr-doped semi-insulating GaAs. If the Cr concentration falls below the donor concentration N_D as illustrated, a n-type surface layer with a net donor concentration given by (N_D-N_{Cr}) will result (Asbeck, 1982).

Recently, considerable effort has been devoted to the use of a liquid encapsulated Czochralski (LEC) growth technique to grow semi-insulating GaAs (AuCoin *et al.*, 1979). The concentration of donor impurities in semi-insulating material grown by this method is lower than in GaAs grown by the horizontal Bridgman technique, and it is possible to obtain semi-insulating GaAs with resistivities of 10^8 ohm cm or higher without the deliberate addition of Cr to the melt (Hobgood *et al.*, 1981). The yield of device-quality semi-insulating material from the LEC process has been observed to be quite good, and the initial results on the use of this material in device fabrication are very encouraging (Kirkpatrick *et al.*, 1982). These results suggest that it may be possible to establish a better supply of semi-insulating GaAs for device purposes if the material is grown by the LEC technique rather than the horizontal Bridgman technique. It should be noted, however, that the compensation mechanisms in semi-insulating LEC material are not fully understood at present. It is conceivable that the compensating centers in this material may also exhibit an outdiffusion effect in some cases. This would result in thermal conversion similar to that observed in Cr-doped semi-insulating GaAs.

Typical electron concentration profiles for low-dose Si, S, or Se implants in GaAs are shown in Fig. 5. These results were obtained from measurements of capacitance vs voltage on the implanted and annealed samples. Calculated profiles for the implanted species obtained using LSS range statistics (Gibbons et al., 1975) are also shown in Fig. 5. The calculated and measured profiles are quite similar for Si and Se, indicating that a high percentage of the implanted ions are effective in doping the GaAs and that there is little or no diffusion of these dopants during implantation or post-implantation annealing. The calculated and measured profiles for the S-implanted sample are quite different. Only about 20% of the implanted S is effective in doping the GaAs, and the depth of the doped layer is much greater than expected. Data obtained from samples implanted with a radioactive S isotope indicate that these phenomena are the result of diffusion of the S during post implantation annealing (Eisen and Welch, 1980). A signifcant amount of the implanted S is lost from the GaAs as a result of this diffusion, and this dopant loss probably accounts for the apparent low doping efficiency.

The electron mobility in implanted layers with electron concentration profiles such as those shown in Fig. 5 is usually quite good. For example, mobilities of about 5000 cm^2 V s^{-1} have been obtained in layers with a net donor concentration of about 1×10^{17} cm^{-3} (Hobgood et al., 1981). The electron mobility obtained in n-type layers formed by implantation into semi-insulating GaAs depends, of course, on the purity of the semi-insulating material. In a study of the electron mobility measured for n-implants in GaAs grown from a pyrolytic boron nitride crucible using LEC methods, the mobilities obtained were consistent with a compensating acceptor concentration of about 1×10^{16} cm^{-3} (Hobgood et al., 1981).

The uniformity of n-type layers formed by implantation has been demonstrated to be very good. An example of this uniformity is presented in Fig. 6, which shows the distribution of FET pinchoff voltages for FETs fabricated using the process illustrated in Fig. 7c. The pinchoff voltages for such FETs depends largely on the uniformity of the FET active layer formed by ion implantation. The pinchoff voltage distribution measured over an area of 1.7 $\times$ 1.7 cm^2 (Fig. 6a) shows a standard deviation of about 5%, while that measured over a smaller area (300 μm $\times$ 600 μm) is only about 1.2% (Fig. 6b).

Low-dose n-type implants in GaAs have been used in the fabrication of field-effect transistors and more widely in integrated circuits that use FETs, varactor diodes (Immorlica and Eisen, 1977, Niikura et al. 1978), and IMPATT diodes (Bozler et al. 1976). The uniformity of doping over relatively large areas which was illustrated above, is essential for reproducibility of device characteristics in complex integrated circuits. Examples of three different fabrication approaches used to make GaAs integrated circuits are shown in Fig. 7. The mesa implanted DMESFET approach shown in Fig. 7a involves the formation of a continuous n-type layer by implantation into semi-insulating GaAs and the use of mesa etching in order to provide device

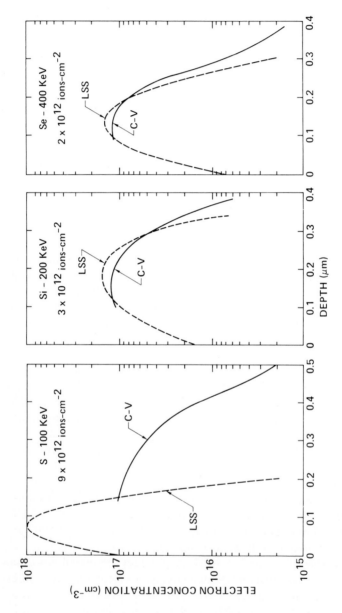

Fig. 5. Comparison of electron concentration profiles for GaAs samples implanted at room temperature with S, Si, or Se at the indicated energy and with the indicated dose. The measured profiles were derived from capacitance-voltage data and the dashed estimates of the profile of the implanted species were obtained using LSS-range parameters (Morgan *et al.*, 1981).

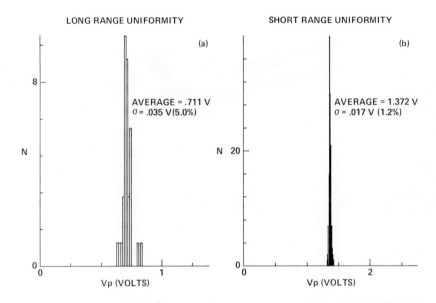

LONG RANGE UNIFORMITY

SHORT RANGE UNIFORMITY

(a)

AVERAGE = .711 V
σ = .035 V (5.0%)

(b)

AVERAGE = 1.372 V
σ = .017 V (1.2%)

Vp (VOLTS)

Vp (VOLTS)

Fig. 6.   Examples of (a) long-range and (b) short-range uniformity of pinch-off voltages for test FETs on GaAs integrated circuit wafers fabricated using the planar ion-implanted process illustrated in Fig. 7c (Morgan *et al.*, 1981).

isolation. This approach affords greater uniformity of device characteristics than when the active layer is formed by epitaxial growth techniques. However, mesa etching does not fully utilize the potential of ion implantation. Proton bombardment could alternatively be employed for isolation in planar device structures. The planar fabrication scheme for the enhancement mode FET shown in Fig. 7b utilizes several different implantations into localized areas of the GaAs substrate to form FET active layers, heavily-doped contacts, and p-type gate regions for junction FETs. Magnesium is used as the p-type dopant (see Section V). This fabrication approach has the potential of yielding low-power digital integrated circuits but has not yet been fully developed. A planar integrated circuit technology for fabricating ion-implanted DMESFETS in GaAs is illustrated schematically in Fig. 7c. In this technology, called Schottky diode FET logic (SDFL), the logic circuits employ FETs for inversion and gain and utilize high-speed Schottky barrier-switching diodes for the logic switching. The planar ion-implanted process used to fabricate these circuits is the most advanced in terms of application to high complexity integrated circuits. The feasibility of GaAs large-scale integration has been demonstrated using this process, by the fabrication of

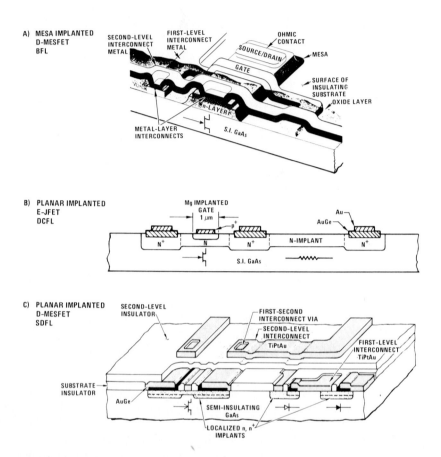

Fig. 7.   Schematic representations of various GaAs integrated circuit fabrication technologies: (a), mesa implanted DMESFET, BFL (Van Tuyl *et al.*, 1977, Leichti, 1977), (b) planar implanted EJFET, DCFL (Troeger *et al.*, 1979), (c) planar implanted DMESFET, SDFL (Welch and Eden, 1977, Welch *et al.*, 1979, Welch *et al.*, 1980).

fully functional 8 bit by 8 bit multipliers with latched input and outputs containing 1008 logic gates (Lee *et al.* 1982). (An example of such circuits was given in Chapter 1, Figs 5. and 6.)

The active layer for the FETs in GaAs integrated circuits requires an electron concentration of about 10^{17} cm^{-3}, with a thickness of about 2000 Å. These requirements can be met by using Si, S or Se. However, Si and Se have been preferred as dopants since they do not exhibit the extensive diffusion often shown by S after post-implantation annealing. In the SDFL technology illustrated in Fig. 7c, the switching diodes require an active layer significantly deeper than that for the FET, with a slightly lower maximum electron concentration. This requirement can be met with S, since the diffusion results in an n-type layer which is 4000–5000 Å deep for an implantation energy of about 400 keV. However, the doping requirements for the active layer of the Schottky diode can also be met if Si is used as the implanted dopant. Evidence for a preferential lateral diffusion of implanted S has been observed during the development of the SDFL technology (Lee *et al.* 1980). This work suggests that S diffuses further in a $<011>$ direction than in a $<01\bar{1}>$ direction. This effect may be associated with a difference in the strain resulting from the stress between the GaAs surface and the Si_3N_4 caps. While similar data are not available for implanted Si or Se, it seems likely that such a preferential lateral diffusion might be observed for them also, although one might expect it to be somewhat smaller in magnitude. When the contact regions of FETs are implanted as illustrated in Fig. 7c, such effects may play a significant role in device performance.

IV. HIGH-DOSE n-TYPE IMPLANTS

The data for Se-doped bulk GaAs shown in Fig. 1 indicate that when the Se concentration is of the order of 10^{19} cm^{-3}, the measured free electron concentration is significantly lower than the donor concentration. Implanted doses of the order of 10^{14} cm^{-2} are required in order to produce such donor concentrations by ion implantation. For the purpose of the discussion in this section, high-dose n-type implants will be assumed to be those with an implanted dose of 5×10^{13} ions cm^{-2} or higher. Such high doses of n-type dopants are of interest because they provide regions of low resistivity in devices, particularly in areas where ohmic contacts are to be applied. They are typified by less than 100% activation of the implanted species. The activation which is realized is dependent on the temperature at which the implantation is carried out and on the nature of the annealing cap, if one is used, or on the details of the capless technique if a cap is not employed. This section discusses these effects and presents data which are typical of implantation doping results for high-dose n-type implants. The application of such high-dose implants to device fabrication is also discussed.

Electron concentration profiles for Se implanted into GaAs at a variety of temperatures are shown in Fig. 8. Much higher activation of the implanted Se is achieved for the implants performed at elevated temperatures than for the room-temperature implant. This result is typical of the differences among high-dose, room-temperature, or elevated-temperature implants of group VI donors in GaAs. Data for the disorder introduced by Te ion bombardment

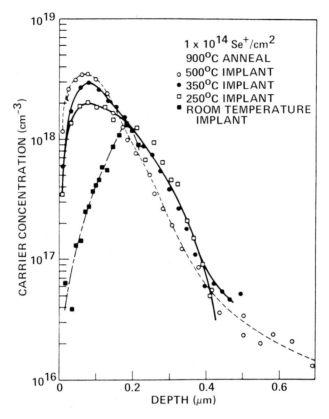

Fig. 8. Electron concentration profiles for Se-implanted GaAs samples annealed at the indicated temperatures using pyrolytically deposited Si_3N_4 cap (Donnelly, 1976).

of GaAs as a function of the implant temperature are shown in Fig. 9. There is a rapid drop in the disorder at temperatures above about 140°C. At lower temperatures an amorphous layer is produced by Te implantation, whereas at higher temperatures ($\geq 140°C$) the implanted layer is heavily damaged but still retains its crystalline character. The final activity of high doses of n-type dopants is much larger when the implant is carried out at temperatures which do not result in the implanted layer becoming amorphous. The regrowth of amorphous layers in GaAs appears to be much more complicated than in Si and such regrown layers may contain substructure. Channeling determinations of lattice locations of implanted Te indicate that, when the implant is carried out at elevated temperatures, the implanted Te is largely substitutional (Fig. 10). On the other hand, when implantation is per-

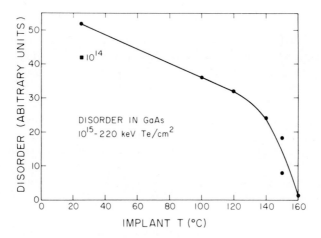

Fig. 9. Disorder in Te-implanted GaAs samples as a function of implantation temperature, as determined by channeling-effect techniques (Eisen *et al.*, 1973).

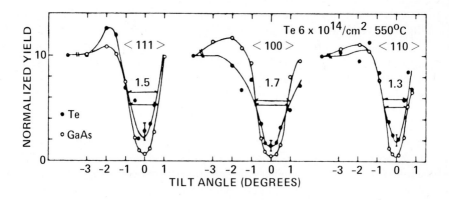

Fig. 10. Channeling angular scans for 1 MeV He$^+$ backscattered from GaAs and Te atoms along each of the major axes of the GaAs sample. The sample was implanted at 550°C to a dose of 6 × 10^{14} Te cm^{-2} (Takai *et al.*, 1973).

formed at room temperature, the implanted ions are found to be slightly displaced from lattice sites after post-implantation annealing. This difference in the lattice location of group VI dopants for room-temperature or elevated-temperature ($\gtrsim 200$°C) implants may at least partially account for the difference in activity observed between room-temperature and high-temperature implants of these dopants.

Electron concentration profiles measured in Se-implanted GaAs samples as a function of Se dose are shown in Fig. 11. With increasing doses of implanted Se up to about 1×10^{14} cm^{-2} the maximum electron concentration increases; however, higher Se doses do not result in any significant increase in the maximum electron concentration. This effect is also illustrated in Fig. 11, which shows that the maximum electron concentration decreases as a function of dose above about 1×10^{14} Se ions cm^{-2}. The data in Fig. 11 were obtained by using an aluminium oxynitride cap during the post-implantation annealing. The maximum electron concentration achieved was similar to that shown in Fig. 8 for samples annealed with a pyrolytically deposited Si_3N_4 cap. However, when a reactivally sputtered Si_3N_4 cap was used, the maximum electron concentrations measured were significantly below those obtained with either the pyrolytically deposited Si_3N_4 or an aluminium oxynitride cap (Gamo et al. 1977). This illustrates the fact that activation of high-dose implants depends not only on the cap material but also on the method of deposition of the cap.

Electron concentration profiles for several doses of Si implants carried out at room temperature are shown in Fig. 12. The behavior of Si implanted to high doses differs from that of the group VI dopants. The figure shows that electron concentrations above 10^{18} cm^{-3} can be achieved by implanting high doses of Si at room temperature. These high concentrations are attained by using an annealing temperature of 850°C, whereas an anneal temperature of at least 900°C seems to be required for high activation of high-dose Se implants. These differences make Si an attractice choice for obtaining high electron concentrations in some device applications.

The data for bulk-grown Se-doped GaAs shown in Fig. 1 indicate that electron concentrations greater than 10^{19} cm^{-3} can be achieved in such material. However, the maximum electron concentrations obtained in the high-dose n-type implants which were discussed above were no higher than about $3–4 \times 10^{18}$ cm^{-3}. Higher concentrations have been achieved in certain cases. These include the use of double implantation and pulsed laser or electron beam annealing. The implantation of high doses of a group VI n-type dopant such as Se results in an effective non-stoichiometry: the implanted dopants reside on the As lattice sites and this results in the introduction of a number of Ga vacancies equal to the number of implanted dopant atoms. It has been suggested that the implantation of Ga so as to achieve a Ga concentration equal to that of the implanted group VI dopant would minimize the Ga vacancy concentration and result in higher maximum electron concentrations (Heckingbottom and Ambridge, 1973). One example in which this has proved very successful is shown in Fig. 13. Here, implantation of both Se and Ga at 400°C, followed by annealing at 950°C, resulted in a

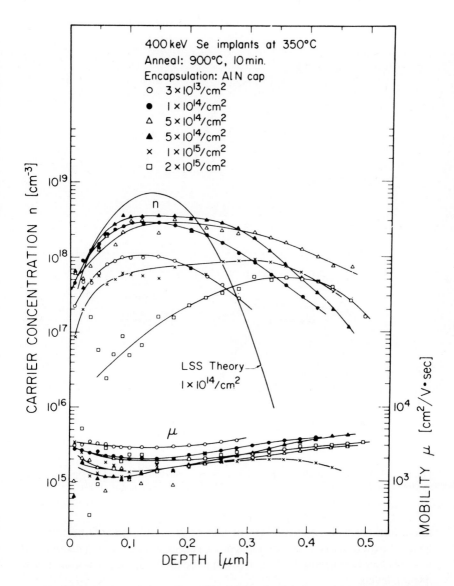

Fig. 11. Electron concentration and mobility profiles for GaAs samples implanted with Se under the indicated conditions and annealed at 900°C using an aluminium oxynitride cap. The profile of implanted Se calculated from LSS range parameters for a dose of 1 × 10^14 cm^-2 is also shown (Gamo *et al.*, 1977).

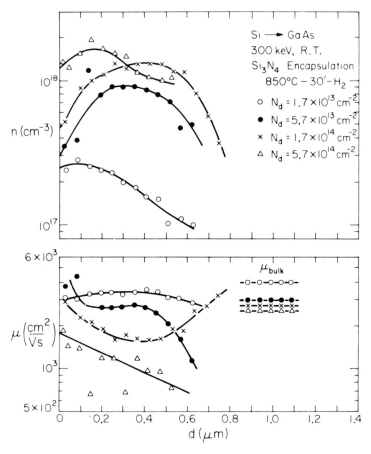

Fig. 12.   Electron concentration and mobility profiles for Si-implanted GaAs samples annealed at 850°C for 30 min. using a reactively sputtered Si_3N_4 cap (Tandon *et al.*, 1979).

maximum electron concentration of almost 2×10^{19} cm^{-3}. Other double-implant experiments, however, have not given such encouraging results, and it is not clear how useful this technique may be for obtaining very high n-type doping levels.

In the past several years there has been considerable interest in the application of pulsed laser and electron-beam annealing techniques to GaAs. Several laboratories have found that maximum electron concentrations significantly above 10^{19} cm^{-3} can be obtained when GaAs implanted with high doses of n-type dopants is annealed by these pulsed techniques. One example of such high doping levels is shown in Fig. 14. The data are for Se-

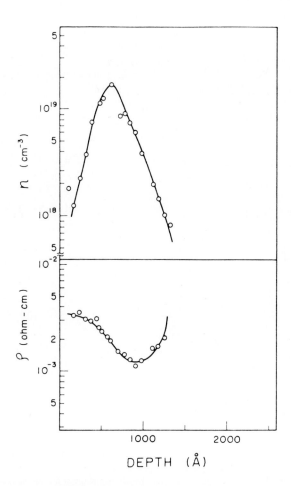

Fig. 13. Electron concentration (*n*) and resistivity (*ρ*) profiles for a GaAs sample implanted with Se (100 keV 4.4 × 10^{14} cm^{-2}) and Ga (90 keV 5 × 10^{14} cm^{-2}) at 400°C and annealed at 950°C for 15 min. using a Si_3N_4 cap (Inada et al., 1979b).

implanted samples which were annealed with or without a cap using a pulsed electron beam. The maximum electron concentrations were about 2 × 10^{19} cm^{-3} in both cases; however, greater diffusion of the implanted dopant occurred in the sample annealed without a cap. For pulsed annealing of high-dose n-type implants in GaAs, the electron mobility is generally significantly below the value one would expect in uncompensated material having the measured high electron concentrations. The reason for this lower mobility is not clear, although it has been suggested that it may result from defects

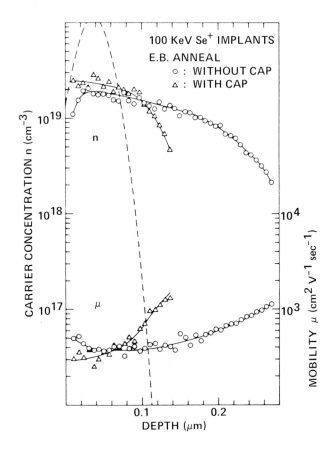

Fig. 14. Electron concentration and mobility profiles for Se-implanted GaAs samples annealed by pulsed electron beam irradiation (1.2 J cm^{-2}) with and without the use of Si$_3$N$_4$ cap during annealing (Inada *et al.*, 1979a).

introduced by the pulse itself (Davies *et al.* 1980). It has also been suggested that the decrease in sheet electron concentration which has been observed during thermal annealing of a previously pulsed-annealed sample (Pianetta *et al.* 1980) may be associated with motion of these defects during the thermal anneal (Davies *et al.* 1980).

The most important application of high-dose n-type implants in device fabrication probably lies in increasing the electron concentration in the portions of a device in which ohmic contacts are applied. While applications to such devices as solar cells have been demonstrated in the laboratory, it is likely that high-dose n-type implantation in GaAs will be most useful when applied to discrete FETs and integrated circuits. In power FETs, for example, increased doping under the ohmic contacts is essential in order to maximize breakdown voltages in the devices. In FET-based integrated circuits, increased doping of the contacts can be used to decrease the source resistance of the FETs; this results in an increase in the operating speed of the integrated circuits and can be most effectively accomplished if a self-aligned gate technique such as that employed by Yokoyama *et al.* (1981) is used. This technique uses Schottky barrier metallization, which exhibits stable barrier properties after annealing at the temperatures required for post implantation annealing ($\sim 850°C$). This metallization acts as a mask during the contact-implantation step and makes it possible to use implantation to provide increased doping up to the edge of the Schottky barrier, while significantly decreasing the source resistance.

The applications for high-dose n-type implants discussed above do not require the highest possible electron concentration that can be obtained by implantation. Thus, conventional implantation and annealing processes can be used and, in fact, the doses may be somewhat below the nominal value of $\geq 10^{14}$ cm^{-2} for high-dose n-type implants. There is one potential application for high-dose n-type implants which would require the highest electron concentration possible; that is, to raise the electron concentration under the contact-metallization of devices to allow non-alloyed ohmic contacts to be formed. The electron concentrations required to achieve non-alloyed contacts are well above 10^{19} cm^{-3} and therefore difficult, or impossible, to achieve at present. The ability to fabricate non-alloyed ohmic contacts would make it possible to eliminate one metallization step and therefore one mask level in device fabrication. It might also facilitate the alignment of Schottky barrier gates between ohmic contacts. At present, when Schottky barriers and ohmic contacts are applied in separate steps, this requires very good alignment accuracy. (A review of various approaches to ohmic contact formation to GaAs is given in Chapter 11.)

V. p-TYPE IMPLANTS

The group II elements Be, Mg, Zn and Cd act as p-type dopants in GaAs, and each has been investigated as an implanted p-type dopant. High doping levels can be obtained for room temperature implantation of these species in GaAs. High values of doping efficiency have been reported for anneals at approximately 800°C using SiO$_2$ as the encapsulant (Hunsperger *et al.* 1970, Yuba *et al.* 1974). Zinc and Cd exhibit extensive diffusion during post-implantation annealing (Zölch *et al.* 1977). Diffusion of Be and Mg is also observed; however, at least in the case of Be, this is seen only for annealing temperatures of about 800°C or higher, when the maximum implanted Be concentration is somewhat above 3×10^{18} cm^{-3}.

The low mass of Be ions results in only a small fraction of their energy being available for the production of displacements of Ga and As atoms during implantation. Therefore, significantly lower defect densities are found in Be-implanted GaAs layers following implantation than when the other p-type dopants are used. This reduction in implantation damage may be responsible for the fact that signifcant activation of Be can be obtained with annealing temperatures as low as 600°C. It also makes Be an attractive choice as a p-type dopant, since it offers the likelihood of a lower defect density in the implanted region, and this may lead to better p–n junctions.

Hole concentration profiles for GaAs samples implanted with 10^{15} Be$^+$ cm^{-2} and annealed at different temperatures are shown in Fig. 15. The profile for a sample annealed at 650°C is Gaussian in character, with a maximum hole concentration of about 2×10^{19} cm^{-3}. As the annealing temperature is increased the profile broadens and the peak hole concentration decreases. For annealing carried out at 800°C or 850°C, the profile becomes almost flat, with a concentration of about 3×10^{18} cm^{-3} to a depth beyond 1 μm. The profiles shown for the two highest annealing temperatures are typical of those reported for Be-implanted GaAs annealed at 800°C or higher. At these temperatures, the implanted dose is sufficient to achieve maximum Be concentrations above about 3×10^{18} cm^{-3} (McLevidge et al. 1977; Zölch et al. 1977; Comas et al. 1977). This diffusion can be avoided and higher hole concentrations can be achieved if lower annealing temperatures are used (Fig. 15). It is possible, however, that in a given application the best characteristics may not be achieved when annealing is carried out at temperatures as low as 650°–700°C. For example, it has been reported that annealing to 900°C is required in order to restore the intensity of photoluminescence in GaAs to the value observed before Be implantation (Chatterjee et al. 1975). Annealing at about 900°C is also required in order to achieve low leakage current in Be-implanted p–n junctions (Helix et al. 1978).

Magnesium implantation has been employed in some device applications. When rather shallow p-type layers are desired, Mg may be an easier p-type dopant to work with than Be, because the implantation energy required would be within a range in which implanters are more readily operated. For example, Be implanted at an energy of less than 20 keV (a value at which high-energy implantation machines may not yield their best results) would give a junction depth of approximately 1500 Å, whereas the energy required to achieve such a junction depth with Mg would be about 70 keV. Since Mg has a rather low mass in comparison to Zn and Cd, it would be expected that Mg doping would afford some of the benefits of low damage which are associated with the use of Be (Zölch et al. 1977). The doping efficiency measured for Mg-implanted samples has been observed to decrease

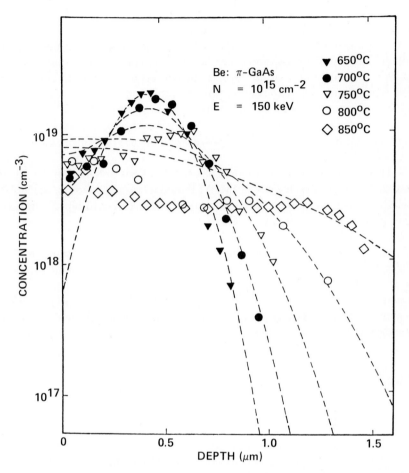

Fig. 15.   Hole concentration profiles for Be-implanted GaAs samples annealed at the indicated temperatures (Zölch *et al.*, 1977).

at temperatures above about 750°–800°C, in a manner similar to that mentioned above for Be (Zölch *et al.* 1977). This result suggests that the change in shape of the doping profile may also be similar to that shown in Fig. 15 for Be-implanted GaAs. Doping profiles, reported for GaAs implanted with 120 keV Mg ions and annealed at temperatures ranging from 600° to 900°C, are qualitatively in agreement with this hypothesis (Yeo *et al.* 1979). However, the result for the 900°C anneal is significantly lower than the profile obtained after an 800°C anneal. Such a difference with annealing temperature does not seem to occur to the same degree in the case of Be implantation.

The implantation of p-type dopants may be used in the fabrication of GaAs devices which involve p–n junctions. High quality p–n junctions have been fabricated by using Be implantation (Helix *et al.* 1978; Yuan *et al.* 1980). These junctions exhibit very low reverse currents and sharp breakdowns. The magnitude of the reverse current has been found to depend on the type of annealing cap used in post-implantation annealing (Helix *et al.* 1978). For annealing carried out at 900°C, the lowest reverse currents were obtained using a plasma deposited Si_3N_4 layer with a very low oxygen content. Higher reverse current was observed with the use of a silicon oxynitride cap or a SiO_2 cap.

The use of implantation to form p–n junctions has potential in the fabrication of such GaAs devices as IMPATT diodes, varactor diodes, and solar cells. Recent work has been carried out on the fabrication of bipolar transistors and integrated circuits in GaAs using both Se and Be implantation (Yuan *et al.* 1980, McLevige *et al.* 1982).

Magnesium implantation using the processing scheme illustrated in Fig. 7b. has been applied to the fabrication of GaAs integrated circuits (Troeger *et al.* 1979). The p-type gate of an enhancement-mode junction FET is fabricated by implanting Mg into the n-type channel of the device. In this fabrication technique the energy of the implanted Mg may be adjusted to achieve the desired threshold voltage for the FETs.

VI. SUMMARY AND CONCLUSIONS

From the foregoing discussion of the implantation of the n-type and p-type dopants in GaAs it can be seen that n-type layers with good mobility and with doping levels of approximately 10^{17} electrons cm^{-3} can be produced using several dopants as well as several different annealing techniques. Higher electron concentrations can also be achieved, but the choice of dopant and of annealing conditions may become more critical as the desired maximum electron concentration increases. Electron concentrations of $1-3 \times 10^{18}$ cm^{-3} are not difficult to achieve, but doping levels in excess of 10^{19} cm^{-3} may require special implantation (e.g., double implants) or annealing conditions (such as pulsed annealing techniques). Carrier concentrations in excess of 10^{19} cm^{-3} are more easily achieved with p-type doping than with n-type doping. However, p-type doping profiles may be affected in some cases by concentration-dependent diffusion effects. The use of short (1–10 s) thermal annealing techniques, which have only recently undergone some preliminary investigation, may be of value in the future.

Implantation in GaAs has been applied to the fabrication of a variety of devices in the laboratory. The most widespread applications by far, however, are to the fabrication of GaAs digital and monolithic microwave integrated circuits. GaAs integrated circuits are being developed in more than twenty laboratories around the world. In most cases, implantation is used as a part of the integrated circuit fabrication process. In this application, it displays the same advantages which have led to such widespread use of ion implantation in the manufacture of silicon integrated circuits. These include uniformity and reproducibility of doping and the ability to readily mask integrated circuit wafers so as to confine the doping to the desired localized regions. As GaAs integrated circuits move from the laboratory into large-scale manufacture, implantation should continue to play an important role in the technology. In the long run, the uniformity of implantation doping will probably depend primarily upon the uniformity of the semi-insulating substrate material used. Over the past few years, this substrate uniformity has been improving. It is possible that epitaxial techniques such as molecular beam epitaxy (MBE) and metal organic chemical vapor deposition (MOCVD) may ultimately be developed to the point where greater uniformity of n-type layers suitable for FET channels can be obtained using these techniques than is possible by implantation. If such a development should occur, then epitaxial techniques may well supplant implantation in the fabrication of FET active layers, particularly for enhancement mode devices. However, implantation is still likely to play a major role in integrated circuit fabrication because it readily affords a method for realizing optimum doping levels in many other areas of integrated circuits. For example, it may be applied in self-aligned gate technologies to decrease source resistance, especially in enhancement mode devices. In addition, implantation will very likely play a role in the fabrication of integrated circuits based upon higher performance devices such as high-electron-mobility transistors and heterojunction bipolar transistors.

REFERENCES

Arai, M., Nishiyama, K., and Watanabe, N. (1981). *Jpn. J. Appl. Phys.* **20**, L124.
Asbeck, P. M. (1982). Private communication.
Asbeck, P. M., Tandon, J., Welch, B. M., Evans, C. A., Jr., and Deline, V. R. (1980). *IEEE Electron Device Lett.* **EDL-1**, 35.
AuCoin, T. R., Ross, R. L., Wade, M. J., and Savage, R. O. (1979). *Solid State Technology* **22**, 59.
Bozler, C. O., Donnelly, J. P., Murphy, R. A., Laton, R. W., Sudbury, R. W., and Lindley, W. T. (1976). *Appl. Phys. Lett.* **29**, 123.
Bujatti, M., Centronio, A., Nipoti, R., and Olzi, E. (1982). *Appl. Phys. Lett.* **40**, 334.
Chatterjee, P. K., Vaidyanathan, K. V., McLevige, W. V., and Streetman, B. G. (1975). *Appl. Phys. Lett.* **27**, 567.

Comas, J., Plew, L., Chatterjee, P. K., McLevige, W. V., Vaidyanathan, K. V., and Streetman, B. G. (1977). *In* "Ion Implantation in Semiconductors 1976" (F. Chernow, J. A. Borders, and D. K. Brice, eds.), p. 141. Plenum Press, New York.

Davies, D. E., Lorenzo, J. P., and Ryan, T. G. (1980). *Appl. Phys. Lett.* **37**, 612.

Davies, D. E., McNally, P. J., Lorenzo, J. P., and Julian, M. (1982). *IEEE Electron Device Lett.* **EDL-3**, 102.

Donnelly, J. P. (1977). *Inst. of Physics Conference,* Series No. **33b**, 166.

Donnelly, J. P., Lindley, W. T., and Hurwitz, C. E. (1975). *Appl. Phys. Lett.* **27**, 41.

Eisen, F. H. (1980). *In* "Laser and Electron Beam Processing of Materials" (C. W. White and P. S. Peercy, eds.), p. 309. Academic Press, New York.

Eisen, F. H., and Welch, B. M. (1977). *In* "Ion Implantation in Semiconductors 1976" (F. Chernow, J. A. Borders, and D. K. Brice, eds.), p. 97. Plenum Press, New York.

Eisen, F. H., Harris, J. S., Welch, B. M., Pashley, R. D., Sigurd, D., and Mayer, J. W. (1973). *In* "Ion Implantation in Semiconductors and Other Materials" (B. L. Crowder, ed.), p. 631. Plenum Press, New York.

Eisen, F. H., Welch, B. M., Mueller, H., Gamo, K., Inada, T., and Mayer, J. W. (1977). *Solid State Electron.* **20**, 219.

Fan, J. C. C., Chapman, R. L., Donnelly, J. P., Turner, G. W., and Bozler, C. O. (1979). *Appl. Phys. Lett.* **34**, 780.

Gamo, K., Inada, T., Krekeler, S., Mayer, J. W., Eisen, F. H., and Welch, B. M. (1977). *Solid State Electron.* **20**, 213.

Gibbons, J. F., Johnson, W. S., and Mylorie, S. W. (1975). "Projected Range Statistics: Semiconductors and Related Materials." Dowden, Hutchinson and Ross, Stroudburg.

Heckingbottom, R., and Ambridge, T. (1973). *Rad. Effects.* **17**, 31.

Helix, M. J., Vaidyanathan, K. V., and Streetman, G. G. (1978). *IEEE J. Solid-State Circuits* **SC-13**, 426.

Higgins, J. A., Kuvas, R. L., Eisen, F. H., and Ch'en, D. R. (1978). *IEEE Trans. Electron Devices* **ED-25**, 587.

Hobgood, H. M., Eldridge, G. W., Barrett, D. L., and Thomas, R. N. (1981). *IEEE Trans. Electron Devices* **ED-28**, 140.

Hojo, A., Toyoda, N., Mochizuki, M., Mizoguchi, T., and Nii, R. (1981). GaAs Integrated Circuit Symposium, San Diego, California, October 27–29, 1981 (unpublished).

Hunsperger, R. G., and Marsh, O. J. (1970). *Rad. Effects.* **6**, 263.

Immorlica, A. A., Jr., and Eisen, F. H. (1976). *Appl. Phys. Lett.* **29**, 94.

Immorlica, A. A., Jr., and Eisen, F. H. (1977). *Proc. Sixth Biennial Cornnel Electrical Eng. Conf.* p. 151.

Inada, T., Tokunaga, K., and Taka, S. (1979a). *Appl. Phys. Lett.* **35**, 546.

Inada, T., Kato, S., Hara, T., and Toyoda, N. (1979b). *J. Appl. Phys.* **50**, 4466.

Kasahara, J., and Watanabe, N. (1980). *Jpn. J. Appl. Phys.* **19**, L151.

Kasahara, J., Arai, M., and Watanabe, N. (1979). *J. Electrochem. Soc.* **126**, 1997.

Kirkpatrick, C. K., Ch'en, R. T., Holmes, D. E., Asbeck, P. M., Elliot, K., Fairman, R. D., and Oliver, R. J. (1982). *In* "Semiconductors and Semimetals" (R. K. Willardson and A. C. Beer, eds.), Vol. 20. Academic Press, New York.

Lee, C. P., Zucca, R., and Welch, B. M. (1980). *Appl. Phys. Lett.* **37**, 311.

Lee, F. S., Kaelin, G., Welch, B., Zucca, R., Shen, E., Asbeck, P., Lee, C. P., Kirkpatrick, C., Long, S. I., and Eden, R. C. (1982). *IEEE J. Solid State Circuits* **17**, 4.

Liechti, C. A. (1977). *Inst. of Physics Conference,* Series No. **33a**, 227.

Malbon, R. M., Lee, D. H., and Whelan, J. M. (1976). *J. Electrochem. Soc.* **123**, 1413.

McLevige, W. V., Helix, M. J., Vaidyanathan, K. V., and Streetman, B. G. (1977). *J. Appl. Phys.* **48**, 3342.

McLevige, W. V., Yuan, H. T., Duncan, W. M., Frensley, W. R., Doerbeck, F. H., Morkoc, H., and Drummond, T. J. (1982). *IEEE Electron Device Lett.* **EDL-3**, 43.

Morgan, D. V., Eisen, F. H., and Ezis, A. (1981). *Proc. IEE,* **128** (Pt. I), 109.

Murphy, R. A., Lindley, W. T., Peterson, D. F., Foyt, A. G., Wolfe, C. H., Horwitz, C. F., and Donnelly, J. P. (1972). *Inst. of Physics Conference,* Series No. **17**, 224.

Niikura, I., Nobuyuki, T., Shimura, Y., Yokoyama, S., Mihara, M., Hayashi, T., and Hara, T. (1978). *Electron. Lett.* **14**, 9.

Nishi, H., Okamura, S., Inada, T., and Hashimoto, H. (1981). *Inst. of Physics Conference,* Series No. **63**, 365.

Pianetta, P. A., Stolte, C. A., and Hansen, J. L. (1980). In "Laser and Electron Beam Processing of Materials" (C. W. White and P. S. Peercy, eds.), p. 328. Academic Press, New York.

Picraux, S. T. (1973). In "Ion Implantation in Semiconductors and Other Materials" (B. L. Crowder, ed.), p. 641. Plenum Press, New York.

Sansbury, J. D., and Gibbons, J. F. (1970). *Rad. Effects.* **6**, 269.

Sealy, B. J., and Surridge, R. K. (1975). *Thin Solid Films* **26**, L19.

Shah, N. J., Ahmed, A., and Leigh, P. A. (1981). *Appl. Phys. Lett.* **39**, 322.

Speight, J. D., Leigh, P., McIntyre, N., Groves, I. G., O'Hara, S. and Hemment, P. (1974). *Electron. Lett.* **10** (7), 98.

Steeples, K., Saunders, I. J., and Smith, J. G. (1980). *IEEE Electron Device Lett.* **EDL-1**, 72.

Takai, M., Gamo, K., Masuda, and Namba, S. (1973). *Jpn. J. Appl. Phys.* **12**, 1926.

Tandon, J. L., Nicolet, M.-A., and Eisen, F. H. (1979). *Appl. Phys. Lett.* **34**, 165.

Troeger, G. L., Behle, A. F., Friebertshauser, P. E., Hu, K. L., and Watanabe, S. H. (1979). *IEEE IEDM Tech. Digest,* 497.

Vaidyanathan, K. V., Helix, M. J., Wolford, D. J., Streetman, B. G., Blattner, R. J., and Evans, C. A., Jr. (1977). *J. Electrochem. Soc.* **124**, 1781.

Van Tuyl, R. L., Liechti, C. A., Lee, R. E., and Gowen, E. (1977). *IEEE J. Solid State Circuits* **SC-12**, 485.

Vieland, L. J., and Kudman, I. (1963). *J. Phys. Chem. Solids* **24**, 437.

Welch, B. M., and Eden, R. C. (1977). *IEEE IEDM Tech. Digest,* 205.

Welch, B. M., Shen, Y. D., Zucca, R., and Eden, R. C. (1979). *IEEE IEDM Tech. Digest,* 493.

Welch, B. M., Shen, Y. D., Zucca, R., Eden, R. C., and Long, S. I. (1980). *IEEE Trans. Electron Devices* **ED-27**, 1116.

Wohllenben, K., and Beck, W. (1966). *Z. Naturforsch* **21a**, 1057.

Woodall, J. M., Rupprecht, H., Chicotka, R. J., and Wicks, G. (1981). *Appl. Phys. Lett.* **38**, 639.

Yeo, Y. K., Park, Y. S., and Yu, P. W. (1979). *J. Appl. Phys.* **50**, 3274.

Yokoyama, N., Mimura, T., Fukuta, M., and Ishikawa, H. (1981). *Int. Solid State Circuits Conf. Tech. Digest* **24**, 218.

Yuan, H. T., Doerbeck, F. H., and McLevige, W. V. (1980). *Electron. Lett.* **16**, 637.

Yuba, Y., Gamo, K., Masuda, K., and Namba, S. (1974). *Jpn. J. Appl. Phys.* **13**, 641.

Zölch, R., Ryssel, H., Kranz, H., Reichl, H., and Ruge, I. (1977). In "Ion Implantation in Semiconductors, 1976" (F. Chernow, J. W. Borders, and D. K. Brice, eds.) p. 593. Plenum Press, New York.

CHAPTER 11

Contacts and Interconnections on Semiconductors

J. E. E. BAGLIN

IBM, Thomas J. Watson Research Center
Yorktown Heights, New York, USA

H. B. HARRISON, J. L. TANDON* AND J. S. WILLIAMS

Royal Melbourne Institute of Technology
Melbourne, Australia

Present Address: 15251E Don Julian Road,
    P. O. Box 1212, The City of Industry,
    California, USA

357

ION IMPLANTATION
AND BEAM PROCESSING
ISBN   0 12 756980 4

I. INTRODUCTION

In the manufacture of an integrated circuit, many devices that are electrically isolated from one another are formed into the semiconductor. These devices then require electrical interconnections to complete the integrated circuit. With the extremely demanding constraints expected to be placed upon the technology of integrated circuit fabrication in the future, in which device geometries will be dramatically reduced to achieve larger packaging densities and larger scales of integration, multi-layers of closely packaged, fine-dimension interconnections between devices will be necessary (Cooper, 1981; Keyes, 1977).

These interconnections are placed across the surface of the semiconductor and are most often insulated from the underlying substrate and from one another by a dielectric. Where appropriate, vias (contact openings) are made in the dielectric to provide electrical connections (contacts) to the semiconductor and between interconnecting layers. The interconnecting layers are often referred to as layers of metallization, although this is more of an historical nomenclature, since present integrated circuits can make use of materials other than metals for device interconnections; for example, polycrystalline Si and diffused layers in Si (Naguib and Hobbs, 1974). Future generations of Si integration will make larger use of silicides and refractory metals in order to gain a performance advantage over the rising resistance of thin polysilicon interconnections and increased sidewall capacitance of diffused layers, both of which increase signal propagation delays (Sinha, *et al.* 1982; Sinha, 1981). True metal interconnection layers (e.g. Al on Si) are also commonly used (Philofsky and Hall, 1975). Other dual and tri-metal systems such as Mo–Au and Ti–Pt–Au are often required in special applications (e.g. connections across GaAs).

The many requirements of the interconnection materials on semiconductors used in integrated circuits are often conflicting and in most cases they are technologically very demanding. For example, they must be multi-level compatible and must display excellent adhesion to underlying and overlaying dielectrics. Furthermore, interconnections must provide continuous coverage that is devoid of local hot-spot generation, over a sometimes rugged surface terrain. They also must exhibit very low electrical resistivity. Typical electrical resistivity properties currently attainable range from 900 $\mu\Omega$ cm ($20\Omega/\square$ for 4 500 Å) for polycrystalline Si to less than 5 $\mu\Omega$ cm for electron-beam evaporated Al (Lyman, 1980). In addition, at least one layer must be bondable, and all layers must display high resistance to electro-migration, thermal aging, oxidation and corrosion (Philofsky and Hall, 1975).

The above properties relate mainly to the interconnections across the semiconductor surface. However, depending on application required, the interconnection material must be connected to the semiconductor (or to other layers) so that it will provide either (a) a low electrical contact resistance (ohmic contact), or (b) a rectifying (Schottky) contact. Under normal device operating conditions both these connections must have excellent contact stability and low noise properties as a function of time and temperature (Rhoderick, 1978). These requirements are specifically related to the interface properties of the interconnecting materials. For example, for a metal semiconductor interface, the difference in work function between the materials leads to a finite contact potential. In addition, for the case of a metal/n-type semiconductor interface, a finite interfacial region of fixed positive charge (depletion region) exists in the semiconductor. The width of this depletion region depends on the work function difference (barrier height potential) and the free electron concentration at the semiconductor interface (Rhoderick, 1978).

Free charge can move across the interfacial barrier (contact interface) in one of three ways. Firstly, if the depletion width is large, the mechanism for carrier transport is over the potential barrier created at the interface (thermionic emission). This case is typical of the metal to lightly n-doped semiconductor interface, and an external potential will either increase or decrease the depletion width, thus assisting or inhibiting the emission of free charge over the barrier. This situation affords ease of current flow in one direction and prevents flow in the other. This contact constitutes a *Schottky* barrier diode. In comparison with a pn junction diode, Schottky diodes can have roughly half the forward potential drop, a considerably lower reverse current and a far superior device switching characteristic. They have wide application in integrated circuits.

A second carrier transport regime is appropriate for the interface between a metal and a heavily doped semiconductor. In this case, the depletion width can become so thin that, via a tunneling process (field emission), it is transparent to the charge flow. The resulting current-voltage characteristic is linear, and the contact is said to be ohmic. In integrated circuit applications, an ohmic contact at a metal-semiconductor interface must offer minimum resistance to current flow in either direction over a wide temperature range. Ohmic contacts are characterized by their specific contact resistance, ρ_c, which has units of Ω cm^2.

The third region of carrier transport is, in fact, intermediate between ohmic and Schottky behavior. This regime is termed "thermionic field emission", and the contacts exhibit an intermediate voltage-current characteristic that is often referred to as "soft" Schottky. These three regimes of current transport across a metal–semiconductor interface, and their importance in integrated circuit technology, are discussed in detail in a recent review (Nicollian and Sinha, 1978).

In integrated circuit applications, the current status of interconnection and contact technology has been largely determined by the properties of the semiconductor substrate and less influenced by the properties of metal overlays. A particular aspect of ohmic contact formation illustrates this. In silicon, heavily doped n-type and p-type layers are readily produced, and ohmic contacts of very low specific contact resistance, ρ_c are easily made. For example, a Pt metal overlay on an n-type or p-type substrate doped to $\sim 3 \times 10^{20}$ cm^{-3} can give a typical ρ_c of $\leq 4 \times 10^{-7}$ Ω cm^{-2} (Ting and Chen, 1971; Harrison, 1980; Naguib and Hobbs, 1974). In contrast, higher band-gap GaAs is not easily doped to $> 10^{19}$ donors cm^{-3} by conventional methods (see Section III,B), and ohmic contacts to n-type GaAs are difficult to form: at best they give ρ_c values an order of magnitude greater than for Si (Macksey, 1977). Another major difference between Si and GaAs relates to their reactivity with interconnecting and contact metals during thermal processing. Most metals react with Si to form metal silicides, and this property is being increasingly exploited (Section II), whereas suitable metal–GaAs reactions are not readily available.

This chapter does not attempt to review the vast field of interconnections and contacts on semiconductors as these have been the subject of many specialist books and reviews (e.g. Rhoderick, 1978; Padovani, 1971; Rideout, 1975; Rosenberg *et al.* 1978; Sinha and Poate, 1978; Macksey, 1977; Nicollian and Sinha, 1978). Rather, it concentrates on some specific areas in which beam processing has been recently applied to interconnection and contact technology in Si (Section III) and GaAs (Section III). Particular attention is given to areas of current technological concern, such as the use of silicides as contacts (and interconnects) in order to improve the performance and reliability of Si integrated circuits (Section II) and the difficult process of forming ohmic contacts to n-type GaAs (Section III).

II. SILICON

A. Current Technology

Some of the problems of constructing stable metal–Si device contacts are illustrated by the difficult case of Al–Si (Rosenberg *et al.* 1978). In order to establish a stable contact, Al deposited on an n-doped Si substrate must be sintered, allowing the Al to reduce native SiO$_2$ at the interface. This step can also allow the growth of Al spikes into the Si (which can be detrimental to the underlying device) and the interdiffusion of Si and Al so that a p-type layer is produced. These processes can alter the barrier height substantially and give widely varying contact properties, from ohmic and hard Schottky,

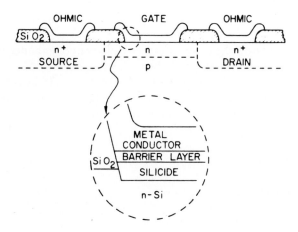

Fig. 1.   Schematic diagram of a shallow silicide contact in a simple FET structure. From Tu and Mayer (1978).

depending on the underlying Si doping and the precise sintering conditions. The introduction of a barrier layer can prevent spiking in Al-based systems, but this requires extra processing steps.

Most of the other metals available for forming contacts with Si will react during process heat treatments to form metal silicides. Such a reaction is beneficial for contamination reduction, since the important silicide–Si contact interface then lies buried within the unexposed Si substrate; moreover, the physical integrity of the junction is assured, and spiking does not occur. Many of the silicides of noble metals, refractory metals and rare earths are themselves metallic in nature, with excellent conductivity, and they offer a range of barrier heights in contact with Si. They therefore represent attractive interconnection and contact materials themselves. Furthermore, it is possible to overlay these silicide contacts with metallic conductors such as Al–Cu or Ti–W, whose properties may make them preferable for interconnection lines between individual devices on a Si wafer. It remains a design challenge to produce metal–silicide–Si combinations in which the silicide will function as a diffusion barrier and thus prevent undesirable interaction between the interconnecting metal and the Si substrate (Rosenberg *et al.* 1978; van Gurp *et al.* 1979). Alternatively, a separate barrier layer may be interposed, as illustrated in Fig. 1.

In the discussions to follow, emphasis will be placed on the silicon–silicide system, and ways in which ion, laser and electron beam technology can assist in fabricating successful silicides for contact and interconnection applications. Techniques involving ion beam treatment have been shown to be potentially useful in a variety of different ways, ranging from interface "cleaning" to achieving low-temperature silicide growth or local transient annealing.

In order to see how the beam effects complement or enhance the conventional processes of growth of metal silicides by heating the wafer in a furnace, we shall first briefly review the processes of silicide growth by furnace sintering in an inert gas ambient or in a vacuum. We shall then examine some specific ion beam techniques for enhancing such processes.

B. Furnace Sintering

1. Nucleation Kinetics

The most direct way to produce a thin film silicide is to heat a deposited metal layer on a Si substrate and allow thermal diffusion to supply the growth of the silicide until all the metal is consumed and the reaction has ceased. This would normally begin with nucleation of the silicide at the metal–Si interface, followed by growth of a steadily thickening planar layer of silicide (whose growth is sustained by diffusion either of metal atoms or of Si atoms through the silicide to be bound at the opposite (growth) interface). The growth rate would be diffusion limited, and the silicide thickness, x, would scale as $\sqrt{t}$ (t = time of heating) at a given temperature T. An example of such diffusion is shown in Fig. 2a in the profiles from Rutherford backscattering (RBS) after a succession of heat treatments in the Ni–Si system (Baglin and Atwater, 1981). The phase Ni_2Si is first formed in the temperature range 225°–350°C, and its growth obeys the $\sqrt{t}$ law, as shown in Fig. 2b. The intercepts on the time axis probably represent the nucleation times required before development of the planar layer structure, and such offsets are among the less reproducible quantities in silicide growth measurements. Nucleation can be very sensitive to interface cleanliness and orientation.

As shown in Fig. 2a, at 325°C, when the deposited Ni layer has been fully consumed, a layer of the phase NiSi begins to develop at the interface. This illustrates that in the terms of our discussion the Ni_2Si–Si interface is not in itself a "stable" interface at 325°. It is artificially stabilized by the ready supply of diffusing Ni atoms, but when their source is exhausted, further reaction with Si can occur, and the NiSi layer grows to completion. This process is reversible, as may be demonstrated by depositing Ni on NiSi and allowing Ni_2Si to re-form. In fact, given judicious choice of reaction temperatures and Ni:Si availability, Ottaviani *et al.* (1981) have shown that they can produce films of most known Ni–Si phases by diffusion (even those not seen in simple heating of Ni on Si), as illustrated in Fig. 3.

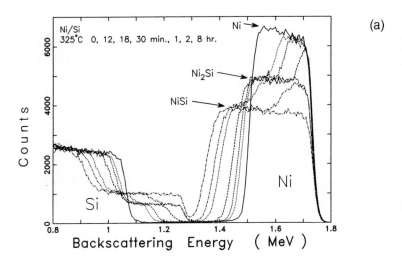

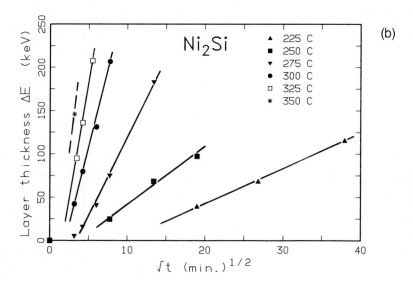

Fig. 2.   (a) RBS spectra showing the interaction of Ni on a Si substrate after heating in a He furnace at 325°C for 0, 12, 18, 30 min., 1, 2 and 8 hr. A layer of Ni₂Si grows first and, when all the Ni has been consumed a NiSi layer begins to grow. (b) Kinetics of growth of Ni_2Si from the Ni–Si<100> interface. From Baglin and Atwater (1981).

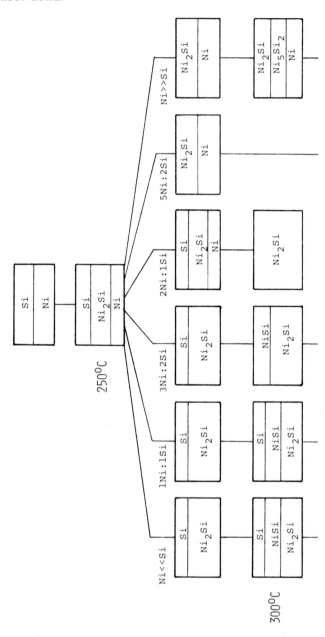

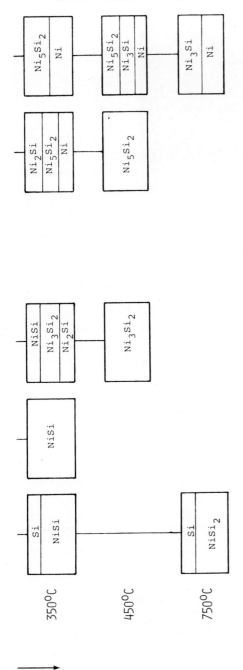

Fig. 3. Schematic diagram illustrating possible thin film reaction paths leading to the formation of pure compounds Ni_3Si, Ni_5Si_2, Ni_2Si, Ni_3Si_2, $NiSi$ and $NiSi_2$. The diagram assumes that Ni and Si are initially deposited in the correct proportions (on a non-interacting substrate). From Ottaviani $et\ al.$ (1981).

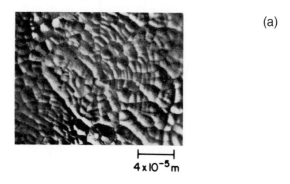

(a)

4×10^{-5} m

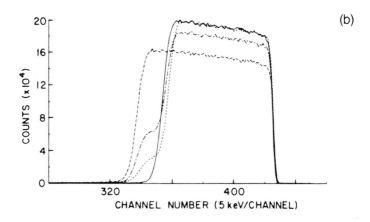

(b)

COUNTS ($\times 10^4$)

320   400

CHANNEL NUMBER (5 keV/CHANNEL)

Fig. 4.   (a) Optical micrograph illustrating heterogeneous nucleation of the silicide IrSi$_3$ in columns through a film of IrSi$_{1.75}$ on Si at temperatures above 960°C. (b) Corresponding RBS spectra (Ir portions only) for various locations on a sample such as that of Fig. 4(a). Some areas contain IrSi$_{1.75}$ only, some only IrSi$_3$ and some a mixture of both phases. From Petersson *et al.* (1979).

The point of this illustration is to show that the "stability" of a given silicide phase in contact with Si clearly depends on the resident interface supply of mobile Ni or Si atoms, and upon the temperature. That supply of mobile atoms can be manipulated to generate unusual compounds of choice, analogously to limiting the Si supply by preparing a silicide from metal and Si layers deposited on an inert substrate.

At temperatures up to 700°C, the NiSi–Si interface appears to be very stable; there is no evidence of a tendency to form $NiSi_2$. However, abruptly at 750°C, the growth of $NiSi_2$ "columns" passing through and normal to the film occurs. This heterogeneous nucleation leads to further (lateral) nucleation and rapidly the whole film is converted to $NiSi_2$. Such a nucleation process observed in the more dramatic case of $IrSi_{1.75} \rightarrow IrSi_3$ is illustrated in Fig. 4. The growth of the new silicide layer is non-planar, and hence the RBS profiles simply become lower and broader where conversion has occurred (Fig. 4b), and the quantity of final silicide phase grown does not scale with $\sqrt{t}$. Because of the mode of growth (and assisted in this case by epitaxy), the crystallites of the nucleated phase become large, and the film is characteristically rough and thus technologically undesirable, even though it displays a creditable conductivity and is completely stable.

The abrupt nucleation displayed at 750°C by NiSi–Si and at 960°C by $IrSi_{1.75}$–Si can be understood as a consequence of film morphology (Baglin et al. 1980; Anderson et al. 1979). Volume energy and interface/stress energy terms, ΔH_m, become dominant in the expression for the change of free energy, ΔG, which determines the onset of the nucleated transition:

$$\Delta G = \Delta H_f + \Delta H_m - T \Delta S \tag{1}$$

where ΔH_f is the heat of formation of the new phase from the old one. In most cases (e.g. for $Ni \rightarrow Ni_2Si$), ΔH_f dominates ΔH_m and the entropy term. However, for a whole class of silicides, including those of Co, Ni, Pd, Zr, Rh, Ir, Hf and Pt, ΔH_f for forming the final (Si-rich) phase can be quite small, leaving the condition for the reaction to occur ($\Delta G < 0$) to be:

$$T_c \geq \Delta H_m / \Delta S \tag{2}$$

where T_c is the critical temperature required to initiate nucleation. Many silicides displaying this behavior would otherwise be technologically attractive, and there is a possibility of modifying the pattern of nucleation by ion beam treatment.

2. Stress

In almost all polycrystalline silicide films, growth starting from the metal–Si system produces large internal stresses in the silicide. This stress can lead to cracking or detachment from the Si substrate, and such dangers are particularly evident for thick films of the refractory metal silicides such as $TaSi_2$ or WSi_2. Crowder and Zirinsky (1979) have reported stress of 2.5×10^{10} dyne

cm^{-2} in grown $TaSi_2$ films 1000 Å thick even after 1000°C annealing. With a sample at high temperature for long enough, the film undergoes a relaxation, which should improve adhesion (Angilello *et al.* 1978). One partial solution to this problem has been found in co-deposition of Ta and Si to form a layer close to stoichiometric composition in which a brief high-temperature heat treatment will cause nucleation of the $TaSi_2$ phase in very small crystallites. Such a layer tends to be more stable than a Ta–Si grown film, and internal stress after 1000°C annealing for one hour is reported as $\sim 1.5 \times 10^{10}$ dyne cm^{-2} (Angilello *et al.* 1981). At room temperature the resistivity of such films can be acceptably low, decreasing by a factor of 10 to a value of 40 $\mu\Omega$ cm as the annealing temperature is raised above 700°C, corresponding to the onset of grain growth of $TaSi_2$.

In all such cases, the heat treatment needed to form the silicide is shorter and perhaps at a lower temperature than that needed for growth from the metal–Si system. This reduced thermal exposure is generally attractive in device processing. Ion beam treatment can offer an elegant alternative means of artificially adjusting the composition of interfaces or deposited films prior to brief thermal treatment to form a desired silicide phase. Such a process similarly can require a much reduced thermal exposure for the sample, while creating a silicide whose high temperature stability is improved.

3. Contaminants

The density of grain boundaries in a silicide film can have a significant effect on its growth kinetics and subsequent resistivity and stability. Naturally, if the film grows by the grain boundary diffusion of one constituent, its growth kinetics will depend on grain size. However, a matter of concern is the effect of possible contaminants, such as oxygen, that grain boundaries can accommodate. Crider *et al.* (1981) have shown that the introduction of slight oxygen contamination during deposition of a Pt film on clean Si substrates can slow down the subsequent growth of Pt silicides by as much as three orders of magnitude, as compared with the performance of Pt deposited in a clean (10^{-9} Torr) vacuum or in the presence of an inert gas impurity. This effect may be attributed to partial clogging of grain boundaries with oxide, and it serves to illustrate how sensitive these processes are to contaminated layers. From a practical point of view, however, routine use of UHV (ultra-high vacuum) deposition is not attractive, and as we shall see, ion beam treatment might be helpful in overcoming such contaminant-related problems.

4. Electrical Resistivity

Low electrical resistivity is one of the most important considerations in selecting a metal silicide for both interconnection and contact fabrication, provided that its physical stability can be assured. Some candidate silicides are listed in Table I, together with values of resistivity reported for furnace-grown layers. These values depend on the means of silicide preparation, the consequent impurity content, and the size of the silicide grains. In a recent vivid demonstration of what can be achieved, Tung et al. (1982) prepared $CoSi_2$ films by molecular beam epitaxy at elevated temperatures in UHV. The epitaxial single-crystal silicide film displayed the excellent resistivity of 10 $\mu\Omega$ cm (cf. 25 $\mu\Omega$ cm for furnace grown $CoSi_2$). Ion beam mixing and melt-annealing may enable the growth of such good films without requiring extraordinary precautions for the metal film deposition. These techniques will be illustrated below.

5. Polycide Process

Contacts and interconnections incorporating high-conductivity silicides of Pt, Pd, Co, Ni, Ir, Rh and Ti or the refractory metals Mo and Ta have been subjects of much study. Many of these silicides lend themselves to the "polycide" technology sketched in Fig. 5, in which a gate contact is fabricated using the well-tried bonding of a layer of doped polysilicon with the gate

TABLE I
Electrical resistivity ($\mu\Omega$ cm) for various furnace-grown silicide films.

Silicide	Resistivity	Formed from	Reference
$TiSi_2$	13–16	metal/poly Si	Murarka (1980)
	25	co-sputtred alloy	Murarka (1980)
$NiSi_2$	50–60		Murarka (1980)
$CoSi_2$	18–25		Murarka (1980)
$ZrSi_2$	35–40	metal/poly Si	Murarka (1980)
$NbSi_2$	50	metal/poly Si	Murarka (1980)
$MoSi_2$	40–100	co-sputtered	Roberts (1982)
Pd_2Si	25–35	metal/Si	Wittmer (1980)
PdSi	20	metal/Si	Ottaviani et al. (1981)
$TaSi_2$	35–45	metal/Si	Murarka (1980)
WSi_2	30–50	co-evaporated	Roberts (1982)
	40–60	co-sputtered	Roberts (1982)
PtSi	28–35	metal/Si	Murarka (1980)

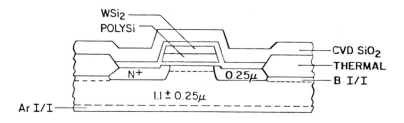

Fig. 5. Schematic diagram of one-micron polycide MOSFET. From Crowder (1982).

oxide layer, followed by a grown silicide layer of much lower resistivity. Silicides grown on polysilicon in this way appear to benefit from having less tensile stress than silicides grown on silicon dioxide. These silicides may then be directly oxidized (at $\sim 1000°C$), so that they develop a protective coat of SiO_2 by silicon diffusion and leave the silicide protected from subsequently deposited layers of conductor in a multilevel system. The integrity of the silicide film can be threatened by the oxidation step, especially in the case of WSi_2 or $TaSi_2$, where a shortage of mobile Si to satisfy the oxidant at the surface can allow dissociation of the silicide and destruction of the film (Zirinksy *et al.*, 1978). In such a criticial oxidation step ion beam mixing can be used to break up a barrier layer of oxide at the Si–silicide interface, and thus aid the important flow of Si from the substrate.

C. Ion Beam Effects

Ion beam effects can be used in a variety of ways to exercise control over some of the important physical variables in the preparation of conducting silicide layers. We shall proceed to quote examples from published exper-imental results which relate to some of the problems of conventional process-ing already outlined.

1. Ion Implantation

a. High Fluence Implantation. With high doses of implanted Si^+ ions in a metal film, it is possible to alter the composition of the film (by analogy with metallurgical implantation work (Myers, 1978) and perhaps by analogy with co-deposition of metal and silicon). Such experiments have been reported by Chapman *et al.* (1979), who implanted 10^{17} Si cm^{-2} at 120 keV into 2000 Å Pd films, thereby introducing almost 20 at. % of Si in the upper half of the Pd film. Although the work was performed at a temperature of $-100°C$, they found that the condensed phase Pd_2Si had formed, mixed with residual Pd. The experiment demonstrates the possibility of producing silicide phases by ion implantation well below the temperature required ($\geq 100°C$) by thermal activation. In this instance, however, a pure Pd_2Si layer could not be generated, since the sputtering limit in the Pd–Si system was reached at about 20 at. % implanted Si. The formation of the crystalline phase at such a low temperature is indicative of microscopic local activation caused by the ions themselves. This becomes very important even in cases where the composition of the film is otherwise determined (as in a co-deposited, amorphous layer). This activation is crucial to the success of ion beam mixing, in which the ion beam also serves to assist the intermixing of materials across an interface (as discussed in Chapter 7).

b. Growth-Inhibiting Implantation. In a further experiment, Chapman *et al.* (1979) bombarded a Pd film only 1000 Å thick deposited on SiO_2. The ion penetration in this case extended through the Pd–SiO_2 interface and into the SiO_2. The substrate was maintained at $-100°C$. After a Si^+ ion dose of 10^{17} cm^{-2}, it was found that X-ray diffraction patterns showed the presence of an amorphous phase, Pd_4Si. Although there was no evidence of extensive dissociation of the SiO_2 at the interface, it is believed that the expected local breaking of Si–O bonds by the ions would liberate enough oxygen atoms to diffuse as a small impurity into the Pd–Si film, thus stabilizing the amorphous phase Pd_4Si by incorporating with Pd_4Si in a Bernal type arrangement.

Ion implantation of N^+ or O^+ throughout a metal film can have a large effect on the subsequent silicide growth kinetics. Scott *et al.* (1980) implanted 80 keV O^+ ions (1.6×10^{16} cm^{-2}) in Ni films ($\sim 1500Å$) on Si substrates before subjecting them to silicide-forming furnace treatment at 290°C. The expected growth of Ni_2Si proceeded at a normal rate initially, but slowed abruptly before the Ni layer was fully consumed, and at that time a layer of NiSi began to develop at the interface. Their model of the process is illustrated in Fig. 6. Ni is the principal diffusing species in growing Ni_2Si, and when Ni is incorporated in the silicide at the Ni interface, its oxygen content remains behind and forms SiO_2 with Si at that interface. Eventually the SiO_2 forms a continuous barrier layer which inhibits the diffusion of Ni to reaction site and initiates the growth of NiSi at the Si interface. In the case of pure Ni films of this thickness, Ni_2Si and NiSi layers are not expected to develop together, as mentioned earlier. Thus, the deliberate introduction of a small oxygen impurity concentration by implantation can evidently offer a means of control over silicide growth kinetics and the phases which will grow at a given temperature.

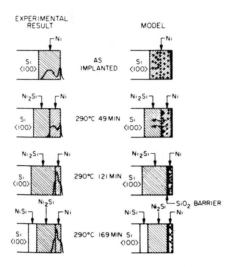

Fig. 6. Model of SiO_2 barrier formation mechanism. The black dots represent oxygen atoms. Ni diffuses through Ni_2Si to sustain the silicide growth, thus exposing residual oxygen to Si at the Ni_2Si interface and allowing SiO_2 to form. Once the barrier is formed, NiSi begins to grow. From Scott *et al.* (1980).

In similar studies of the effect of N^+ implantation in Ni layers on Si$<$100$>$, Wielunski *et al.* (1981a) were able to completely prevent reaction at temperatures below 375°C for 5 × 10^{16} N^+ cm^{-2}. A lower dose (0.9 × 10^{16} N^+ cm^{-2}) caused NiSi to be the first and only phase grown at 313°C. At higher doses the reaction is halted presumably by the accumulation of a Si_3N_4 layer acting as a barrier to the diffusion of Ni.

Pre-implantation of a Ti film on Si$<$100$>$ with N^+ ions (2 × 10^{17} cm^{-2}) followed by 675°C heating for 3 hrs was shown by von Seefeld *et al.* (1980) to produce the phase Ti_5Si_3, which is richer in Ti than the more usual compound $TiSi_2$, which remained at the silicon interface. This might be interpreted as a result of inhibition of Si diffusion by a nitride layer, or alternatively as a consequence of the N impurity stabilizing the Ti_5Si_3 phase, as the authors proposed.

There are many possible applications of reactive ion implantation to the manipulation of the subsequent thermal growth of silicides. However, it should be stressed that useful impurity concentrations demand large implant doses, with attendant sputtering problems and lengthy exposures.

2. Ion Beam Mixing

The basic concepts and implementation of ion beam mixing of interface layers have been presented in Chapter 7. In the pages that follow, we highlight various ways in which ion mixing phenomena may be of special value in the preparation of good contacts to Si devices.

a. Interface Cleaning. It is all too easy for a thin native oxide to be left on a Si substrate before deposition of a metal. At elevated temperatures, such an oxide layer, if continuous, can inhibit the nucleation of silicide phases at the metal–substrate interface. Worse, if the oxide layer is patchy, an inhomogeneous layer of silicide will grow.

Irradiation with inert ions in the region of such a contaminated interface can enable the silicide to nucleate and grow in the normal way, as demonstrated for the case of Ni on Si<100> by Wielunski *et al.* (1982). These authors prepared substrates deliberately coated with enough oxide to prevent thermal silicide formation. After irradiating the Ni–(SiO$_2$)–Si sample with 10^{13} to 3×10^{14} Xe cm^{-2}, normal thermal growth kinetics were restored. They also noted that lateral uniformity of thermally grown Ni$_2$Si layers on Si was significantly improved by this irradiation. These results show how ion irradiation, by displacing interface atoms, can make the silicide growth process more tolerant to interface impurities or irregularities. This is of considerable practical significance in high density device technology, where adequate interface cleanliness is often more difficult to ensure.

b. Interface Mixing. The ability of a flux of energetic ions to produce physical mixing of atoms across an interface between two substrates has been discussed in Chapter 7. In many respects, the process resembles thermal diffusion, although generally it can be achieved at relatively low substrate temperatures.

At high temperatures, the "ion mixing" phenomenon will be dominated by radiation-enhanced diffusion of the constituents at an interface. This is caused by the increased defect density introduced by the radiation. At lwer temperatures, "enhanced" thermal diffusion gives way to the effects of multiple collision cascades produced individually by the incoming energetic ions. Figure 7 shows a typical plot of interface mixing rate as a function of the inverse of sample temperature, *T*. Raising the sample temperature has a relatively small effect in the cascade mixing regime; however, if one approaches the regime of "enhanced diffusion", a small increase of *T* can speed up a reaction greatly. In some of the following examples, it has proved useful to work with elevated sample temperatures.

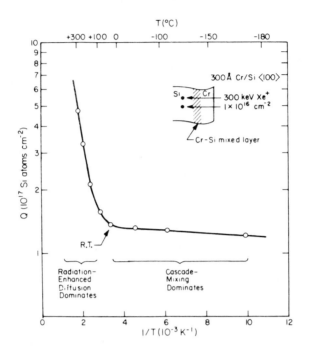

Fig. 7. Ion beam mixing effect as a function of reciprocal implantation temperature. In this example, Xe$^+$ (300 keV, 10^{16} cm^{-2}) ions were used to mix Cr and Si. The behavior of this curve is expected to be general. From Mayer *et al.* (1981a).

For a given T, the thickness of the cascade-mixed layer increases with the square root of the ion dose, and in some materials a very small dose of heavy inert ions can induce the growth of thick (2000Å) silicide layers. In this practical respect, ion beam mixing differs from the process of producing altered layers by high-dose implantation of one species, where the sputtering limit and excessive implantation time govern the operation.

c. Nucleated Silicides. We consider again the use of ion beam mixing at a clean silicon–metal interface. Such mixing serves to initiate nucleation of the silicide, after which normal furnace treatment will satisfy diffusion-limited growth kinetics for the nucleated phase.

Tsaur and Hung (1980) have carried out this interface mixing for samples of Er on Si<100>. The samples were irradiated with about 10^{14} Xe cm^{-2} at 200°C and reacted at 300°–350°C. The disilicide proceeded to grow layer-by-layer with a $\sqrt{t}$ dependence, whereas in the absence of the ion bombardment, no reaction would occur below 380°C, at which temperature complete conversion occurred abruptly after nucleation of the phase (Baglin *et al.*

1980b). Figure 8 displays backscattering spectra which illustrate the differing behavior of unheated and interface-mixing samples. The irradiation evidently facilitates nucleation of the $ErSi_2$ at a temperature (325°C) low enough for planar diffusion-limited reaction to occur in furnace treatment.

Presumably, similar effects of interface mixing could be used beneficially in the case of the rare-earth and other silicides discussed earlier. Their nucleation controlled reaction kinetics would otherwise make them technologically unworkable, despite their attractions of high conductivity and thermal stability.

d. Metastable Phases. Silicide phases not accessible by furnace annealing techniques can be generated by ion beam mixing of an otherwise stable Si–silicide interface. One such example is the work of Tsaur *et al.* (1980a), in which a pre-formed film of PtSi (300 Å) on Si was bombarded at room temperature with 300 keV Xe^+ to a dose of 1×10^{15} Xe cm^{-2}. The implantation produced a composite layer richer in Si than PtSi, and X-ray diffraction lines of PtSi could no longer be found. However, no diffraction lines corresponding to a new phase were found until the sample was post-annealed (~ 6 min at 400°C). This heat treatment produced homogenization of the layer composition and the appearance of diffraction lines which indicated the metastable phase Pt_2Si_3. This phase does not occur in normal silicide growth in a furnace, yet it proved to be stable in contact with Si up to temperatures of over 500°C. At higher Xe doses (3×10^{15} cm^{-2}) the Pt–Si film was richer in Si near the substrate. Subsequent heating (400°C, 30 min.) then produced both Pt_2Si_3 and Pt_4Si_9 in successive defined layers.

While this result rightly suggests that growth of a particular phase is governed by the resident composition of the mixed layer, it is evident that other factors are also important. Tsaur *et al.* (1980b) attempted to reproduce the Pt_2Si_3 formation, starting with a film of $Pt_{40}Si_{60}$ (amorphous) co-deposited on cooled substrates. Heat treatment at 400°C produced mixed phases Pt_2Si_3 and PtSi. Only if the film was ion-mixed before heating did a homogeneous layer of Pt_2Si_3 form at 400°C (Fig. 9). Evidently, the ion mixing has the effect of dispersing local microscopic anomalies of composition (or condensed PtSi micro-crystallites) which would otherwise nucleate crystallites of PtSi. The sequence of phase formation is graphically reflected in the plot of resistivity versus temperature as the sample was heated at a constant rate (Fig. 10).

An apparently important precondition for generating the metastable phase in this and similar cases is the existence of an amorphous material (created here by ion damage) of approximately correct composition, prior to heat treatment. The transformation from amorphous to metastable crystalline phase is evidently favored over that leading to the equilibrium phase— behavior familiar in such techniques as splat cooling or pulsed annealing (Mader *et al.*, 1967).

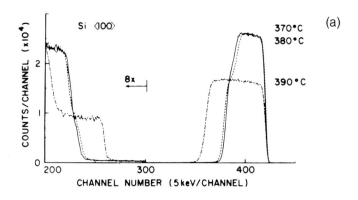

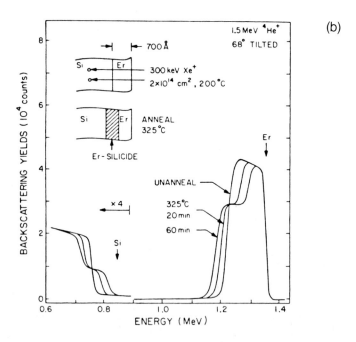

Fig. 8.   RBS spectra illustrating the different behavior of untreated and interface mixed samples of Er–Si<100>. Figure 8(a) shows Er silicide growth abruptly nucleated at 390°C. In a sample pre-implanted with 2 × 20^14 Xe cm^-2 (300 keV) at 200°C, the silicide formed layer-by-layer at only 325°C. (Fig. 8b). From Baglin *et al.* (1980b) and Tsaur and Hung (1980).

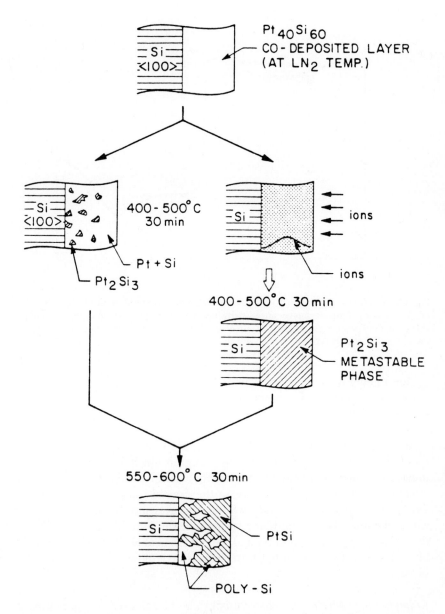

Fig. 9. Formation of Pt_2Si_3 from co-deposited $Pt_{40}Si_{60}$ layer (schematic). The homogeneous layer of Pt_2Si_3 phase can only be obtained by annealing an ion-bombarded film. From Tsaur *et al.* (1980a).

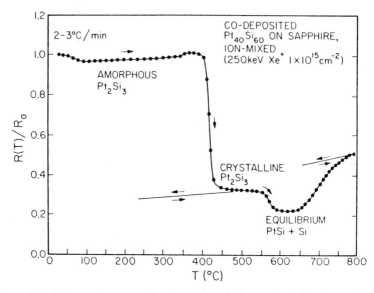

Fig. 10. Resistivity annealing curve for the co-deposited, ion-mixed film of Fig. 9. Heating rate 2–3°C min⁻¹. Distinct changes in resistivity indicate the change from amorphous to metastable crystalline phase Pt_2Si_3 at 550°C, the metastable phase reverts to the equilibrium mixture. From Tsaur *et al.* (1980b).

Ion mixing thus offers one way of creating non-standard silicide phases in thin films. The resulting properties could be of special technical value (e.g. superconducting Pt_2Si_3, at $T_c \sim 4.2°K$, as discussed in Chapter 7).

e. Multilayer Mixing. It is possible to prepare thicker films (perhaps 2000 Å) of silicide at low temperatures by using an ion beam to interface-mix multi-layer films prepared by depositing successive thin layers of Si and metal in correct proportions to obtain the desired silicide. In this case, the ion beam energy is chosen in a way that locates most of the ion damage within the multi-layer film. Using such a scheme, Tsaur *et al.* (1980a,b) produced homogeneous films of $NiSi_2$, $HfSi_2$ and V_3Si at about 500°C, appreciably below the 800°C required to form these compounds by diffusion in a furnace.

f. Single Layer Mixing. Extensive mixing can be achieved by ion bombardment of a thick metal (> 1000 Å) on Si, with the ion energy chosen to center the damage in the developing mixed layer. Formation of normal silicide phases can take place either subsequently, by furnace annealing, or during bombardment, by maintaining an elevated sample temperature. In either case, much lower temperatures are required than those needed for growth by normal thermal diffusion, since only the short-range transport of atoms into bonding locations is required after mixing. This is particularly attractive in forming the refractory metal silicides, whose growth by diffusion requires undesirably high temperatures and often presents other problems related to silicide film adhesion, uniformity and stress.

Tsai et al. (1980) used As^+ ion mixing to produce layers of WSi_2, $TaSi_2$, and $MoSi_2$ which had good uniformity and conductivity. In order to avoid bubble formation which results from high-dose implants of inert gas ions, As^+ was chosen. Films of W, Ta and Mo each of about 400 Å were e-beam deposited at room temperature on to single crystal Si$<100>$ or poly-silicon coated substrates. They were then implanted with a dose of 2×10^{16} As cm^{-2}, at energies chosen to locate the implanted As in the Si near the metal interface. In each case, when the sample was maintained at $\sim 350°C$, a complete layer of stoichiometric disilicide composition formed during implantation, and X-ray diffraction showed hexagonal disilicide patterns in all cases, indicating that the compound was fully crystallized. Growth of these silicides by thermal diffusion would normally require at least 800°C. When implantation was performed at 75°C instead of 350°C, no sign of silicide crystallization was found, even though the extent of mixing was similar.

The resistivity of the as-formed silicides was relatively high, but it improved substantially after 30 min. annealing at higher temperatures (Fig. 11). A steep drop in the resistivity of WSi_2 and $TaSi_2$ films at about 700°C corresponded to a phase change to their normal tetragonal form. ($MoSi_2$ grows thermally in the hexagonal phase.) Presumably, the resistivity drop is due to increased grain sizes and improved crystalline order. Resistivities obtained by thermal diffusion growth are comparable to the results of 1000°C annealing of the ion-mixed films. Whether satisfactory resistivities can be obtained without this excursion to high temperature remains open to question.

A further interesting example of silicide phase formation during ion-mixing bombardment is that of epitaxial Pd_2Si described by Ishiwara and Kuzuta (1980). The phase Pd_2Si grows epitaxially by thermal diffusion on Si$<111>$ at 700°–900°C. However these authors report the reaction of 800 Å Pd on Si$<111>$ during implantation of 5×10^{16} Ar cm^{-2} (200 keV) at room temperature (producing an epitaxial layer of Pd_2Si). Noting that Si will be amorphized by the entering ion beam long before the epitaxial growth is completed, and that the Pd_2 Si structure is evidently resistant to radiation damage at room temperature, they suggest that the initial layers of epitaxial Pd_2Si formed upon Pd deposition and probably provide the template for subsequent epitaxy.

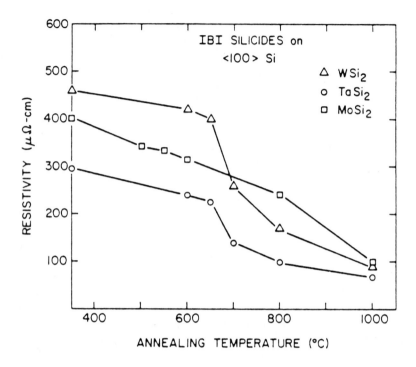

Fig. 11.   Resistivity of silicides formed by ion beam mixing at 350°C and then annealed for 30 min. at various temperatures. The 700°C drop for $TaSi_2$ and WSi_2 coincides with a phase change to the normal tetragonal form. From Tsai *et al.* (1980).

Silicides of Pt, Hf, Nb, Pd, Ni, Co, Fe, Cr and Ti have also been produced by ion beam mixing (Poate and Tisone, 1974; Chapman *et al.*, 1979; Tsai *et al.*, 1980; Tsaur, 1980; Wang *et al.*, 1980), and form reproducibly at relatively low temperatures.

Silicides of Pt, Hf, Nb, Pd, Ni, Co, Fe, Cr and Ti have also been produced by ion beam mixing (Poate and Tisone, 1974; Chapman *et al.*, 1979; Tsai *et al.*, 1980; Tsaur, 1980; Wang *et al.*, 1980), and form reproducibly at relatively low temperatures.

3. Intense Pulsed Ion Beams

The growth of homogeneous layers of metal silicides has been achieved by irradiating metal films on Si with a pulse of ions carrying sufficient energy (typically 1–2 J cm^{-2}) to melt the sample surface briefly (Baglin *et al.*, 1982a;

Chen *et al.*, 1982; Neri *et al.*, 1980). Intermixing of metal and silicon can occur during the brief existence of the liquid phase, and upon cooling, silicide formation can take place. This work may be likened to pulsed annealing of silicides reported with pulsed lasers or electron beams, although ion beams may possess some advantages over these techniques. The ion energy deposition profile is readily predictable and not significantly dependent on the liquid or solid state of the film; there is no reflection of energy at the metal surface, such as that suffered by laser light; and the ion energy is deposited substantially below the sample surface, a more favorable situation than that of light, which is exponentially absorbed, or that of broad-spectrum dispersed electron beams.

In a typical single pulse of ions needed to produce a 1000 Å layer of $NiSi_2$, the total implanted dose will amount to perhaps 10^{13} ions cm^{-2}. In this respect, the technique contrasts with the processes of ion mixing and recoil implantation, where doses of more than 10^{16} cm^{-2} are often needed. Such a small ion dose could not bring about the extensive atomic transport observed here simply by ion mixing or radiation enhanced diffusion in the solid phase. Furthermore, heat transfer calculations indicate that sufficient energy is delivered in one pulse to reach melting or eutectic temperatures at the metal–silicon interface. It is believed that silicides produced by this treatment will have formed during the cooling of a liquid metal–Si mixture (Baglin *et al.*, 1981).

a. Nickel and Cobalt Silicides. Figure 12 shows backscattering spectra from a sample that was made by irradiating a Ni (400 Å) –Si< 100> wafer at room temperature with a single pulse of 280 keV protons at various energy densities. At low power, an interface layer of NiSi formed (its identity being verified by X-ray diffraction). (Apparently the Ni_2Si found in thermal processing was being by-passed.) At higher energy density, a completed layer of NiSi formed. At still higher densities, this phase was found to be mixed with $NiSi_2$, and the lowest curve corresponds to complete conversion to $NiSi_2$—a layer which proved to be epitaxial when studied by channeling and TEM (Chen *et al.*, 1982). In some instances, the epitaxial structure displayed curved grains similar to those reported previously for epitaxial bilayer films which were thermally grown. For energy densities still greater than this, a Si–rich mixture with $NiSi_2$, NiSi and Ni_2Si was formed upon cooling, thus segregating Si in the form of cellular structures recognizable as the result of constitutional supercooling, with Si columns surrounded by silicide walls. Such structures have become familiar in pulsed laser annealing, where rapid movement of the melt front occurs during cooling. A situation of technical interest is the case where just sufficient energy density was used to produce uniform epitaxial $NiSi_2$ (Fig. 12). Although the best channeling (as indicated

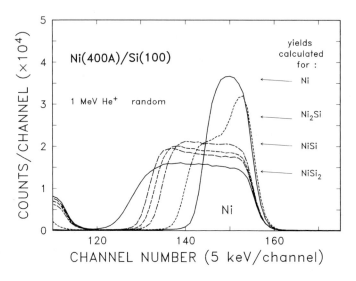

Fig. 12.   Growth of silicides by pulsed ion beam annealing. The RBS spectra indicate the growth of Ni silicides produced by irradiating Ni (400 Å)–Si<100> samples with proton pulses of various intensities in the vicinity of 1 J cm^{-2}. Arrows indicate the Ni profile heights anticipated for each phase should it be present. Ni$_2$Si apparently is not formed. From Baglin *et al.* (1982a).

by minimum yield, χ_{min}) for this layer was 15% (for 2 MeV He$^+$ channeling) and not as good as the value of 5% obtainable by furnace annealing, the NiSi$_2$ film produced was indeed a large-grain homogeneous film. One would expect this to display good conductivity.

Cobalt films on Si<100> have been found to respond to pulsed ion beam treatment in the same way as Ni. First, CoSi and then CoSi$_2$ layers develop, as energy density for the pulse is increased, with the CoSi$_2$ displaying epitaxy and curved grain structures (Baglin *et al.*, 1982).

b. Palladium, Rhodium and Iridium Silicides. Growth of the silicides of Pd, Rh and Ir has been demonstrated using pulsed proton beam treatment of metal–Si. The backscattering profiles obtained (for a series of different energy values) are shown in Figs. 13 and 14. In each case, the evidence indicates (by RBS plateaux) that multiple layers of well-defined composition were formed. In the case of Pd, these include the composition of the normal phases found after thermal annealing (Pd$_2$Si, PdSi), and these phases were verified in X-ray diffraction patterns. The X-ray pattern for the lower power samples also contained a line not corresponding to any of the standard silicides. It is conceivable that this "mystery" line originated from the Pd-rich phase Pd$_3$Si, of which the top curves of Fig. 13 show a hint.

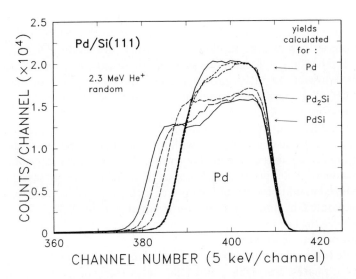

Fig. 13. Growth of Pd silicides by pulsed proton beam annealing at several intensities. RBS spectra from Pd–Si<111> annealed with a pulsed proton beam at various intensities indicate the growth of Pd_2Si, followed by PdSi. From Baglin *et al.* (1982a).

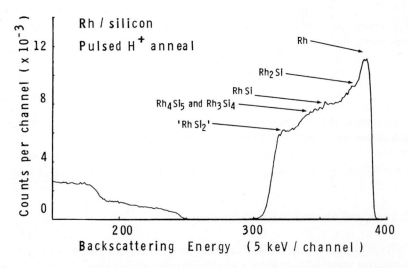

Fig. 14. Growth of Rh silicides by pulsed proton beam annealing at several intensities. Arrows indicate the calculated height of the Rh profile (RBS) if the stated compounds should be present. RhSi and the mixture Rh_4Si_5–Rh_3Si_4 implied by the plateaux were confirmed by x-ray diffraction. No stable phase "$RhSi_2$" has been reported in the literature. From Baglin *et al.* (1982b).

Similarly, the Rh–Si result of Fig. 14 displays a plateau corresponding to the expected phase RhSi and possibly one or both of Rh_4Si_5 and Rh_3Si_4. These phases can also be recognized by X-ray diffraction. The diffraction lines corresponding to at least one other unidentified compound phase were present, however. The RBS profile suggests the composition of the Si-rich layer "$RhSi_2$", a phase not reported in the equilibrium diagram, and perhaps this is the source of the unexplained diffraction lines.

The simultaneous appearance of several expected and unexpected phases in the Pd and Rh cases is consistent with the concept of these phases condensing during fast cooling of a melted layer of initially graded composition. Depending on local composition and cooling rate, metastable phases could also be produced in that process, and in most cases the layers of condensed phases were separated by thin layers of the residual eutectic composition, these having been the last to solidify in the cooling process. Such layers are consistent with present observations.

In the Ir–Si interaction, no unexpected plateaux occur in the RBS profile. The same phases, IrSi, $IrSi_{1.75}$ and $IrSi_3$, seem to occur as those generated sequentially in furnace annealing. One significant difference is that, in furnace annealing, $IrSi_3$ forms by nucleation abruptly and irregularly at high temperature, whereas in this case a layer of composition near that of $IrSi_3$ appears in contact with the other layers.

c. Titanium, Molybdenum, Tantalum and Tungsten Silicides. Pulsed ion beam processing has not been so readily applied to the growth of thick silicide layers of Ti, Mo, Ta and W. At very high energy density, a layer of composition near $TiSi_2$ has been observed, and Mayer *et al.* (1981b) have reported forming $MoSi_2$ layers, also at high power. First efforts with W and Ta have led to very little interface alteration. Further work needs to be done in order to determine the possibilities in these systems. Since the effectiveness of the pulsed ion beam presumably depends on eutectic melting at the metal–Si interface, it should be expected that these systems with high eutectic melting temperatures will not interact unless a high beam energy density is supplied.

D. Laser and Electron Beam Treatment

Both continuous wave (cw) and pulsed lasers and electron beams can be used to prepare metal silicide films, and the prospect of applying such techniques to produce silicide contacts on Si is attractive. In the case of lasers, coupling of the source energy into the metal-coated wafer is inhibited because of reflection from the metal-surface. Furthermore, as the silicide grows, it presents a less reflective surface, and unless extraordinary control is used, the abrupt rise in power absorption can excessively raise the silicide temperature. This problem may be avoided by overlaying the metal with a thin anti-reflection layer of Si. Another approach is to heat the interface with long wavelength laser radiation from the back side of a thin Si substrate. The use of radiation which deposits most of its energy near the sample surface permits the reaction temperatures for silicide growth to be reached in the local region of the growing contact, without the need to heat the entire wafer, as furnace processing demands. This advantage is shared by laser, electron and ion beam treatment (as mentioned in Section II, C, 3).

Continuous wave laser treatment has generally been applied by moving the beam spot across the sample with a "dwell time" of the order of 10^{-3} sec. In this mode, solid-phase diffusion in the metal-silicon system can usually produce adequately thick silicide films. Single phase silicides are then generated, as in furnace annealing, and their physical integrity, uniformity and electrical properties can be excellent. Short-pulsed treatment (beam pulse length 10–100 ns) briefly produces a metal–silicon eutectic liquid which rapidly cools, precipitating a mixture of silicide phases and segregating in a rough cellular structure that incorporates crystallites of unreacted Si. The phases may be metastable, possibly with unique properties. Barrier heights have been measured for such multi-phase Pt–Si films (Doherty et al., 1980). Values around 0.7 eV, presumably averaged over several silicide phases, fall below that for furnace-grown PtSi; namely 0.82–0.85 eV.

The subject of laser (or electron) beam processing of silicides has been covered in a number of articles (e.g. Sigmon, 1981; Poate et al., 1978; Sigmon et al., 1980; von Allmen et al., 1980; Shibata et al., 1980a,b; and in Chapter 7 of this volume). Rather than repeat the same material, we shall refer the reader to Chapter 7 for detailed discussion, and proceed here to quote just a few examples of laser and e-beam treatment in which silicide layers, potentially suitable for interconnections, have been produced.

1. Continuous Wave Lasers

Shibata et al., (1980a,b) used a cw Ar laser operated in the multi-line mode and focused to a 50 μm beam spot. The beam was scanned at 12 cm sec^{-1} over the sample, which was maintained at elevated temperature. Thin films of Pd, Pt, Mo, W and Nb (400–1300 Å) were deposited on <100> silicon substrates, and the metal layer was covered with a 200 Å anti-reflection coating of Si. During laser irradiation, the Pd–Si and Pt–Si samples were held at 50°C, and the others at 350°C.

In the case of Pd–Si, at a laser power level, p, of 0.7 times that needed to melt Si, a single raster scan produced a microscopically smooth, homogeneous layer of Pd_2Si, as observed by RBS and verified by X-ray diffraction.

At $p = 0.8$ to 1.4, the reaction produced a uniform layer of PdSi (with a trace of Pd_2Si), the surface of which, though good, showed "laminar" features along the direction of beam scan. From observations of film smoothness and the progressive planar growth of the Pd_2Si layer as p was raised from 0.45 (threshold) to 0.7, it was evident that the silicide was produced by solid-phase diffusion. Thus, cw laser treatment constitutes a fast equivalent of furnace treatment. The PdSi growth occurred abruptly and may have resulted either from laser-induced nucleation and solid-phase growth or from eutectic melting; either might account for the beam-induced morphology.

In the Pt–Si system, only a mixture of phases could be produced (including the metastable Pt_2Si_3 at high laser power). The smooth film (containing Pt_3Si, PtSi, $Pt_{12}Si_5$ and Pt_2Si) produced by $p = 0.5$ would appear to have grown in the solid phase, although these reactions are not yet fully understood.

In the case of the refractory metals Mo, W and Nb, growth of the disilicide began at approximately $p = 0.9$, a single scan producing only a thin, smooth interface layer of a well-defined single phase. Multiple scans could be used to continue the conversion. Ten scans at $p = 0.85$ were enough to convert 400 Å of W; a single scan at $p = 0.88$ converted 530 Å of Mo. Well-behaved solid-phase growth seems to have occurred in these refractory metals, with a microscopically uniform film being produced. Information on the resistivity of these films has not been obtained.

2. Continuous Wave Electron Beams

Sigmon *et al.,* (1980) produced results similar to those discussed above by irradiating Pt–Si, Pd–Si and Nb–Si samples with a scanned beam of 30 keV electrons. At low power, complete conversion of 1100 Å Pt–Si to PtSi was found, the film having fine-grained (1 μm) orange-peel morphology and uniform composition. In the case of Pd–Si, a similar Pd_2Si layer formed at low power, while at higher power, uniform PdSi displaying a "laminar" pattern in the beam scan direction was found. In the Nb–Si system, only $NbSi_2$ formed. The observations are summarized in Table II.

This work indicates clearly the ability of cw electron beam treatment to produce silicide films of good quality, and it incidentally implies their solid–phase growth at temperatures well below those demanded by furnace annealing (e.g. the case of PdSi which grows at $\geq 800°C$ in a furnace but was here generated at a temperature estimated by Sigmon *et al.* (1980), to be $375°C$). It is noteworthy that excellent resistivity values were measured for the Pt and Pd silicides formed in this way.

III. GALLIUM ARSENIDE

A. Contact Technology

The performance of various GaAs devices depends substantially on the quality of the ohmic contacts which provide the means for coupling external signals to the devices concerned. Ohmic contacts with low specific contact resistance, ρ_c, aid in improving the frequency characteristics, noise properties and power capability of active components fabricated on GaAs. In addition to possessing low contact resistance, it is desirable that contacts be uniform, stable and reproducible.

During the past decade, ohmic contact formation to GaAs has been studied extensively. Although making contacts to p-type GaAs has not constituted a major problem, it has been very difficult to produce reliable low-resistance contacts to n-type GaAs (Rideout, 1975). The reason for this relates to the fundamental current transport mechanisms and the difficulty in generating heavily doped n-type layers (i.e. $n \geq 10^{19}$ cm^{-3}) (as discussed in Section III of Chapter 10). Indeed, in order to achieve a low-resistance "ohmic" contact at the interface between a metal and a high band-gap semiconductor, the free carrier concentration at the interface must be sufficient to reduce the barrier width to a few tens of Angstroms and hence allow majority carriers to tunnel across the interfacial region (Padovani, 1971). Sufficiently high near-surface electron concentrations to enable direct ohmic contacting to non-alloyed metal contacts are difficult to obtain, either by implantation or furnace annealing (as discussed in Chapter 10). Contacts are

TABLE II

Properties of silicide films produced by scanned electron beam processing.[a]

Metal film	Metal thickness reacted (Å)	Reacted phase	Beam power ÷ radius (kW cm^{-1})	Estimated surface temperature[b] (°C)	Resistivity ($\mu\Omega$ cm)	Surface texture
Pt	1000	PtSi	0.93	240	17.9	fine grain orange peel
Pd	1400	Pd$_2$Si	1.12	290	38.5	fine grain orange peel
Pd	1400	PdSi	1.36	375	20.2	"laminar"
Nb	~400	NbSi$_2$	1.73	525	—	—

[a] From Sigmon et al. (1980)
[b] $T_{sub.} = 50°C$

conventionally formed by furnace alloying of selected metallic overlays with the underlying GaAs substrate. However, the long furnace heating times needed to form the desired alloy from a molten eutectic surface layer and the underlying semiconductor cause several problems. These include undesirable interdiffusion of some contact and semiconductor constituents; poor wetting between the semiconductor and the metal layer; formation of high-resistivity intermetallic compounds; and the formation of microscopic crystallites, which result in surface roughness and poor contact edges (Eckhardt, 1980). As a result, conventional furnace alloying can lead to non-uniform contacts, regions of high specific contact resistivity and a lack of contact reproducibility and reliability, all of which are detrimental to device performance.

The advent of novel beam processing techniques in recent years has had a considerable impact on ohmic contact formation to GaAs. Transient annealing methods provide the possibility of short-duration thermal cycling of precisely defined areas on the semiconductor (Barnes *et al.*, 1980) and thus allow a measure of control over the contact formation processes which is not available with furnace annealing. For n-type GaAs, two approaches have been investigated:

1. Pulsed beam (laser and electron) processing of high-dose implanted GaAs, which has been used to provide high electron concentrations (see Chapter 10) and facilitate direct (non-alloyed) contact to metal overlays.
2. Pulsed (liquid phase) or rapid solid-phase annealing, which has been used to alloy conventional and non-conventional metal overlays.

Both methods give promising results.

In this section, the major approaches that have been employed in obtaining ohmic contacts on n-type GaAs are briefly reviewed. Following discussion of conventional furnace processes for fabricating contacts, recent advances made possible by ion implantation and beam processing are emphasized. Finally, some comments are made on the future generation of ohmic contacts on n-type GaAs, in terms of their resistance, reproducibility and reliability.

B. Furnace Processing

1. Alloyed Contacts

In contrast to the well-established technique for the formation of ohmic contacts on Si by solid-phase reactions (e.g. silicide contacts as described in Section II), more success has been achieved with the alloying technique on

GaAs. In this technique, the metallization system is allowed to melt and resolidify during the furnace heat treatment (Rideout, 1975). In general, the basic approach involves a eutectic metal composition with a dopant element (e.g. Au–Ge, Au–Sn, Au–Si, Au–Te). Upon melting and subsequent resolidification of the metal system, the ohmic behavior is believed to be realized by the regrowth of a heavily doped GaAs layer at the metal–GaAs interface (see, for example, Anderson et al., 1978a).

As already mentioned, the furnace alloying technique possesses inherent problems. In particular, melting and resolidification often cause "balling up" of overlay metals, which results in the non-uniformity of the alloyed regions. Although this problem is typically circumvented by adding Ni or Pt to the metallization system (to essentially "wet" the surface), the high reactivity of these metals with GaAs makes the alloying process very difficult to control. Thus, the values of specific contact resistance, ρ_c, of these furnace-alloyed contacts are strongly dependent on the alloy cycle. During the past few years, extensive efforts have been made to optimize the furnace alloy cycle for reproducible, low ρ_c contact (Macksey, 1977; Anderson et al., 1978a). Best contacts are achieved for short-time alloy cycles (0.5–2 min.) in the temperature range 430°–500°C. The exact dynamic alloy cycle chosen to achieve the best results seems to depend on several parameters, including the heat capacity of the furnace employed, the thermal mass of the sample, and the metallization system used. However, under carefully controlled alloying conditions, contacts with a ρ_c as low as 10^{-6} Ω cm^2 (but more typically $\sim 10^{-5}$ Ω cm^2) have been reported (Macksey, 1977). These are to be compared with values of $\leq 10^{-7}$ Ω cm^2 for silicide contacts in Si (Ting and Chen, 1971).

2. Sintered Contacts

In the sintering technique, ohmic contacts are formed by solid phase reactions resulting in metal–Ga or metal–As compounds during furnace heat treatment. Since no melting is involved in this technique, good uniformity of the contacts can be expected. However, in contrast to Si, where a vast collection of silicides can be formed by reaction of metals with underlying Si, little is known about suitable reactions between metals and the GaAs system. Indeed, few studies of sintered contacts to GaAs have been reported. Sintering of Ge–Pd and Ge–Ni systems on n-type GaAs (Sinha et al., 1975; Anderson et al., 1978b) have produced only partial success, with typical ρ_c values $\sim 10^{-4}$ Ω cm^2. The ohmic behavior in these systems may be attributed to a combination of the n-type doping of GaAs with Ge, and the reaction of Pd or Ni with GaAs, so that an intermediate layer with low barrier height is formed.

To establish the merit of sintered ohmic contacts on GaAs, a lot more work on the different non-eutectic metallic mixtures is needed. The reaction kinetics of such mixtures with GaAs and the properties of the layers formed also need to be established. An ideal mixture should perhaps include a dopant element (e.g. Ge) for the generation of a heavily doped interfacial layer to provide ohmic behavior.

3. Non-Alloyed Contacts

For non-alloyed contacts, a thin, heavily doped, n-type GaAs layer is formed by other means (e.g. by ion implantation, Mozzi *et al.*, 1979; molecular beam epitaxy, Barnes and Cho, 1978; Stall *et al.*, 1979), prior to the deposition of the metal(s). Metals so deposited are not alloyed or reacted with GaAs, and the ohmic behavior arises from current transport across the metal–GaAs barrier because of a tunneling process. Very low values of ρ_c ($\sim 10^{-7}$ Ω cm^2) have been reported for such non-alloyed contacts (Mozzi *et al.*, 1979, Stall *et al.*, 1979) because ρ_c is merely a function of the doping concentration in the underlying GaAs layer (Fig. 15). However, as indicated by the scatter of results covering three orders of magnitude in ρ_c (Fig. 15), high n-type doping ($\geq 10^{19}$ cm^{-3}) is not readily or reproducibly obtained with conventional furnace annealing of ion implanted GaAs. In addition, molecular beam epitaxy is an ultra-high vacuum technique not yet compatible with standard device processing for high throughput.

Non-alloyed contacts possess excellent surface morphology, since no reactions between the metals and GaAs are involved. The reproducibility of ρ_c depends on the reproducibility of doping in the underlying GaAs layer, which in turn, is dependent on the reproducibility of the ion implantation or epitaxial doping process. The contacts, however, may be unreliable under low-temperature ($\sim 250°$C) long-term heating because either deactivation of the interfacial dopant concentration (Pianetta *et al.*, 1981) or the reaction of the metals with GaAs during such cycles is possible. For ideal non-alloyed contacts, metals which do not react during heat treatment with Ga, As or the dopant in the underlying GaAs layer should prove to be most useful.

C. Beam Processing

1. Pulsed Annealing

Pulsed lasers and electron beams have been used successfully to form ohmic contacts to n-GaAs. These methods can be employed either to provide high electron concentrations through a process of liquid-phase epitaxial growth of ion-implanted GaAs (see Chapter 10, Section III), or to mix metal overlays with the underlying GaAs through a process of rapid melting and resolidification (see Chapter 7). These approaches are discussed below.

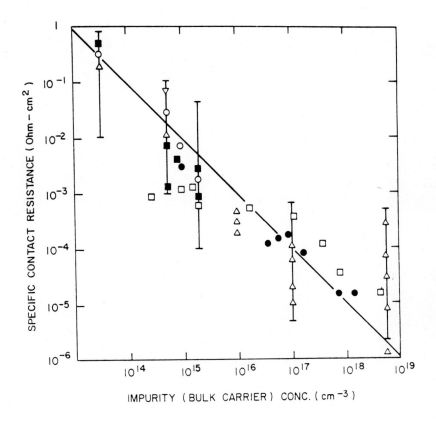

Fig. 15. Specific contact resistance *vs.* bulk doping concentration. From Barnes *et al.* (1980). Solid (empirical) curve is from Goldberg and Tsarenkov (1970) and data points are from Padovani (1971).

The main thrust of ion implantation for low-resistance ohmic contacts has been in the creation of localized heavily doped n-type regions under contacts. Single-ion room-temperature implantations followed by capped furnace annealing have resulted in doping concentrations ($n \sim 2 \times 10^{18}$ cm^{-3}) comparable with levels obtained by conventional epitaxial growth techniques (Tandon *et al.*, 1979). Dual-ion (Inada *et al.*, 1979) or hot implantations (Gamo *et al.*, 1977) have yielded peak electron concentrations in excess of the 2×10^{18} cm^{-3} level after furnace annealing. Such levels are not quite high enough for direct (non-alloyed) contacts. However, as outlined in Section III of Chapter 10, pulsed laser (or e-beam) annealing offers a more promising method of activating high-dose, n-type implants, and electron concentrations exceeding 2×10^{19} cm^{-3} have been reported for capless

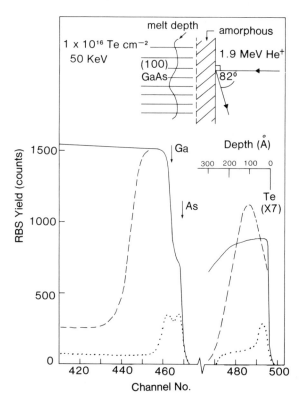

Fig. 16. High resolution random (solid curve) and < 100> aligned (dotted curve) spectra following pulsed Nd:YAG laser annealing of 1 × 10¹⁶ Te cm⁻² implanted GaAs (50 keV). The dashed curve refers to the aligned spectrum before laser annealing. From Barnes *et al.* (1979).

annealing of high-dose (10^{15} cm⁻²) single donor-ion implantations (Barnes *et al.*, 1978; Tandon and Eisen, 1979; Sealy *et al.*, 1979; Pianetta *et al.*, 1980).

The early work of Barnes *et al.* (1978, 1979, 1980) indicated some important features of high-dose implantation and pulsed laser annealing for forming ohmic contacts to n-type GaAs. Firstly, as discussed briefly in Chapters 2 and 10, pulsed laser annealing can facilitate complete removal of ion-implantation damage (thus providing extended defect-free crystal), with the incorporation of high concentrations of dopants onto Ga or As lattice sites. These features are illustrated by the high-resolution Rutherford backscattering and channeling spectra in Fig. 16 for pulsed Nd:YAG laser annealing of n-type GaAs implanted with 10^{16} Te⁺ cm⁻² (50 keV). Perfect recrystallization, as measured by channeling, is achieved for an energy density of 2.2 J cm⁻². The quality of the recrystallization for the high doses of 10^{16} Te cm⁻²

is superior to that which can be achieved by conventional furnace annealing (Brawn and Grant, 1976). This result, together with the observed high Te substitutionality and substantial redistribution, as shown by the Te portion of the spectra, is typical of rapid liquid-phase epitaxial recrystallization of GaAs. Indeed, Fig. 16 shows that more than 90% of the Te atoms reside on Ga or As lattice sites following pulsed annealing. This result implies that the solid solubility is $> 10^{21}$ Te cm^{-3}, which exceeds the equilibrium value, and previous values obtained with furnace annealing (Brawn and Grant, 1976), by more than an order of magnitude. However, the measured electrical activity is not as high as the substitutional solubility might suggest: maximum activities for Te-implanted n-type GaAs of the order of 5×10^{19} cm^{-3} have been reported (Barnes et al., 1980; Pianetta et al., 1980). Nevertheless, this value is still considerably above that obtained by conventional furnace annealing. Reasons for incomplete dopant activity in pulsed-laser annealed GaAs have been reviewed elsewhere (Williams, 1982). These include the quenching-in of point defects, which provide carrier trapping sites, the trapping of dopants on non-active "anti-sites", and the tendency for the surface to decompose during liquid-phase annealing.

The decomposition effect is illustrated in Figs. 17 and 18. Depending on the laser conditions, after laser irradiation the GaAs surface typically exhibits an excess Ga content. This is illustrated both by the channeling spectra in Fig. 17 (e.g. hatched area) and the rough and patchy surfaces shown in the scanning electron micrograph (Fig. 18a). Etching the samples in warm HCl was found to greatly diminish the surface Ga, as shown by both the SEM micrograph of Fig. 18b and the appropriate channeling spectrum in Fig. 17. For contacting applications, it is necessary either to choose pulsed annealing conditions that minimize decomposition or to subsequently remove the surface Ga (which results in electrically noisy behavior, as discussed by Barnes et al., 1980).

Despite incomplete activity following pulsed annealing of high-dose implants and a tendency for the surface to decompose during liquid-phase epitaxy, reproducible contacts to n-GaAs which exhibit low specific contact resistance have been reported. For example, reproducible, non-alloyed ohmic contacts have been fabricated following pulsed annealing of high-dose Te (Barnes et al., 1978), Se (Pianetta et al., 1980) and Si (Mozzi et al, 1979; Inada et al., 1979) implants into n-GaAs, and ρ_c values $\leq 10^{-6}$ Ω cm^2 have been reported under optimum pulsed annealing conditions. However, the reliability and stability of the contacts on GaAs during subsequent low-temperature ($\sim 250°C$) heat treatments still remains an issue of concern, since deactivation of pulsed laser annealed GaAs has been reported (Pianetta et al., 1981) and the stability of the non-alloyed metal overlays has not been fully assessed.

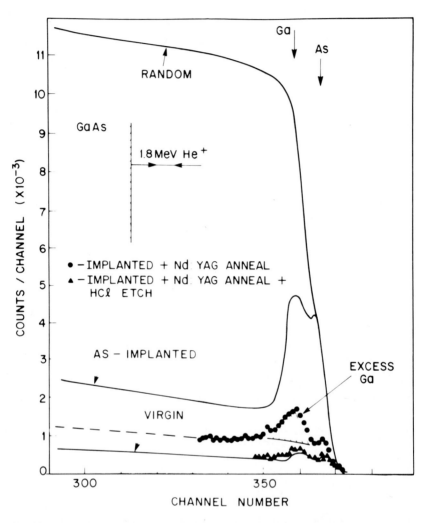

Fig. 17.   Random and $<100>$ aligned RBS spectra from Te implanted (100) GaAs which was Nd:YAG laser annealed. Spectra taken before and after etching in warm HCl. From Barnes *et al.* (1978).

A second method of forming contacts to lightly doped n-type (n $\sim$ 10^{17} cm^{-3}) GaAs essentially substitutes pulsed laser or electron beam induced alloying for conventional furnace alloying of deposited metal overlays. The first applications of lasers to the formation of alloyed ohmic contacts were reported by Pounds *et al.* (1974), but the ρ_c values in this study were rather high. More recently, Margalit *et al.* (1978) used a Q-stitched ruby laser to

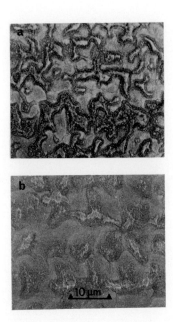

Fig. 18. Secondary electron (SEM) micrograph of GaAs surface (a) after Nd:YAG laser annealing; (b) after subsequent etching of the surface with warm HCl. From Barnes *et al.* (1978).

alloy Ge–Au contacts on GaAs and obtained a ρ_c value of 7×10^{-5} Ω cm^2. The use of optimized laser and electron beam annealing in forming alloyed contacts to GaAs to obtain low ρ_c values has been investigated in considerable detail by several groups (e.g. Gold *et al.*, 1979; Eckhardt *et al.*, 1979; Eckhardt, 1980; Tandon *et al.*, 1980; Lee *et al.*, 1980). These studies indicate that the contacts exhibit good ohmic behavior, are reproducible, have improved surface morphology, and have lower ρ_c values (typically $\leq 10^{-6}$ Ω cm^2) than those usually formed by conventional furnace processing.

As far as the energy absorption necessary to alloy contacts is concerned, pulsed electron beams are preferable to pulsed laser beams because the high optical reflectivity of the metals does not affect the electron beam. Indeed, Gold *et al.* (1979) and Eckhardt (1980) used Ge as the top layer on Au–Ge depositions in order to improve absorption of the incident pulsed laser irradiation. When metals were used as the top layer, the alloying process was extremely difficult to control and poor results were obtained (Gold *et al.*, 1979).

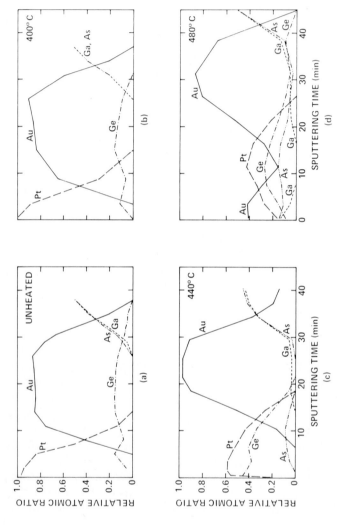

Fig. 19.   AES depth profiles of relative atomic distribution of elements in pulsed electron beam irradiated Au–Ge–Pt ohmic contacts on GaAs (a) before heating, and (b) after heating, and (b) after 400°C, (c) after 440°C and (d) after 480°C (2 min.) furnace heating in H₂. The electron beam parameters were: mean energy ≈ 20 keV, pulse duration ≈ 10⁻⁷ s, energy density ≈ 0.4 J cm⁻². The unirradiated contacts had similar distributions to the irradiated contacts. From Lee *et al.* (1980).

Apart from measurements of the specific contact resistance and observations of surface morphology, few studies have attempted to investigate the alloy mechanisms or the composition and structure of pulsed-alloyed contacts. However, some understanding of the reasons for the improved contacting properties can be obtained from the electron beam annealing studies of Tandon and co-workers (Tandon *et al.*, 1980; Lee *et al.*, 1980, 1981). In these studies, pulsed electron beam alloying of Au–Ge–Pt contacts was examined using Auger Electron Spectroscopy (AES). Prior to electron beam irradiation, Au and Ge were co-deposited ($\sim$80:20) directly onto n–GaAs, followed by a further deposition of Pt. Following electron beam irradiation, under conditions necessary to produce good ohmic contacts ($\rho_c \sim 4 \times 10^{-7}$ Ω cm^2), it was found that little mixing of the Au and Pt layers had occurred (Fig. 19a). In fact, AES combined with sputter profiling did not indicate any appreciable difference between as-deposited and electron beam irradiated structures. This clearly demonstrates that the Pt–Au metals did not melt. It is suggested that the ohmic behavior resulted from doping of the near-surface of GaAs with Ge (possibly by a localized interface-melting process) and generated a highly active n-type layer at the metal–GaAs interface. (Indeed, in a different experiment carried out by Badertscher *et al.* (1980), pulsed laser irradiation of Ge layers on n–GaAs produced interfacial melting and high doping of surface layers upon solidification.) In contrast, furnace-alloyed contacts (470°C for 3 min in H$_2$) result in considerable intermixing of metals and Ge with the GaAs (Fig. 20c). The furnace heating and aging treatments described below (cf. Figs. 19 and 20) give further insight into the different mechanisms of contact formation for electron beam and furnace alloyed contacts.

Auger electron spectroscopy (AES) depth profiles of the above Ge–Au–Pt contacts before and after the heat treatments, are shown in Fig. 19. Prior to measuring the AES depth profiles, ρ_c measurements were made on these contacts (Table III). A comparison of the AES and ρ_c measurements reveals interesting features. The irradiated contacts heated at 400°C show depth profiles for the constituent elements similar to those for the unheated ones and, therefore, these possess a similar value of ρ_c. This indicates that heating at 400°C for 2 min is insufficient to induce significant reaction between the metals and GaAs. The increase in the ρ_c value of the sample heated at 440°C can be clearly attributed to the movement of Ge away from the metal–GaAs interface into the top Pt layer; this strongly confirms the importance of Ge in the formation of ohmic contacts. At this temperature, Ge most probably reacts with the Pt to form intermetallic compounds (Wittmer *et al.*, 1977). The restoration of the low ρ_c value for the sample heated at 480°C can be correlated with the penetration of Ge into GaAs to provide high electrical activation at the metal-GaAs interface. The migration and intermixing of Au

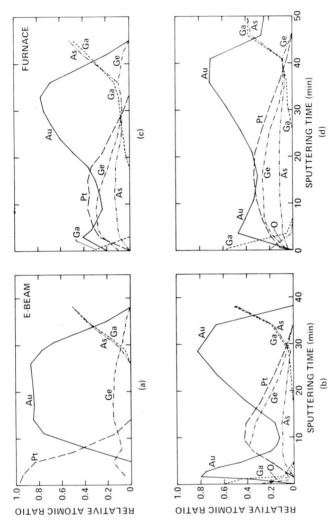

Fig. 20. AES depth profiles of relative atomic distributions of elements in Au–Ge–Pt contacts on GaAs before and after aging at 250°C for 500h: (a) electron beam irradiated, before aging; (b) electron beam irradiated, after aging; (c) furnace alloyed, before aging; (d) furnace alloyed, after aging. The electron beam parameters were the same as in Fig. 19. Furnace alloying was done at 470°C for ∼3 min. in H₂. From Lee *et al.* (1981).

TABLE III

Specific contact resistance, ρ_c, irradiated Au–Ge–Pt contacts on GaAs before and after furnace heating.

Heating temperature (°C)	ρ_c ($\Omega\,cm^2$)
Unheated	4×10^{-7}
400	3×10^{-7}
440	7×10^{-6}
480	4×10^{-7}

[a] After Lee et al. (1980).

and Pt, and out diffusion of Ga and As, may well be attributed to the formation of complex intermetallic compounds. With furnace alloying (Fig. 20c) the mixing of the metals (with Ga and As) is inevitable, but this may be necessary, in the absence of controllable interface melting, so that the Ge will migrate into the GaAs.

Although, by using pulsed electron beam irradiation, excellent contacts can be formed with little or no mixing of the Au–Ge–Pt layers with GaAs, they are found to be unreliable under low-temperature long-term heating (Lee et al., 1981). The ρ_c of the irradiated contacts increases significantly (Table IV) after heating at 250°C for 500 hours. This change is attributed to the high reactivity of the metallization system, which causes the Ge to move away from the metal–GaAs interface and combine with the top Pt layer (Fig. 20). In contrast, the ρ_c values of furnace alloyed contacts show no significant change after similar low-temperature long-term heat treatment (Fig. 20), presumably because such heat treatment does not produce any significant change in the distribution of the already reacted elements.

TABLE IV

Specific contact resistance, ρ_c ($\Omega\,cm^2$), of Au–Ge–Pt contacts alloyed by electron beam irradiation or furnace heating before and after aging at 250°C for 500 hours.[a]

	Before Aging	After Aging
Electron beam irradiated contacts	4×10^{-7}	3×10^{-4}
Furnace alloyed contacts	4×10^{-6}	5×10^{-6}

[a] After Lee et al. (1981).

For the pulsed electron beam studies described above, it has been demonstrated that, in order to obtain good contacting properties, complete surface melting and intermixing of deposited metal overlays is not necessary. In such cases, local interface or eutectic melting between an appropriate dopant and GaAs may provide the required interface activation. However, this process will depend on the order of deposition. The other pulsed-alloying studies (e.g. Gold *et al.*, 1980; Eckhardt *et al.*, 1980) may well require complete surface melting and intermixing in order to provide contacting.

Finally, a third method of forming ohmic contacts to GaAs by using pulsed annealing involves the implantation or deposition of a specific metal (e.g. In) which, when alloyed with underlying GaAs, forms a thin layer of a low band-gap ternary compound. This then facilitates direct contact with a metal overlay. The method has recently been demonstrated by Harrison and Williams (1980) for the $Ga_{1-x}In_xAs$ system, but poor specific contact resistance values ($\sim 10^{-4}$ Ω cm^2) were obtained under non-optimized laser conditions. Nevertheless, in order to achieve improved contacting and expand our knowledge of laser mixing mechanisms, this method warrants further investigation. Interesting features of pulsed ruby laser annealing of In$^+$ ion implanted GaAs are illustrated in Fig. 21. The Rutherford backscattering and channeling spectra indicate near-surface melting and liquid–phase epitaxial growth of the GaAs. The In redistributes in the melt, and most of it appears to be zone refined to the surface upon recrystallization. However, a fraction of In appears to be substitutionally located in the underlying GaAs. Similar results, giving higher bulk incorporation of In, were obtained from laser annealing of vapor deposited In on GaAs (Harrison and Williams, 1980).

2. Rapid Continuous Wave Annealing

As described above, the local heating time during pulsed annealing is typically 10 to several hundreds of nanoseconds, Little solid-phase diffusion or annealing can take place in this time, and the damage removal and alloying invariably result from melting of the GaAs near-surface or from more localized interface (eutectic) melting phenomena. Annealing, alloying and solid-phase reactions can also be induced in a time scale between that of the pulsed regime and the long-time annealing of conventional furnace processing. As discussed in Chapter 2, scanned cw lasers or electron beams can locally heat surface regions in about 1–100 msec, whereas rapid bulk heating methods (e.g. strip heaters, incoherent light sources) can heat and cool the entire substrate in a matter of seconds. These methods allow annealing, diffusion and reaction processes to proceed in the solid phase, or they can be used to induce

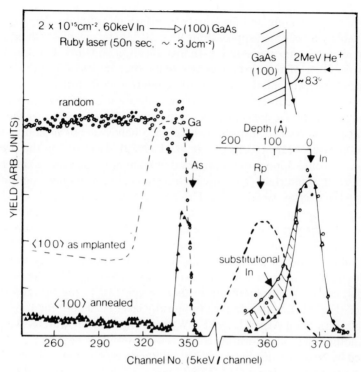

Fig. 21. High resolution channeling spectra from 60 keV In$^+$ implanted GaAs before and after pulsed ruby laser annealing. From Harrison and Williams (1980).

surface or interface melting and alloying in a more controllable manner than conventional furnace heating.

Rapid solid-phase annealing methods have been used in removing ion implantation damage in GaAs (see Chapters 2 and 10, and Williams, 1982). However, layers doped heavily enough to allow direct (non-alloyed) contacts to n-GaAs have not been produced by such methods. Indeed, most of the difficulties encountered during conventional furnace annealing (e.g. surface decomposition and incomplete activation of dopants) are still present during the more rapid annealing treatments (Williams, 1982). In addition, gross surface damage (evaporation and decomposition) occurs if the GaAs is allowed to melt for times of the order of milliseconds; thus liquid phase annealing is not viable in this time regime.

A more promising application of rapid cw annealing methods for contacting applications has been in the processing of metal layers on GaAs. For example, Eckhardt and co-workers (Eckhardt *et al.* 1979, Eckhardt *et al.*

1980; Eckhardt, 1980) found that cw lasers gave more reproducible results than pulsed annealing and also the best surface morphology. The lowest reproducible values of ρ_c (approaching 1×10^{-6} Ω cm^2) were obtained for cw Argon ion laser annealed Au–Ge–In metallization on GaAs. For this system, depth profiling of the surface constituents after deposition and following *optimized* laser annealing revealed some interesting features. Laser annealing caused little redistribution of the metallization constituents apart from a reduction in the Ge concentration of the metallization layer near the GaAs interface. This result contrasts with furnace behavior but is similar to the pulsed electron beam results of Lee *et al.* (1980), described in the previous section. It would appear that optimized annealing in the millisecond region may also allow interface (eutectic) melting to take place without significantly altering the overlay metal layers. This again indicates that heavy Ge doping of the GaAs surface is the prime requirement for good ohmic contacts.

This good control over interface alloying without gross re-distribution of deposited metals is not only beneficial in terms of lower contact resistance but leads to superior surface morphology. This is illustrated by the results of alloying co-evaporated Au–Ge layers with GaAs (Fig. 22). The Normaski interference micrographs illustrate that, in contrast to the furnace alloyed surface (Fig. 22a), both a free-running ruby laser (15 J cm^{-2} for 1 msec) and a single scan of an Argon laser (2.5 W) result in a near-featureless surface.

Another method of forming contacts using rapid cw heating has been described by Nissim *et al.* (1981a, b). This method involves the cw laser processing of a sn spin-on dopant (SnO_2–SiO_2) on n-GaAs. Laser scanning induces Sn diffusion into the GaAs and initiates an interface reaction which leads to the formation of a Sn_3As_2 compound. The rapid laser processing at temperatures in the range $600°$–$800°C$ is thought to produce formation, melting, and resolidification of the interfacial Sn_3As_2 layer without damaging the underlying Sn-doped GaAs. Reproducible non-alloyed contacts with $P_c \sim 10^{-6}$ Ω cm^2 were obtained using this technique.

Rapid bulk annealing in the time scale of 1 to 100 seconds (see Chapters 2 and 10) has been used with some success to remove implantation damage from GaAs. Although not yet investigated in detail, this method may have considerable application to ohmic contact formation. For example, during simple rapid bulk heating, it should be fairly easy to control interface (eutectic) melting and processes similar to those described above for Sn layers on GaAs. Indeed, recent results of Johnson *et al.* (1983) indicate that interface (eutectic) melting can be controlled for the Sn–GaAs system to produce heavily doped GaAs amenable to direct contacting. These studies have also shown that temperature gradient zone migration processes can be induced during rapid bulk heating with an incoherent light source. As they may have possible contacting applications such techniques and their operative alloying mechanisms obviously warrant further study.

(a)

(b)

(c)

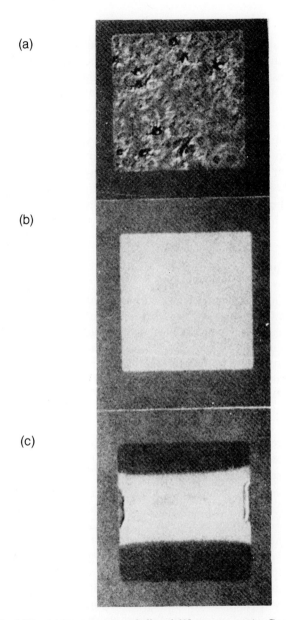

Fig. 22. Microscopic appearance of alloyed 115 μm–square Au-Ge contacts to n-GaAs. (a) Thermal anneal, 450°C, 60 sec. (b) Ruby laser anneal 15 J cm^{-2}, 1 msec. (c) Scanned Argon laser anneal 2.5 W. From Gold *et al.* (1979).

3. Ion Beam Mixing

As discussed in Chapter 7, ion beam mixing can result in the formation of interesting alloy compositions. In Chapter 7 and in Section II of this chapter it has been demonstrated that silicide reactions, which are important in fabricating contacts to Si, can be induced by ion beam mixing processes. Ion beam mixing has not yet been used to fabricate contacts to GaAs, but worthwhile possibilities exist. Recent studies (Williams *et al.*, 1983) have examined ion beam mixing of Al, In, and Sb layers on GaAs. Although some mixing was induced within the temperature range $-130°$ to $200°C$, ternary compounds did not form and contacting properties were not investigated. In view of the success of laser mixing (interface melting) of Ge and Sn on GaAs, studies of the effect of ion beam mixing on the Ge–GaAs and Sn–GaAs systems may prove to be worthwhile.

D. Future Developments

The application of ion implantation and transient anneal techniques to the formation of ohmic contacts to GaAs have shown much promise, since they have provided a degree of reproducibility and contact uniformity not possible with conventional furnace alloying. Use of these techniques in device fabrication is not widespead, but recent reports indicate that rapid annealing for contact formation is compatible with standard MESFET fabrication (Dobkin *et al.*, 1982) and can lead to significant improvement in device performance (Eckhardt, 1980). However, the long-term reliability of ohmic contacts produced by rapid annealing techniques has not been adequately assessed. Thus, more detailed studies of the novel processing techniques discussed in this section are needed before their full potential for device fabrication will be realized.

As reviewed in this section, rapid annealing offers many interesting possibilities for contact formation to GaAs. For example, high-dose implantation followed by pulsed annealing can result in high electron concentrations ($n \gtrsim 10^{19}$ cm^{-3}) at the surface of GaAs to enable non-alloyed contacts of low resistance ($\sim 10^{-7}$ Ω cm^2). Similar results can be obtained from laser processing of deposited dopant layers (e.g. Ge, Sn) on n–GaAs, where doping appears to result from interface (eutectic) melting. However, future studies must be directed towards (a) understanding the doping mechanisms (e.g. incomplete activity for pulsed annealing of ion implanted layers and the mixing processes operating during rapid heating); and (b) an assessment of deactivation and metal reactions which may take place during subsequent thermal processing. For example, the contacting metal(s) in such a case should be chosen on the basis of their contact reliability. The systems chosen should be stable under long, low-temperature heating cycles which simulate the thermal conditions for a typical device operation.

Several different approaches using rapid heating have been used to directly alloy metallic layers deposited on GaAs. The shorter heating-cycle methods (pulsed and cw laser annealing) may provide the means of achieving locally high temperatures without appreciably raising the temperature of the entire wafer. This would allow new contacting metals and eutectic mixtures (not necessarily those having low melting temperatures appropriate to furnace alloying) to be explored. All rapid annealing methods offer a degree of control over the alloying processes which is not possible with furnace alloying. This control appears to hinge on the ability to induce interface (eutectic) melting processes without long-range intermixing of overlay metals. However, the rapid annealing methods need to be studied in more detail so that our understanding of the precise interface mixing mechanisms will be improved. Indeed, high melting temperature eutectic-metal compositions may prove to be more valuable in contacting applications which require rapid heating (or ion beam mixing) than the more conventional Au:Ge based systems so far examined.

IV. CONCLUSION

We conclude this chapter by repeating the observation that the scaled devices, dense packing, and multiple layer VLSI anticipated in the immediate future of the semiconductor industry will demand new and subtle materials and fabrication techniques. Ways must be found of producing interconnection and contact structures that are small, highly conductive and stable in three dimensions at lower process temperatures. In some cases they will need to have tailored barrier heights. The contacts should also form metallurgical diffusion barriers so that the overlaid interconnect metallization will be isolated from the semiconductor below. As much as 65% of the surface area of a VLSI wafer may be needed for interconnect and contact metallization. Such density of packing reminds us of the need to consider barriers to lateral diffusion of constituents of conducting layers.

Our discussion has centered on some aspects of metal–semiconductor contacts and on materials for interconnect metallurgy. The insights and the ion beam techniques applied here to the silicides and GaAs contact systems can readily be extended into the larger field of interconnect metals and alloys. Much basic research is needed still in order to expose all of the potential benefits which ion, electron and laser beam technology has to offer in this field.

REFERENCES

Anderson, R., Baglin, J. E. E., Dempsey, J., Hammer, W., d'Heurle, F., and Petersson, S. (1979). *Appl. Phys. Lett.* **35**, 285.
Anderson, W. T., Christou, A., and Davey, J. E. (1978a). *IEEE J. Solid State Circuits* **13**, 430.
Anderson, W. T., Christou, A., and Davey, J. E. (1978b). *J. Appl. Phys.* **49**, 2998.
Angilello, J., Baglin, J., d'Heurle, F., Petersson, S., and Segmuller, A. (1978). *In* "Thin Film Interfaces and Interactions" (J. E. E. Baglin and J. M. Poate, eds.), p. 369. The Electrochemical Society, Princeton.
Angilello, J., Baglin, J. E. E., Cardone, F., Dempsey, J. J., d'Heurle, F. M., Irene, E. A., MacInnes, R., Petersson, C. S., Savoy, R., Segmuller, A. P., and Tierney, E. (1981). *Journal of Electronic Materials* **10**, 59.
Badertscher, G., Salathe, R. P., and Luthy, W. (1980). *Elect. Lett.* **16**, 113.
Baglin, J. E. E., and Atwater, H. (1981). Unpublished data.
Baglin, J. E. E., d'Heurle, F., and Petersson, S. (1980a). *In* "Thin Film Interfaces and Interactions" (J. E. E. Baglin and J. M. Poate, eds.), p. 341. The Electrochemical Society, Princeton.
Baglin, J. E. E., d'Heurle, F. M., and Petersson, C. S. (1980b). *Appl. Phys. Lett.* **36**, 594.
Baglin, J. E. E., Hodgson, R. T., Chu, W. K., Neri, J. M., Hammer, D. A. and Chen, L. J. (1981). *Nucl. Instrum. Methods* **191**, 169.
Baglin, J. E. E., d'Heurle, F. M., Chen, L. J., and Mayer, J. W. (1982). Unpublished results.
Barnes, P. A. and Cho, A. Y. (1978). *Appl. Phys. Lett.* **33**, 651.
Barnes, P. A., Leamy, H. J., Poate, J. M., Ferris, S. D., Williams, J. S., and Celler, G. K. (1978). *Appl. Phys. Lett.* **33**, 965.
Barnes, P. A., Leamy, H. J, Poate, J. M., Ferris, S. D., Williams, J. S., and Celler, G. K. (1979). *In* "Laser-Solid Interactions and Laser Processing" (S. D. Ferris, H. J. Leamy and J. M. Poate, eds.), p. 647, AIP, New York.
Barnes, P. A., Leamy, H. J., Poate, J. M., and Celler, G. K. (1980). *In* "Laser and Electron Beam Processing of Electronic Materials" (C. L. Anderson, G. K. Celler, and G. A. Rozgonyi, eds.), p. 421. ECS, Princeton.
Brawn, J. R., Grant, W. A. (1976). *In* "Application of Ion Beams to Materials" (G. Carter, J. S. Colligon and W. A. Grant, eds.), p. 59. Inst. Phys., London.
Chapman, G. E., Lau, S. S., Matteson, S., and Mayer, J. W. (1979). *J. Appl. Phys.* **50**, 6321.
Chen, L. J., Hung, L. S., Mayer, J. W., and Baglin, J. E. E. (1982). *In* "Metastable Materials Formation by Ion Implantation" (S. T. Picraux and W. J. Choyke, eds.), p. 319. North Holland, New York. Proc. Symposium on Metastable Phases in Thin Films, Materials Research Society, Boston. (To be published in Nuclear Instruments and Methods.)
Cooper, J. A., Jr. (1981). *Proc. IEEE* **69**(2), 226.
Crider, C. A., Poate, J. M., Rowe, J. E., and Sheng, T. T. (1981). *J. Appl. Phys.* **52**, 2860.
Crowder, B. L. (1982). *In* "Thin Films and Interfaces". (P. S. Ho and K. N. Tu, eds.), p. 369. North Holland, New York.
Crowder, B. L. and Zirinsky, S. (1979). *IEEE Trans.* **ED-26**, 369.
Dobkin, D. M., Gold, R. B., Nissim, Y. I., Gibbons, J. F. (1982) to be published.
Doherty, C., Crider, C. and Leamy, H. (1980). *J. Electronic Materials* **9**, 453.
Eckhardt, G. (1980). *In* "Laser and Electron Beam Processing of Materials" (C. W. White and P. S. Peercy, eds.), p. 467. Academic Press, New York.
Eckhardt, G., Anderson, C. L., Hess, L. D., and Krumm, C. F. (1979). *In* "Laser-Solid Interactions and Laser Processing" (S. D. Ferris, H. J. Leamy and J. M. Poate, eds.), p. 641. AIP, New York.
Eckhardt, G., Anderson, C. L., Colborn, M. N., Hess, L. D., and Jullens, R. A. (1980). *In* "Laser and Electron Beam Processing of Electronic Materials". (C. L. Anderson, G. K. Celler and G. A. Rozgonyi, eds.), p. 445. ECS, Princeton.

Gamo, K., Inada, T., Krekeler, S., Mayer, J. W., Eisen, F. H., and Welch, B. M. (1977), *Solid State Electron.* **20**, 213.

Gold, R. B., Powell, R. A., and Gibbons, J. F. (1979). *In* "Laser-Solid Interactions and Laser Processing" (S. D. Ferris, H. J. Leamy and J. M. Poate, eds.), p. 635. AIP, New York.

Goldberg, Y. U., and Tsarenkov, B. V. (1970). *Sov. Physics-Semi-Conductors* **3**, 1447.

Harrison, H. B. (1980). *Proc. IREE* **41**, 95.

Harrison, H. B., and Williams, J. S. (1980). *In* "Laser and Electron Beam Processing of Materials" (C. W. White and P. S. Peercy, eds.) p. 481. Academic Press, New York.

Inada, T., Kato, S., Hara, T., and Toyoda, N. (1979). *J. Appl. Phys.* **50**, 4466.

Ishiwara, H., and Kuzuta, N. (1980). *Appl. Phys. Lett.* **37**, 641.

Johnson, S. T., Harrison, H. B., and Williams, J. S. (1983). *Appl. Phys. Lett.* (In press).

Keyes, R. W. (1977). *Science* **21**, 565.

Lee, C. P., Tandon, J. L., and Stocker, P. J. (1980). *Electr. Lett.* **16**, 850.

Lee, C. P., Welch, B. M., and Tandon, J. L. (1981). *Appl. Phys. Lett.* **39**, 556.

Lyman, J. (1980). *Electronics* **19**, 115.

Macksey, H. M. (1977). *Inst. Phys. Conf.,* Ser. No. **33b**, 254.

Mader, S., Nowick, A. S., and Widmer, H. (1967). *Acta Met.* **15**, 203.

Margalit, S., Pekote, D., Pepper, D. M., Lee, C. P., and Yariv, A. (1978). *Appl. Phys. Lett.* **33**, 346.

Mayer, J. W., Tsaur, B. Y., Lau, S. S., and Hung, L. S. (1981a). *Nucl. Instrum. Methods* **182/183**, 1.

Mayer, J. W., Thompson, M., and Galvin, G. (1981b). Unpublished data.

Mozzi, R. L., Fabian, W., and Piekarski, F. J. (1979). *Appl. Phys.Lett.* **35**, 337.

Murarka, S. P. (1980). *J. Vac. Sci. Technol.* **17**, 778.

Myers, S. M. (1978). *In* "Thin Films: Interdiffusion and Reactions" (J. M. Poate, K. N. Tu and J. W. Mayer, eds.), Ch. 14, Wiley-Interscience, New York.

Naguib, H. M., and Hobbs, L. H. (1974). *J. Electrochem Soc.* **124**, 573.

Neri, J. M., Hammer, D. A., Ginet, G., and Sudan, R. N. (1980). *Appl. Phys. Lett.* **37**, 101.

Nicollian, E. H., and Sinha, A. K. (1978). *In* "Thin Films: Interdiffusion and Reactions" (J. M. Poate, K. N. Tu and J. W. Mayer, eds.) p. 481. Electrochem. Soc., Princeton.

Nissim, Y. I., Gibbons, J. F., Magee, T. J., and Ormond, R. (1981a). *J. Appl. Phys.* **52**, 227.

Nissim, Y. I., Gibbons, J. F., and Gold, R. B. (1981b). *IEEE Trans. Elect. Devices,* **Ed-28**, 607.

Ottaviani, G. (1981). Unpublished data.

Ottaviani, G., Tu, K. N., and Mayer, J. W. (1981). *Phys. Rev.* **B24**, 3354.

Padovani, F. A. (1971). *In* "Semiconductors and Semimetals" (R. K. Willardson and A. C. Beer, eds.). Vol. 7A, p. 75. Academic Press, New York.

Petersson, S., Baglin, J. E. E., Hammer, W., d'Heurle, F., Kuan, T., Ohdomari, I., de Sousa Pires, J., and Tove, P. (1979). *J. Appl. Phys.* **50**, 3357.

Philofsky, E., and Hall, E. L. (1975), *IEEE Trans P.H.P.* **11**, 281.

Pianetta, P. A., Stolte, C. A., and Hanson, J. L. (1980). *In* "Laser and Electron Beam Processing of Materials" (C. W. White and P. S. Peercy, eds.), p. 328. Academic Press, New York.

Pianetta, P. A., Amano, J., Woolhouse, G., and Stolte, C. A. (1981). *In* "Laser and Electron Beam Solid Interactions and Materials Processing" (J. F. Gibbons, T. Sigmon and L. Hess, eds.), p. 239. Elsevier–North Holland, New York.

Poate, J. M., and Tisone, F. (1974). *Appl. Phys. Lett.* **24**, 391.

Poate, J. M., Leamy, H. J., Sheng, T. T., and Celler, G. K. (1978). *Appl. Phys. Lett.* **33**, 918.

Pounds, R. S., Saifi, M. A., and Hahn, W. C., Jr. (1974). *Solid State Electron.* **17**, 245.

Rhoderick, E. H. (1978). "Metal-Semiconductor Contacts." Clarendon Press, Oxford.

Rideout, V. L. (1975). *Solid State Electronics* **18**, 541.

Roberts, S. (1982). Unpublished data.

Rosenberg, R., Sullivan, M. J., and Howard, J. K. (1978). *In* "Thin Films: Interdiffusion and Reactions" (J. M. Poate, K. N. Tu and J. W. Mayer, eds.), Ch. 2. Wiley-Interscience, New York.

Scott, D. M., and Nicolet, M.-A. (1981). *Nucl. Instrum. Methods* **182/183**, 655.

Scott, D. M., Grunthauer, P. J., Tsaur, B. Y., Nicolet, M.-A., and Mayer, J. W. (1980). *In* "Thin Film Interfaces and Interactions" (J. E. E. Baglin and J. M. Poate, eds.), p. 148. The Electrochemical Society, Princeton.

Sealy, B. J., Kular, S. S., Badawi, M. H., and Stephens, K. G. (1979). *In* "Laser-Solid Interactions and Laser Processing" (S. D. Ferris, H. J. Leamy and J. M. Poate, eds.), p. 610. AIP, New York.

Shibata, T., Gibbons, J. F., and Sigmon, T. W. (1980a). *Appl. Phys. Lett.* **36**, 566.

Shibata, T., Sigmon, T. W., and Gibbons, J. F. (1980b). *In* "Laser and Electron Beam Processing of Electronic Materials" (C. L. Anderson, G. K. Celler and G. A. Rozgonyi, eds.), p. 520. The Electrochemical Society, Princeton.

Sigmon, T. W. (1981). *In* "Laser and Electron Beam Solid Interactions and Materials Processing" (J. F. Gibbons, L. D. Hess and T. W. Sigmon, eds.), p. 511. North Holland, New York.

Sigmon, T. W., Regolini, J. L., Gibbons, J. F., Lau, S. S. and Mayer, J. W. (1980). *In* "Laser and Electron Beam Processing of Electronic Materials" (C. L. Anderson, G. K. Celler and G. A. Rozgonyi, eds.), p. 531. The Electrochemical Society, Princeton.

Sinha, A. K., (1981). *J. Vac. Sci. Tech.* **19**, 778.

Sinha, A. K., and Poate, J. M. (1978). *In* "Thin Films: Interdiffusion and Reactions" (J. M. Poate, K. N. Tu and J. W. Mayer, eds.), p. 407. The Electrochem. Society, Princeton.

Sinha, A. K., Smith, T. E., and Levinstein, H. J. (1975). *IEEE Trans. Elect. Dev.* **ED-22**, 218.

Sinha, A. K., Cooper, J. A., Jr., and Levinstein, H. J. (1982). *IEEE, EDL.* **3**, 90.

Stall, R., Wood, C. E. C., Board, K., and Eastman, L. F. (1979). *Electron. Lett.* **15**, 800.

Tandon, J. L., and Eisen, F. H. (1979). *In* "Laser-Solid Interactions and Laser Processing" (S. D. Ferris, H. J. Leamy and J. M. Poate, eds.), p. 616. AIP, New York.

Tandon, J. L., Nicolet, M.-A., and Eisen, F. H. (1979). *Appl. Phys. Lett.* **34**, 165.

Tandon, J. L., Kirkpatrick, C. G., Welch, B. M., and Fleming, P. (1980). *In* "Laser and Electron Beam Processing of Materials" (C. W. White and P. S. Peercy, eds.), p. 494. Academic Press, New York.

Ting, C., and Chen, C. Y. (1971). *Solid-State Electronics,* **14**, 433.

Tsai, M. Y., Petersson, C. S., d'Heurle, F. M. and Maniscalco, V. (1980). *Appl. Phys. Letters,* **37**, 295.

Tsaur, B. Y. (1980). *In* "Thin Film Interfaces and Interactions" (J. E. E. Baglin and J. M. Poate, eds.), p. 205. The Electrochemical Society, Princeton.

Tsaur, B. Y., and Hung. L.-S. (1980). *Appl. Phys. Lett.,* **37**, 922.

Tsaur, B. Y., Mayer, J. W., and Tu, K. N. (1980a). *J. Appl. Phys.* **51**, 5326.

Tsaur, B. Y., Mayer, J. W., Graczyk, J. F., and Tu, K. N. (1980b). *J. Appl. Phys.* **51**, 5334.

Tu, K. N., and Mayer, J. W. (1978). *In* "Thin Films: Interdiffusion and Reactions" (J. M. Poate, K. M. Tu and J. W. Mayer, eds.), p. 360. Wiley-Interscience, New York.

Tung, R. T., Poate, J. M., Bean, J. C., Gibson, J. M., and Jacobson, D. C. (1982). *In* "Thin Films and Interfaces" (P. S. Ho and K. N. Tu, eds.) p. 79. North Holland, New York.

van Gurp, G. J., Daams, J., van Oostrom, A., Augustus, L., and Taminga, Y. (1979). *J. Appl. Phys.* **50**, 6915.

Venkatesan, T. N. C., Auston, D. H., Golovchenko, J. A., and Surko, C. M. (1979). *In* "Laser-Solid Interactions and Laser Processing" (S. D. Ferris, H. J. Leamy, J. M. Poate, eds.), p. 629. AIP, New York.

von Allmen, M., Lau, S. S., Maenpaa, M., and Tsaur, B. Y. (1980). *Appl. Phys. Lett.* **36**, 205.

von Seefeld, H., Cheung, N., Tonn, D., and Nicolet, M.-A. (1980). *In* "Thin Film Interfaces and Interactions" (J. E. E. Baglin and J. M. Poate, eds.), p. 311. The Electrochemical Society, Princeton.

Wang, K. L., Bacon, F., and Reihl, R. F. (1980). *In* "Thin Film Interfaces and Interactions" (J. E. E. Baglin and J. M. Poate, eds.), p. 232. The Electrochemical Society, Princeton.

Wielunski, L., Scott, D. M., Nicolet, M.-A., and von Seefeld, H. (1981). *Appl. Phys. Lett.* **38,** 106.

Wielunski, L. S., Lien, C.-D., Liu, B. X., and Nicolet, M.-A. (1982). *In* "Metastable Materials Formation by Ion Implantation". (S. T. Picraux and W. J. Choyke, eds.) p. 139. North Holland, New York.

Williams, J. S. (1982). *In* "Laser Annealing of Semiconductors" (J. M. Poate and J. W. Mayer, eds.) p. 385. Academic Press, New York.

Williams, J. S., Johnson, S. T., Short, K. T. and Sood, D. K. (1983). *Rad. Effects.* (In press).

Wittmer, M. (1980). *In* "Laser and Electron Beam Processing of Electronic Materials" (C. L. Anderson, G. K. Celler and G. A. Rozgonyi, eds.), p. 485. The Electrochemical Society, Princeton.

Wittmer, M., Finstad, T., and Nicolet, M.-A. (1977), *J. Vac. Sci. Tech.* **14,** 935.

Zirinsky, S., Hammer, W., d'Heurle, F. M., and Baglin, J. E. E. (1978). *Appl. Phys. Lett.* **33,** 76.

INDEX

411